Phillip

M000234760

Portraits in Oils

Phillipe Mailhebiau

Portraits in Oils

The Personality of Aromatherapy Oils and their link with Human Temperaments

Translated from the French
by Susan Y. Chalkley in association with
First Edition Translations Ltd, Cambridge

Index compiled by Lyn Greenwood

Illustrated by Daniel Lack

SAFFRON WALDEN
THE C.W. DANIEL COMPANY LIMITED

This is an abridged version of
La Nouvelle Aromatherapie
published in Switzerland by Editions Jakin

First published in Great Britain in 1995
by the C.W. Daniel Company Limited
1 Church Path, Saffron Walden,
Essex, CB10 1JP, England

ISBN 0 85207 237 6

Design and Production in association
with Book Production Consultants plc,
25–27 High Street, Chesterton, Cambridge CB4 1ND,
Typeset by Cambridge Photosetting Services,
Printed and bound by WSOY, Finland

Contents

Introduction

All theories are grey,
but green and vibrant is the tree of life.
Goethe

AROMATHERAPY: ITS PLACE WITHIN NATURAL MEDICINE

On the fringe of so-called traditional or conventional medicine – currently the only kind recognised and enjoying specific status and privileges – we are today witnessing what is known as alternative medicine undergo a consequent boom. Although alternative medicine still remains somewhat scorned by official medicine, it receives more and more recognition from the public and from many people in the medical and paramedical professions.

On closer inspection, the term *traditional* when applied to allopathic and chemotherapeutic medicine appears inappropriate, since these methods – which date back several decades – cannot pose as tradition. In the same way, the epithet *alternative*, commonly used for natural therapies, seems inadequate since it implies the restricted character of any exchanges, alternatives by definition being mutually exclusive. (In the same vein, the French term for "alternative medicine" – "médecines paralèlles" – would seem to be equally inadequate since it implies not only the similarity of the objectives but, as in English, the limited nature of any exchanges, parallels on principle not being able to meet.) In addition to inappropriate terminology and in a struggle where passions and interests most often prevail over reason, we see the protagonists of natural therapies describe chemotherapy as poisonous, whilst allopathic practitioners disparage alternative medicine as the province of charlatans. Such simplistic opposition leads one to think that both may be capable of poisoning and charlatanism.

In the face of these cliquish quarrels, the reflection of a change in mentality – the basis of which is, however, less about the defence of ethics than about the pecunary interest represented by the health market – the person in search of improved well-being scarcely knows which doctor to turn to. Whilst a growing number of people are striving to break free from the clutches of allopathic and hospital-based medicine, which often presents the image of quasi-dogmatic scientific imperialism, they are still afraid of giving much credit to natural medicine, which is supported more often by dangerous charlatans than qualified therapists. In this period of change favourable to opportunists and vendors of hope, looking after one's body and one's health sometimes becomes a problem. Medical abuses are on the increase and public confidence is consequently shaken, despite the rarity of cases denounced which actually only means that one cannot see the wood for the trees.

Logic would require that we pass judgement on therapeutic efficacy and commitment, not in respect of medicine in general but of the doctors in particular, since medical competence depends less on the training provided as on those who make use of it; whilst no therapy is simply a panacea, doubtless neither is any totally devoid of interest, and it just shows that it is possible, in the practice of health care, to do good as well as harm. Although not within the scope of this work, we feel it necessary to emphasise that the chemotherapeutic principles – bases of symptomatic intervention medicine and valid in cases of emergency – and the "terrain"[1] principles on which natural medicine is based – these being more disposed towards depth treatments – can be considered as complementary. For that reason, their original motives still need to be preserved, in other words the restoration and maintenance of individual and collective health.

These days, the dehumanisation of medicine and public disinformation, reinforced by the aberrations of the social system and health policies, tend to restrict medical action to simple intervention to the detriment of prevention. This observation is driving a growing number of doctors and therapists towards "terrain" medicine, which imbues the patient as much as the practitioner with a sense of responsibility and is more rounded but also more specific than symptomatic intervention. Aromatherapy, especially when practised in relation to the aromatic characterologies, falls within the ranks of such "terrain" therapies, particularly as a result of the psychosensory impact of the fragrances we shall be discussing.

What about Aromatherapy today? Logically included within the framework of natural medicine – which the French also describe as "médecines douces" or "gentle medicine" – it is, on the face of it, accessible and harmless. In the manner which it is often practised, however, Aromatherapy cannot claim the title of natural medicine, in the untarnished sense of the term, and still less that of "gentle" medicine.

As regards what is natural, on the one hand, many essential oils on the market are synthetic essences or adulterated, doctored mixtures, in any case neither botanically nor biochemically defined, being reduced, in effect, to doubtful products of which some can prove dangerous. In this sphere as in any other, exploitation of the need for health care governs the sale of cheap, very poor-quality essential oils; this fact is reinforced by current aromatherapeutic practice which is generally based on bibliography that is rather unreliable and lacks rigour in its prescriptions.

Assisted by a team of pharmacists, botanists, biologists and chemists, we have studied and analysed several thousand varieties of essences and batches of specific biochemical characteristics. We were able to observe that quality varies greatly and that adulteration is rife, which often makes their therapeutic application hazardous. Many firms assuming the title of "laboratory" are, in fact, simply companies that resell essences supplied by wholesalers who market synthetic products and essences that are not biochemically defined and which cost less than authentic essential oils. Whilst such products are acceptable for the perfumery industry and the soap trade, they should be banned for therapeutic use; and we regret to say that we have found them in far too many pharmacies and stores specialising in pharmaceutical and chemical products.

The suer is therefore deceived not only as regards the nature of the products, but – even more distressing – is exposed to iatrogenic effects due to the poor quality of the product.

It is our wish that this work, as well as conveying the basics of therapeutic instruction, should assist consumers and above all those prescribing essential oils in realising the mediocre quality and uncertain origin

of the essences they most often use, in order that they henceforth learn to select them according to genuine criteria of quality.

On the other hand, as regards its classification as a "gentle medicine", Aromatherapy is inappropriately and imprudently presented as innocuous. Essential oils are tricky to use and if such use is poorly tailored to the needs of the patient concerned, it can be accompanied by serious side effects. Some essential oils, even the best-quality ones, can become harsh poisons in improper dosages. For example, the ingestion of ten drops of essential oil of Hyssop (*Hyssopus officinalis*) can lead to an epileptic fit as a result of the pinocamphone this essence contains. Other ketones are equally dangerous, particularly the thujones in *Salvia officinalis*, which are abortifacient in incorrect dosages, and the indiscriminate use of *Artemisia herba* alba and *Thuya occidentalis* even causes violent haemorrhages. The furocoumarins in Bergamot, an essence nevertheless regularly recommended in sun lotions that one can make up oneself, are photosensitising and lead to depigmentation in high doses. Used improperly, the phenolic essential oils are toxic to the liver and the essences which are rich in monoterpenes have a revulsive effect on the skin – to mention just a few examples.

Whilst one may, if necessary, resort to the use of certain essential oils as part of family healthcare – essential oil of True Lavender (*Lavandula vera*) to counteract an insect sting, for example, or Italian Helichrysum (*Helichrysum italicum*) for a bruise – the prescribing of aromatics should be based on a thorough knowledge of the way in which they act and the dosages need to be respected. It is regrettable that one should read in certain popularised works and magazines the recommendation to add essence of Thyme, Sage or Pine (these terms are, moreover, incomplete) to one's bath: essential oils are not water-soluble in their natural state. Another even more disturbing example is when Oregano is advocated as an inhalation while in fact *carvacrol*, a phenol constituting 60% of essence of *Origanum compactum*, is extremely revulsive and irritant to the mucous membranes. Some writers suggest complex compounds for ingestion consisting of eight, ten or even twelve drops of essence per dose, which is absurd. People have also been known to recommend essential oils that do not exist, such as essences of Hawthorn or Robert Geranium, but this is less serious, at least as far as the reader is concerned.

These days, one therefore needs to have a minimum of knowledge in order to avoid been taken in by erroneous publications by unqualified and unreliable writers who encourage an ill-formed public to buy anything by any means whatsoever.

Aromatherapy is therefore not innate knowledge but a specialised medical field, and only a few basic remedies can be used by everyone with the utmost guarantee that they are totally safe.[2]

In addition, an understanding of the characterology of the essences makes it possible to ascertain its olfactory affinities and to recognise in the people with whom one is in contact certain psychosomatic features of the characters described in the monographs. From a therapeutic point of view, this approach opens the door to personalised treatments which go beyond the scope of symptomatic aromatherapy by combining efficient physicochemical action with a decisive psychosensory effect.

We therefore invite the reader on this aromatic and undoubtedly inspiring journey and we hope that the essences, once they become more familiar, will form precious allies in maintaining health and, we might even suggest, in stimulating personal growth.

---

[1]We have decided to keep this French concept of "terrain", derived from agriculture. In the French medical vocabulary, particularly in holistic and natural medicines, this word defines the general predispositions of an individual, be it from the genetic, physiological or psychic viewpoint, including his specific strengths and weaknesses. This concept, which has gained considerable respect in the past decades, places the emphasis on the individual rather than his environment in the search for the origin of his pathology. In the same way that the specific qualities or shortcomings of the soil will or won't allow plants for weeds to grow, it is considered that an individual's terrain, whether it is balanced or not, either keeps him in good health or allows pathologies to develop. *"The virus is nothing ; the terrain is everything"*, concluded Claude Bernard at the end of his life.

[2]On this matter, see: *L'Aromathérapie pratique et familiale. Comment utiliser 33 huiles essentielles majeures sans risque et avec un maximum d'efficacité,* published by Editions Jakin, Lausanne, Switzerland.

PREFACE TO THE ENGLISH EDITION

Intended mainly for the general public, this book is a shortened version of Philippe Mailhebiau's first book *La Nouvelle Aromathérapie: caractérologie des essences et tempéraments humains; Biochimie aromatique et influence psychosensorielle des odeurs,* published by Editions Jakin of Lausanne (Switzerland) 1995. The monographs of the 24 major essential oils have generally been simplified in the present work, both where detailed description and botanical history are concerned and with regard to the properties and indications (written in the original text for a professional readership) and characterologies, whose mythological and symbolic references have been reduced.

In addition, the full volume of more than 600 pages also contains the following chapters not included in the present book:

– a study of the methodology taught by the author, enabling a practical application of the characterologies, and comparable with what Hahnemann did for homoeopathy and Steiner for anthroposophy;

– a thorough analysis of aromatic biochemistry, from the origin of the aromatic molecule to the physicochemical properties and indications of the different biochemical families;

– an exposition on the physiology of olfaction;

– detailed chromatographic analyses of the essential oils covered in the work and their graphic representation based upon the three diathese developed by the author;

– the data sheets of 31 essential oils commonly used in aromatherapy.

In addition to *La Nouvelle Aromathérapie* Edition Jakin also publish a journal called *Les Cahiers de l'Aromathérapie/Aromatherapy Records* which is written in both French and English.

For our part and with the author's agreement, we considered it appropriate to publish a more accessible text for the layperson, the main aim being to familiarise English-speaking readers with the famous *Characterology of Essences* devised by Philippe Mailhebiau. This opens up fascinating new perspectives on Aromatherapy, particularly with regard to the personalisation of "terrain" treatments and the understanding of the psychosensory impact of essential oils, whilst nevertheless being based on a thorough knowledge of botany and biochemistry which are vital to therapeutic punctiliousness.

This introduction to the New Aromatherapy alone constitutes a reference work as fascinating as it is meticulous, thanks to the therapeutic information it contains.

Aromatic Plants and Essential Oil, From Nature to the Laboratory

What the eye sees is not a remedy;
when distillation
has transformed the plant,
then the remedy becomes apparent.
Paracelsus

Whilst the number of botanical species is estimated at approximately 800,000, we do not know exactly how many are aromatic because the term "aromatic plant" relates to plants sufficiently rich in aromatic molecules to be capable of giving off a characteristic odour that forms their main criterion of identity, unlike other species which have no particular fragrance in their natural state. Amongst the latter, some have a perfume which is revealed only if they undergo enzymatic transformation. These particular plants (*Betula lenta*: Sweet Birch, *Gaultheria fragrantissima*: Wintergreen, *Brassica nigra*: Black Mustard...) are seldom used in aromatherapy as the biochemical composition of their essence is very specific.

There are numerous aromatic plants that are not used in aromatherapy, either because of their toxicity (e.g. *Tanacetum vulgare*) or because interest in them arises more out of curiosity than need, since they have no specific characteristics or properties – at least as far as our state of aromatological knowledge stands at present (e.g. *Bupleurum arborescens*). Furthermore, many aromatic plants contain very little essence and that essence is not extractable by steam distillation; the aromatic molecules are in this case extracted with the help of organic solvents, which make it possible to obtain concretes and absolutes, or through lipidic media (enfleurage method). These aromatics are reserved for perfumery and non-biological food flavourings and must not be used in therapy.

Aroma remains one of the distinctive characteristics of the plant kingdom, which is richer in this domain than the other kingdoms. Aromatic plants rely heavily on solar radiation in order to grow and develop their specific aromatic character, and whilst practically all botanical species have their own odour, be it only because of the presence of chlorophyllian pigments, we consider as aromatic plants those rich in a relatively quantifiable essence.

An apple or a pear also has its odour and no doubt develops a number of aromatic molecules, but these do not, for all that, constitute plants with essence capable of comparison with a Lavender, Eucalyptus or Bay Some plants are practically odourless, for example *Equisetum arvense* (Horsetail), a medicinal plant valued for its silica content, but which gives no scent. Horsetail, even more than apple or pear, cannot be considered an aromatic plant despite the relative dusty smell it produces when drying.

Despite the large number of plants with a specific fragrance, there are very few which produce an extractable essence. Only a few hundred are used in the perfumery industry, and if we restrict ourselves to the therapeutic sector alone, the number is generally less than a hundred; this is mainly due to the fact that many essences are still little known and their properties poorly described. In fact, there are few therapists who are fully familiar with more than about fifty essential oils, other than experimentally.

Initially, we will look at the main essences whose species names are known to aromatherapists. This list is obviously not exhaustive, even in so far as characterology [the study of character types] is concerned; a few extremely interesting species – such as *Hyssopus officinalis*, *Cistus ladaniferus* and *Myrtus communis* as well as several others – will be the subject of an in-depth study covered by later works.

Where Essence Originates within the Plant

From a biochemical point of view, plant metabolism presents us with a fair number of aspects that we still find obscure and complex. We do know, however, that all plant metabolic processes originate from a primordial and essential phenomenon of the expression of life on earth, namely photosynthesis. It would be valuable to recall briefly the role it plays.

Chlorophyll, a green pigment, collects the photons from solar radiation through the leaf system. It uses this energy to split the water molecule intrinsic to the life and development of the plant into hydrogen and oxygen. The oxygen is for the most part rejected (regenerating the ambient air) or used in other metabolic reactions, whilst the hydrogen combines with the carbon dioxide absorbed by the plant (purifying the ambient air) to form various sugars.

Photosynthesis, a process perfected by Nature over the ages, constitutes an unrivalled and supreme biochemical reaction taking place on earth which is the prerogative of the plant kingdom.

Cellular metabolism produces complex and variable molecular structures from these sugars by different oxidation-reduction processes, depending on the genetic characteristics peculiar to the species of plant. Aromatic plants produce specific molecules mainly by means of two methods of biosynthesis.

1 – The terpene method from IPP (isopentenylpyrophosphate, a five-carbon molecule). By successive chain formations of this basic structure:

- monoterpenes ($C_{10}H_{16}$),
- sesquiterpenes ($C_{15}H_{24}$),
- then diterpenes ($C_{20}H_{32}$)

are formed.

Again by oxidation-reduction reactions, the aromatic plant forms aromatic compounds with varied biochemical functions from these hydrocarbonic molecules:

alcohols, phenols, aldehydes, ketones, oxides, esters, acids...

2 – The phenylpropane method via shikimic acid. This method directly produces various oxidised compounds:

- phenols, acids, coumarins, themselves bases of synthesis for other molecules:
- lactones, methyl ethers.

3 – In addition to terpenoids and phenylpropanoids, essential oils include a very slight quantity of other molecules such as certain alcohols, aldehydes and acids... which have a very short carbon-containing

chain (fewer than ten carbons) and result from various methods of biosynthesis, as well as sulphurous or nitrogenous compounds.

All these compounds, as well as their various isomers, form biochemical families according to their type of chemical function. These biochemical families are the medium for the numerous properties of essential oils, depending on their natural synergetic combination.

Essence and Essential Oil

Although it is commonly acknowledged that we talk without differentiation about essence and essential oil, one should be aware that they are in fact two different substances.

1. *Essence* is a natural secretion produced by the plant organism. It is contained in various types of producing organs, which differ according to the part of the plant in question:

• smaller and finer epidermal cells than the cells of the epidermis (Rose petals);

• secretory hairs on the periphery of various organs (calyx, leaves, stems). They are formed from a longish pedicel and a head developed from one or a number of secretory cells (*Lamiaceae*);

• bigger and thicker secretory cells found within the plant tissues (stems, bark, roots, seeds, leaves);

• modified cells in secretory sacs found as follows:

    - schizogenous sac: a cell splits in two; the sac will form in between these two newly formed cells (*Myrtaceae* leaf);

    - lysigenic sac: several grouped cells form a sac by lysis of their wall;

    - schizolysigenous sac: formed by the association of the characteristics of the two preceding types of sacs (*Citrus* zests);

    - ducts, or narrow secretory bands, formed by elongated secretory sacs (*Santalum album* wood, *Apiaceae* fruits and roots).

2. *Essential oil* is a natural extract from aromatic plants or trees obtained by steam distillation. In other words, *essential oil is the distilled essence.*

The nature and composition of these two substances are not the same, since oxidation-reduction phenomena during distillation alter the biochemical composition of the essence. The essence is frequently accompanied by resin in the producing organs; the aromatic molecules making up the resin, which are too heavy to be drawn off by steam, are not extracted.

The distillation process must be carried out correctly, according to the plant or part of the distilled plant, in order for the essential oil to be the most representative aromatic image of the essence possible.

An essential oil is made up exclusively of volatile aromatic molecules provided that it is totally pure and has been properly distilled. The presence of vegetable or organic oils, organic solvents, residues or occasionally undefined substances indicates that the product is adulterated.

The Secretory Systems of Aromatic Plants
1 – Secretory hairs

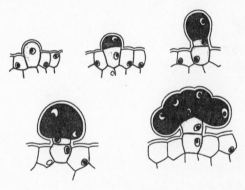

Successive stages in the growth of a secretory hair - *Lavandula, Lamiaceae*
(*adapted from Perrin & Colson*)

Secretory hair of *Pelargonium, Geraniaceae*
(*adapted from Deysson*)

2 – Secretory cells

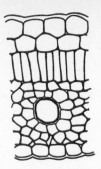

Secretory cell of *Peumus boldus* (leaf)
(adapted from Beille)

3 – Schizogenous sacs

   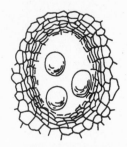

Successive stages in the formation of a schizogenous secretory sac -
Hypericum perforatum, Hypericaceae (adapted from Deysson)

4 – Schizolysigenous sacs

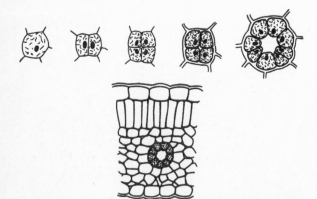

Successive stages in the formation of a schizolysigenous sac -
Citrus aurantium, Rutaceae (adapted from Deysson)

5 – Secretory ducts

 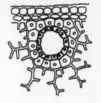

Secretory duct of
Daucus carota seeds, *Apiaceae*
(adapted from Beille)

Secretory duct of
Pinus sylvestris, Abietacea
(adapted from Deysson)

Technique for Distilling Aromatic Plants

The oldest procedure used and the one best adapted to extracting essences from aromatic plants is steam distillation, expression being a specific procedure reserved for extracting zest essence from the various *Citrus* plants.

The distillation apparatus or still is used for the quantitative and qualitative extraction of essential oils. Old stills did not separate the plants from the water; the plants were boiled and essential oils obtained often had a "burnt" smell. In more modern stills, the water and aromatic plants are either separated by a grate in the same vessel or placed in two different vessels.

"Open fire"
still

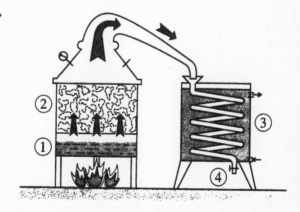

*Still with
a separate fire*

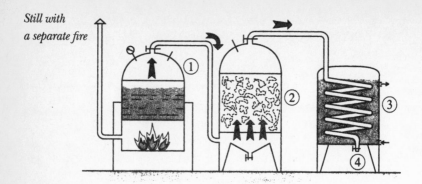

The steam produced by the boiling water (as pure as possible) (1) permeates and passes through the plant matter (2), dissolves and vaporises the aromatic molecules, then carries them towards the cooler (3). Heat exchange takes place between the cold water in the cooler around the coil and the essence-charged steam circulating within it. Gradually, condensation occurs and the steam and extracted essence return to a liquid state.

On leaving the cooler (4), the distillate separates into two distinct liquids: the aromatic water and the essential oil. This separation takes place inside a vessel known as a "Florentine flask"; in the majority of cases, the essential oil, being of a lighter density than water, floats on top of the aromatic water. It is collected up and put into glass flasks to stabilise (internal readjustment between the different molecules); this rest period is essential for it to take on its specific characteristics before being used therapeutically.

The minimum rest period is generally one month, as in the case of Lavender, but for optimum quality it is preferable to wait longer before using the essential oil: three months for Rosemary, a year for Bay. The oils are best kept in a cool cellar.

The aromatic water is also kept as it contains a small amount of aromatic molecules (the amount varies according to the water-solubility of the different molecules in the essential oil) in the water-soluble state. The aromatic water is a natural by-product of distillation with therapeutic properties that complement those of the essential oil.

The distillation temperature and pressure must be as low as possible (about 100°C and slightly higher than atmospheric pressure) so as not to increase the oxidation-reduction phenomena inherent in an essential oil of good odoriferous quality.

The distillation time is almost always more than one hour (1 hr 15 mins. for *Lavandula vera*, 3 hrs for *Pinus sylvestris* and more than 100 hrs for *Santalum album*). Yields are generally low, falling somewhere between 0.02% (*Rosa damascena*) and 1% (*Apiaceae* fruits generally give between 1 and 5% essential oil), except in the case of certain plants from tropical regions (almost 18% for Cloves and even more for exotic resins).

Studies are currently under way to improve the distillation technique by hydrodiffusion or with the aid of liquids in the supercritical state. Steam distillation nonetheless remains the best method for the time being.

The Three Criteria of Origin for an Essential Oil

The term "100% pure and natural" is no longer adequate to qualify an essential oil. This expression is tarnished since it conceals a commercial ambiguity oriented towards selling adulterated and dangerous products behind a benevolent appearance, a situation which is prejudicial to the reputation of genuine essential oils. Before buying and using any essential oil, it is vital to verify three points which, whilst not conferring credentials of absolute quality, do enable the element of confusion to be replaced with the precision needed for therapy.

These three criteria that we have established and which INSA [the Scientific Institute of Aromatology] has registered under the seal of HEBBD [Botanically and Biochemically Defined Essential Oil] will make it possible to define accurately the specific characteristics of origin of an essential oil.

1. BOTANICAL SPECIES

One must in fact know precisely the botanical species of the plant used in distillation. The term "Lavender essence", for example, is insufficient because there is not one but several species of Lavender. Each has its own aromatic characteristic and forms a specific essence in its tissues.

A correctly defined botanical species has the genus name followed by a qualifying epithet, and sometimes the variety – if there is one.

Lavandula is not a species but a genus which covers several types of Lavenders. *Vera, spica, stoechas* and *hybrida* are the different qualifying epithets individualising these various Lavenders.

The combination of the genus with the epithet defines the botanical species: *Lavandula vera* (in English: True Lavender), *Lavandula hybrida* (in English: Lavandin), etc.

The variety needs to be specified for *Lavandula vera* and *Lavandula hybrida* because there are several of them.

There is the *fragrans* variety of *Lavandula vera*, for example, or the "maillette" variety, the first originating in the wild and the second being a cultivated clone.

Lavandula hybrida (a cultivated species) includes the *abrialis* variety, which is becoming rarer; the *super* variety; and the *grosso* variety, which is the most widespread.

The name of the variety enhances the accuracy of classification of the botanical species and its origin. We shall also see that the detail "wild" or "cultured" has its significance in the quality of the product obtained.

Another characteristic example is that of Eucalyptus, for it includes several hundred species and varieties – not all of which are aromatic, however. We can consequently see how it is totally inadequate to talk about "Eucalyptus essence" and that it is vital to specify the type: *Eucalyptus globulus, Eucalyptus radiata, Eucalyptus citriodora, Eucalyptus polybractea*, etc. These different species of Eucalyptus produce specific essences and the curative reputation in the broncho-pulmonary area attributed to this tree is based on the presence of an oxide, *1.8 cineole*, formerly known as *eucalyptol*, in which the *globulus, radiata* and other varieties are rich, but which is absent in the *citriodora* type.

Confusion is no less great for the genera of *Salvia* (Sage) and *Thymus* (Thyme): *Thymus vulgaris, Thymus serpyllum, Thymus zygis, Thymus satureioides... Salvia officinalis, Salvia sclarea, Salvia lavandulaefolia, Salvia triloba*, etc. These aromatic species yield essential oils that are qualitatively and quantitatively very different.

In practice, it is becoming necessary to retain the Latin name, which is in any case the one most commonly used in botanical nomenclature. It allows a botanical species to be defined without any possible confusion whereas the common names, which vary according to regional folklore or country, are liable to sound alike and generally lead to errors.

The terms "Citronella" and "Vervain" (Verbena) are randomly used to refer to plants of very diverse origins whose only common feature is that of exuding a warm, lemony fragrance; for example *Cymbopogon nardus* (Ceylon Citronella), *Cymbopogon winterianus* (Java Citronella) and *Cymbopogon citratus* (Lemongrass, West Indian Lemongrass), to name only a few of the *Cymbopogon (Poaceae)* species. *Melissa officinalis* (Melissa or Citronella, *Lamiaceae*), *Lippia citriodora* (Scented Verbena or Lemon Verbena, *Verbenaceae*), as well as many other plants, also contain lemony aromatic molecules and hence have identical or very similar common names. Here again, the respective properties of the essential oils extracted from these plants must not be confused.

We should be aware that behind the mask of incomplete names falsification is easy, for which reason therapeutic use must exclude any inaccuracy that might lead to one product being prescribed instead of another. Common confusions explain in part why the results obtained in aromatherapy are not always those that are expected. In fact, each species has a specific composition and, though similarities can be observed, they in no way imply an identical mode of action.

Such accuracy expressed by the exact botanical species also makes it possible to identify frauds as regards the plants containing little or no essence. Genuine essential oil of Vervain comes from *Lippia citriodora*, whilst the Vervain essential oil commonly found on sale is merely a pale reflection resulting from a mixture of various *Cymbopogon* essential oils (Lemongrass in particular) or oils from other plants with a lemony smell and even, sometimes, synthetic compounds. It is the same with essential oil of Melissa, which is even rarer and more expensive (*Melissa officinalis*). The genuine essential oils of *Lippia citriodora* and *Melissa officinalis* are extremely precious due to their very low yield and it is quite difficult to find good quality ones.

The private user has practically no way of checking the quality of the essences he is buying and it is up to the distributor, chemists or health-food shop to know which laboratory they are dealing with and what guarantees it provides. It does happen that some pharmacies and specialist shops become misled by inferior quality and poorly controlled products.

Amongst some of the most flagrant cases of abuse and falsification are the sales of non-existent essential oils such as, essential oil of Hawthorn; the flowers of this plant smell very pleasant but steam extraction of the essence is impossible. Consequently the essential oil found on sale is made up of a synthetic product, anisaldehyde, a principal component in the Hawthorn fragrance. Some works mention it, as well, as essential oil of Herb Robert (Geranium), although this indigenous plant does not contain any essence that is capable of extraction and use in therapy. This shows the authors' lack of knowledge. One does indeed find essential oils of Geranium on sale, but they come from various tropical species. Common language has retained the name Geranium, whereas it is, in fact, the Pelargonium which is involved.

We could unfortunately go on mentioning many other examples of this kind which are detrimental to the growth of aromatherapy, but we are able to conclude already that it is essential to demand a guarantee as to the botanical species concerned.

2. THE PARTS OF THE PLANT USED

Although this is of little importance for the "whole plant" distilled species (*Mentha piperita, Origanum majorana, Rosmarinus officinalis,* etc.), the producing organ (p.o.) must be mentioned for certain plants, mainly aromatic trees or bushes, since the essence varies in terms of quality depending on which part is involved.

As regards the *Citrus (Rutaceae)* species, for example, and in particular *Citrus aurantium var. amara,* it is possible to extract two essential oils: from the leaves (Petitgrain bigarade) and the flowers (Neroli bigarade), as well as an essence from the peel of the fruit (zest essence extracted by expression).

Cinnamomum zeylanicum or Ceylon Cinnamon (*Lauraceae*) produces three specific essences:
- essential oil from the leaves, rich in *eugenol* (phenol)
- essential oil from the bark, rich in *cinnamaldehyde* (aldehyde)
- essential oil from the roots, rich in *borneone* (ketone).

The essential oil from the bark is the one most commonly sold and the most valued; it contains more than 75% *cinnamic aldehyde* and a little *eugenol* (less than 10%). The essential oil from the leaves is reminiscent of the odour of the essential oil of *Eugenia caryophyllata* p.o. Cloves (Clove Tree); it is, moreover, used to adulterate it although it has extremely attractive properties itself.

3. BIOCHEMICAL SPECIFICITY

This third detail required for the exact specification of an essential oil results from research dating from the Sixties. Several researchers showed that a plant of a defined botanical species elaborated different essences depending on the conditions under which it grew (soil, climate, latitude and altitude). This fact is due to variations in the expression of the genes of the species. These discoveries were the outcome of the study of a quite precise species which is very prevalent in the scrublands of southern France: *Thymus vulgaris*.

For our part, we have designated these changes in constitution within the same botanical species *biochemical specificity* (b.s.), but other terms are sometimes used.

Depending on its biochemical specificity, the essential oil of a given species will have very specific properties. The precision of this specificity indicates the component or components which grant the essential oil a particular therapeutic action without their necessarily being present in the largest quantity.

In order to explain the significance of biochemical specificity, we will take the case of *Rosmarinus officinalis*, the principal constituents of which are *1.8 cineole* (oxide) and *borneone* (a ketone also known as *camphor*), this composition varying according to where the Rosemary is gathered.

In Morocco, *1.8 cineole* predominates, whereas amongst the old standing bushes of Rosemary in the scrublands of southern France (Provence, Languedoc), *camphor* is the majority component. Where there is a mid-way situation (Provence, Corsica, Spain), there is always *1.8 cineole* and *camphor*, and also an ester, *bornyl acetate*, and a ketone, *verbenone*, which give the essential oil of Rosemary the properties which have the most marked effect in the hepatobiliary area. We will therefore term them respectively:

Rosmarinus officinalis b.s. 1.8 cineole,
Rosmarinus officinalis b.s. camphor,
Rosmarinus officinalis b.s. bornyl acetate, verbenone.

The precision of the biochemical specificity is vital; in the present case, we would point out that essence of Rosemary, reputed to be the regulator of the hepatobiliary functions, may no longer be so according to its biochemical composition. This property relates to an essential oil of *Rosmarinus officinalis b.s. bornyl acetate, verbenone* but certainly not to a Rosemary essence containing a high proportion of *borneone (b.s. camphor)* since this ketone is toxic to the liver.

The essence undergoes changes according to the various external conditions but also according to the vegetative stage. In winter, *Satureja montana* (Winter savory) contains practically nothing but *terpenic hydrocarbons*, whilst at the end of the summer its essence is found to be extremely rich in *carvacrol* (phenol) resulting from the oxidation of these very hydrocarbons. This fact cannot be classed as a territorial and biochemical specificity, but rather as a normal seasonal variation in the vegetative cycle of this hardy perennial.

This phenomenon confirms the use that plants make of their essence, contrary to the theory upheld for a time by some biologists who saw the essence as a plant waste product. Plants use their essence, which is an intrinsic part of their immune system, to deal with attacks and hostile climatic conditions. We thus understand why the best essences generally come from wild plants, which are subjected to the most difficult conditions of existence and have to build up a powerful immune defence for themselves.

In order to illustrate these three criteria, let us take the example of an essential oil which is often chemically reconstituted: Niaouli.

Botanical species: *Melaleuca* (genus) *quinquenervia* (epithet)

Producing organ: leaves

Biochemical specificity: *1,8 cineol, viridiflorol*

We will therefore write it as:

Melaleuca quinquenervia p.o. leaves, *b.s. 1.8 cineole, viridiflorol.*

We cannot emphasise strongly enough the importance of these details if we wish to work with the utmost rigour in aromatherapy.

No valid conclusion concerning the therapeutic efficacy of essences can be drawn by anyone who fails to respect these requirements. The organoleptic properties of an essential oil are not random but result from the combined action and synergy of its different constituents. We must nevertheless stress that whilst one may know the specific properties of the biochemical components of an essential oil, it is not possible to define their principle of action fully.

On the one hand we are not able to analyse all the microparticles contained in an essential oil as shown by gas chromatographies; on the other the accumulation of the specific properties of each component is not the sole therapeutic virtue of an essential oil containing, for example, monoterpenols, aldehydes, esters, acids, etc. (the essential oil of *Pelargonium graveolens* contains more than two hundred components). As soon as one talks about natural substances or living matter, the whole is always greater than the sum of its parts. An essential oil is not only a fairly complex set of specific aromatic molecules which it would, if necessary, be possible to reconstitute, but rather a biological entity the composition of which stems from a living synergy worked by Nature.

An essential oil which is chemically reconstituted (synthetic essence) can be dangerous, because it no longer conforms to the laws pertaining to all natural and living substances; it is a chemical drug, aggressive and often toxic to the human body. A large number of allergies to essential oils result from the fact that those used are of poor quality and subjected to deterpenation, rectification, decolouration and often adulteration with substances that may be pathogenic in the long term.

Essences, Aromas and Characterologies

*Contentment is an agreeable perfume in the soul,
and virtuous acts are as beautiful
as rose petals.*
Yoga-Vasishtha

In previous chapters, we have looked at essences from a physical point of view; however, the study of the biochemical composition constituting their objective reality could not define the fragrant world in its entirety, it being equally possible to take into consideration a subtler, shall we say more energetic, aspect. Alongside the "somatic" side of the essence, its biochemical composition, we can conceive of a dimension which we might easily call its "psyche", a subtle, strange nature, which has fascinated men throughout the centuries - whether seekers, poets or therapists - and which still continues to surprise or captivate us: its perfume. The extraordinary power which perfumes and smells exert upon our senses reveals their significance, and the mystery still surrounding them sometimes unnerves us, often satisfies our need for miracles, in every case touches a cord in us and awakens our feelings. The poet intuitively captures this connection which enables "embalm" to rhyme with "charm":

"April arrives to calm all things, everything to embalm.
I have no other business in this world but to charm." *(Victor Hugo)*

Perfumes: Myths, Legends and Passions
The way in which perfumes were originally used in ancient societies indicates the general awareness people then had of the spiritual dimension of odours. Whether in China, India, Persia, Egypt or Chaldea, with the Jews, Greeks or Romans, the history of these civilisations is rich in pages relating the use of perfumes and aromatics, particularly in religions and their

many rituals. What's more, the ancient beliefs maintained the divine origin of perfumes and their links with the soul of the world, as the Zohar, amongst others, notes: "The soul ascends from the altar through love awoken by scent and is caused to depart from within that it may attain Heaven's Garden of Eden." The domain of the heart, feeling, belief, religion and its ideal, Divine Love, sometimes appealed beyond measure to "heavenly" perfumes such as rose, frankincense, myrrh, sandalwood and jasmine to invoke the deities and win over their good graces.

In India, plants are considered as born of the gods; herbs, roots and fruits are the hairs of Brahma, the Creator. During a *puja* (sacrificial prayer and ritual), one of the many rites of offering to the deities is called *gandha*, which means perfume. In Hindu mythology, the *Gandharvas*, considered in the Vedas to be ancient water gods, then to be the *devas* associated with air, represent harmony and the smell of perfumes. Living in the clouds, they initially symbolise the primordial forces; later called upon to inhabit the *Gandhamadana*, a mythical region of the Himalayas, the *Gandharvas* are found living on perfumes and becoming the musicians of the gods, whose respective dwelling places - Mount Meru for Brahma; the Himalayas for Vishnu, Shiva and Indra - are filled with flowers and aromatic plants exuding exquisite scents.

The Greeks, for their part, attributed the origin of perfumes and flowers to Aphrodite, goddess of love, forever confirming the bond between smell and feeling. Eugene Rimmel describes the origin of the rose in these terms:

"One day Venus, wishing to pick the white rose,
Wounded herself, tinging it with an immortal purple hue.
The flower then appeared to Cupid so beauteous,
That he placed upon it a kiss... from this comes its perfume!"

But according to legend, perfumes are not the prerogative of the gods alone, thanks to the nymph Oenone, priestess of Aphrodite, who allowed Paris to be present at the toilet of the goddess when she was covering herself with heavenly scents. Paris told these secrets to the fair Helen, who made known their precious formulae to all humanity.

Inspired, Homer sings of Hera at her toilet in these terms:
"Here first she bathes, and round her body pours
Soft oils of fragrance and ambrosial showers,

The winds, perfumed, the balmy gale conveys

Through heaven, through earth, and all the aerial ways".

But whether from the heights of Olympus or Nirvana, the gods continue to send forth their wondrous perfumes, thereby drawing the attention of mortals to their presence:

"From the top of her head, her ambrosia-scented hair exudes a divine fragrance", sings Virgil in homage to Venus, and Euripides places this prayer into the mouth of the dying Hippolytus: "O Artemis, chaste goddess, I know that you are close, for I have recognised your heavenly fragrance."

At the dawn of Western civilisation, it was Egypt which evolved to their utmost the sacred ritual of offerings and the art of creating very elaborate perfumes for the purpose of honouring the deities and embalming their statues. *Kyphi*, a sacred perfume known throughout Antiquity - and for which various recipes have come down to us - contained sixteen ingredients, according to Plutarch, including cypress, myrrh, juniper, *Calamus aromaticus*, cardomom, resin, sweet rush and lentisk; it was burned before altars or mixed with wine.

"These ingredients", says Plutarch, "are not mixed at random but in accordance with a formula related in the holy books and read out during preparation to those charged with making this perfume. A soft and beneficial fragrance exudes from it which changes the state of the air. This fragrance steals into the body through the breath, relaxes it gently and imperceptibly, lulls it to sleep and spreads its delightful effect throughout. Everyday anxieties, like as to painful fetters, lose their sorrow and intensity; they weaken and loosen their grip, without recourse to inebriety. Acting thus upon the imagination, so powerful a faculty in dreams, these exhalations make it, as it were, clear and bright like the most perfect mirror."

The Egyptians passed on their knowledge to the Jews who, in turn, made extensive use of perfumes and aromatics whilst adapting them to their own creative spirit. The Bible contains very exact guidance on the art of sacred perfumes; thus in Exodus 30:22: "The Lord spoke to Moses, saying: Take the finest spices, of liquid myrrh five hundred shekels, of sweet-smelling cinnamon half as much, that is, two hundred and fifty, of aromatic cane two hundred and fifty, and of cassia five hundred, according to the shekel of the sanctuary, and of olive oil a hin. You shall make of these a sacred anointing oil blended as by the perfumer..." Then *(Exodus 30:34)*: "The Lord said to Moses: Take sweet spices, stacte, onycha, galbanum with pure frankincense (of each there shall be an equal part). You shall make of these an incense blended as by the perfumer, seasoned with salt, pure and holy."

We might also recall the gesture of Mary Magdalene when she wanted to show her love for Jesus: "While Jesus was at Bethany in the house of Simon the Leper, as he sat at table a woman came in carrying an alabaster flask of ointment of pure nard, very costly; and, having broken the flask, she poured the ointment over Jesus's head." *(Mark 14:3)*.

Also spiritual heirs of Egypt, the Greeks made plentiful use of perfumes in their rites, fumigations of incense and libations of aromatic oil or wine, as Hesiod advised:

"Let pure incense smoke over your altars,

To gain the favours of your immortal gods.

Allow ample libation still to flow

At the dying of the day or as dawn begins to glow."

The Romans, to whom the Greeks handed down their taste for perfumes and their culture in general, also adopted the liturgical rite and made extravagant use of aromatics, as revealed in the amusing song of Ovid:

"Before the vessels from India and the Euphrates

Brought us costly spice

And precious incense, we offered on the altar

A modest tribute of wheat mixed with salt.

Our gods, in those days, to show that they smiled upon us

Knew how to content themselves with simple sacrifices,

A branch of myrtle or sweet-smelling wood

This was the extent of the offering, in company with meadow flowers."

As civilisation became more sophisticated, men soon discovered in perfumes (which apart from their therapeutic vocation were also considered to be of divine origin, a point upon which we will expand no further in this chapter as our work is entirely given over to it) a secular use, the favoured domain of which was naturally that of amorous seduction and then, as morals declined, that of simple pleasure of the senses.

The literature of all ages abounds with accounts of the erotic use of perfumes and spices, associated with conjuring up blossoming maidens or buxom courtesans. Kalidasa, a great Indian poet of the fourth to fifth centuries, in his poem *Meghaduta*, which is strewn with allusions to flowers and their sweet scents, thus addresses a cloud in these terms: "Your expanse, made greater by the scented mists departing the windows of the palace wherein they were used to perfume hair, will linger on the flower-embalmed terraces, where sprightly maidens trace the imprint of their feet with a reddish tint."

Egyptians, Mesopotamians and Jews all made great use of perfumes in the form of oils and unguents with which they anointed the whole body. Stacte, a "royal perfume", was the object of such desire, narrates Athenaeus, that the king of Syria, Antiochus Epiphanius (2nd-3rd century BC), who frequented the public baths, poured a whole bowl of it over one of his envious neighbours. All the onlookers who rushed forward to grab their share fell over one another on the slippery floor, to the king's great glee.

Shakespeare, borrowing from Plutarch, evokes the extent of perfumed sumptuousness reached by Egypt in its dying stages in his *Antony and Cleopatra*: "The barge she (Cleopatra) sat in, like a burnish'd throne, burn'd upon the water; the poop was of beaten gold, purple the sails, and so perfumed that the winds were love-sick with them..."

In Israel, one need only quote Solomon: "Oil and perfume make the heart glad" *(Proverbs 27:9)* and his Song of Songs, the enchanting form of which, although an allegory of mystical love, reveals no less a more profane use for aromatics: "Your anointing oils are fragrant; your name is oil poured out, therefore maidens love you... My nard gives forth its fragrance, my beloved is to me a bundle of myrrh, that lies between my breasts... How much sweeter is the fragrance of your oils than any spice! Your lips distil nectar, my bride; honey and milk are under your tongue, and the scent of your garments is like the scent of Lebanon... His cheeks are like beds of spices, yielding fragrance. His lips are lilies, distilling liquid myrrh... I am my beloved's and my beloved is mine; he pastures his flock among the lilies... Your breasts are like clusters, ever flowing with scented wine... Let us see whether the vines have budded, whether the blossoms have opened and the pomegranates are in bloom. There I will give you my love. The mandrakes give forth fragrance..."

The Greeks long made extravagant use of fragrances and brought the art and use of perfumery to a high degree of refinement; ointments for the whole body, essences poured from flasks to perfume the head or burned in incense-burners at feasts, scenting wines or sprinkled on guests, the lavishness of perfumes reached such a height that laws tried in vain to prevent them from being sold. The familiar expression "to sniff out what's going on" seems to owe its origin to Greek perfumery shops, veritable meeting-places to catch up on all the city gossip, which confirms the favourable influence of pleasant aromas in social exchanges.

Here again, the sensual delights of love are exalted in scented exhalations:

"Wreaths of violets,

And rose and saffron,

Touching me, woven around your head,

"Garlands intertwined

Around your delicate neck,

Fair blooms mingling,

And mysterious fragrance,

The flasks of royal perfume,

That streamed over your lovely hair..."

languishes Sappho after her lover departs.

The comic poet Antiphanes (4th century BC) recounts that the refined individual bathes in a gilded tub and steeps his feet in Egyptian unguent; he rubs his jaws and breast with Phoenician palm oil, his arms and back with mint, his eyebrows and his hair with marjoram, and he uses mother-of-thyme to restore vigour to his legs and his neck.

The Romans for their part delighted in continuing with these scented extravagances and pushing them to truly incredible excesses. Suetonius tells that in the palace built for Nero, "the dining-room ceiling was made from movable ivory blocks and pierced with holes so that the guests might be showered from above with flowers or perfumes; the main one was round and revolved continuously on its own axis, day and night, like the world."

Petronius, likewise reminiscing on Nero in the *Satyricon* recounts: "And now suddenly the ceiling opened up and we saw a huge hoop come down, in all likelihood taken from an enormous barrel, hanging from all around which were gilded wreaths with flasks of perfumes. Whilst we were being invited to remove these gifts, I turned my gaze to the table."

"...I am ashamed to relate what happened next. In a fashion unprecented in our customs, young long-haired slaves brought forward in a silver basin scented oil with which they anointed the feet of the guests, after garlanding them with flowers from thigh to toe. Then the perfume was poured into the wine flask and into the lamps."

A period of respite from this debauchery of scents constituting a somewhat more moral period followed with the fall of the Empire. Then came the Middle Ages, during which aromatics (mainly frankincense and myrrh) were above all put to liturgical use; in castles and at feasts, the custom was to strew the ground with flowers and aromatic plants, a procedure also intended to disguise the putrid smells of hung meat, which was in those days kept under very risky conditions. After the Crusades - which reintroduced to the West the Eastern penchant for lavishness - and with the perfecting of the technique of distillation and the invention of alcohol by the Arabs, together with the obtention of the first rose essence by Avicenna, the use of scents reappeared in the art of seduction.

In 1190, Philip Augustus granted perfumers a charter governing their profession and accorded them the title of master at the end of four years' apprenticeship and three years in a guild.

While the simple practices of the Middle Ages gradually gave way to a more sophisticated way of life, there continued to be a blatant lack of hygiene during the Renaissance. This was offset for the olfactory well-being of high society by the unrestrained use of perfumes, the range of which widened as a result of the discovery of the New World, with perfume spray, toilet vinegars and other scented powders to mask the bodily and excremental smells in people's homes - to the point that Montaigne, in his chapter on "Perfumes" in *Essays*, wrote: "It is said of some, such as Alexander the Great, that their sweat exuded a fragrant odour, by some rare and uncommon constitution, for which Plante and others seek the cause. But the usual way of the body is quite other, and the best to be hoped is that one smells nothing bad. And the sweetness of the purest breaths consists of nothing better than to be unsullied and with no odour that offends, as those of the healthiest children; that is why Plutarch says: '*Mulier tum bene olet, ubi nihil olet.* The most perfect scent of a woman is that she does not smell of anything.' And one is right to suspect people who use pleasing foreign scents and consider that these are being employed to cover up some natural failing. Whence those juxtapositions of ancient poets, to smell pleasant is to stink."

The fashion was for aromatic pastilles, smelling boxes, scented sachets, handkerchieves and gloves, this last reflected in Shakespeare by: "These gloves the count sent me; they are an excellent perfume."[1] And to play a trick on a sleeping drunk: "Carry him gently to my fairest chamber...; balm his foul head in warm distilled waters, and burn sweet wood to make the lodging sweet", advocates the lord in *The Taming of the Shrew.*

We know the heights reached during seventeenth century France (the *Grand Siècle*) and until the end of the *Ancien Régime* by the lack of hygiene and the nauseating smells of Versailles due - as well as to the complete non-existence of modern conveniences - to a curious theory about the permeability of the skin to water, making bathing hazardous. (Baths would, moreover, be considered debilitating until the dawn of the twentieth century, as they were felt to dissipate the animal vitality deemed to be contained in the bodily exhalations of the young and healthy.) A. Corbin relates that "a respectable old lady, disturbed to discover in Louis XVIII's Saint-Cloud the excremental smells that prevailed in Louis XVI's Versailles, confides to Viollet-le-Duc that this show of aristocratic offhandedness awakened nostalgia for her lost youth and the *Ancien Régime* that no longer exists.[2]

The eighteenth century, with the Age of Enlightenment's passion to explain phenomena rationally and in the grip of a sensualist philosophy, witnessed the birth of a great awareness of hygiene and an attempt to combat the putrid, volatile and persistent miasma prevailing in the cities and deemed to be deadly. This was catalogued in a comprehensive

---

[1] Much Ado About Nothing

[2] Viollet-le-Duc, *Dictionnaire de l'architecture*

range of smells, from the disagreeable to the infectious, by the learned brains of the period. It was the time when musk, amber and civet, until now poured on in buckets by the nobility to enhance the *odor di femmina* that was so highly thought of, were relegated in favour of floral scents in keeping with the vogue for a natural healthy life, which was charged with delicately disguising what hygiene still discreetly neglected to do. Smell became the sense which crystallised social repulsions and affinities - the demarcation line between those considered decent, the rich and well-bred possessing a delicate sense of smell; and the rest, the common people, hardly little more than animals and wallowing in their own nauseating emanations, was henceforth drawn by the nose. As the *Dictionnaire de Phrénologie* [Dictionary of Phrenology] then defined it: "Smell is a manifestation of beings, like line, colour and sonority (sic)."

Thenceforth commenced a veritable battle of smells, between the romantic to be celebrated - of which Baudelaire, Flaubert, Zola and so many others fully availed themselves - and the offensive to be eliminated. In the fight against the deleterious miasma, the terror of the times, the perfumer E. Rimmel was not afraid, even in 1870, of endorsing this theory: "It must be proven that perfume is not only intended to mask the disagreeable smell of the miasma, but to reduce it radically, and that it is no longer an object of luxury but an object of utility and one of the true protectors of human health."

Balzac, who concentrated his novel *César Birotteau* on the story of a perfumer, was fascinated by the seduction of olfactory messages and conferred upon them their letters patent of amorous nobility: "She took a few soft steps, as if to billow out her white dress... O my lily! I said, ever perfect and straight of stem, ever white, proud, fragrant, solitary!" Echoing the hygienists, he associates the smell of places with the temperament of their inhabitants when offended, for example, by the odour of boarding-houses, "which smell stuffy, musty, rank... stink of service, office, hospice. It might perhaps be described if we were to invent a process for assessing the basic, nauseating quantities cast off by the catarrhal atmospheres and their like by each lodger, young or old."

The "magic" of perfumes so often celebrated by sensual evocations, affective reminiscences and the imaginative fantasy worlds they conjure up, would be the field of predilection for poetry in the nineteenth century, at the time of romanticism and its sensual-mystical cult of Nature, the flower-bedecked and embalmed temple of soul and body wherein "sublime" aspirations and secretly repressed desires find release in the melancholy and frenzies of an exalted imagination:

"Come then!" cries Alfred de Vigny to Eve, Nature and the eternal Woman:

"Heaven is nothing more to me than a halo

Surrounding you with azure, lighting and protecting you;

The mountain is your temple and the wood its dome;

The bird only sits on the wind-rocked flower,

And the flower only releases scent and the bird only gives forth song

To greater enrapture the air breathed in by your breast."

While Lamartine pours forth:

"Earth is a bundle of twigs

Whose scent makes a man giddy

As to frenzy all his senses;

Wild breezes, full hands,

Bring to God, by their breath,

Everything of incense found on this globe."

And Victor Hugo proclaimed:

"... The resplendent tree

Digs deep into the earth, a hydra beneath its feet;

The fearsome root with its long folded necks,

And a thousand gaping beaks in the black depths,

Sinks down, plunges, reaches the darkness and strives to imbibe it,

And exhales, at the pleasure of air, place and season,

Offers it as perfume to the skies or spits it out as poison,

According to which the root, fragrant or foul,

Issues scent of love or venom of hate."

Poets would eulogise the mysterious oneness of Nature in which mystical, secret connections are formed between scents, sounds and colours: "All is scent, all is sound", reveals Victor Hugo, even before Baudelaire dreams of "A resounding haven wherein my soul is able to imbibe copiously of scent, sound and colour..." and evokes in his famous *Correspondances*:

"Nature is a temple where living pillars
Sometimes let slip words of confusion...
Like long-heard echoes that from afar meld
Into a shadowy deep oneness,
Far-reaching as the night and wide-spread as light,
Fragrances, colours and sound move in unison."

Grandiloquent substitutes and imitations of Nature to which they readily add an imported exoticism - the pleasure garden, then the conservatory, displaying elaborate compositions which must please the sense of smell as much as the eye - are the localities propitious for outpourings of the heart or exaltation of the passions, depending on whether their subtly arranged scents, light or heady, are directed at young maidens or those more skilled in love.

It was the time when people were rediscovering a mysterious and fascinating Orient, a place of cultured pleasures and forbidden delights or, to the contrary but now and then mingling, of fabulous cities and unexplored isles ("In the scented sun-caressed land..."), mythical reflections of a lost paradise where the art of living and loving, evolving in exotic fragrances, would not become tainted by the miasmatic ugliness of city life:

"How distant you are, scented paradise,
Where under a clear blue sky nothing exists but love and joy,
Where all that one loves is worthy of love,
Where in pure sensual delight one's heart is drowned!" *(Baudelaire)*

Thus Baudelaire, a rare poet in the mystery of scents, speaks to us now of olfactory reminiscences awakened by "...some cupboard, Full of the acrid odour of time" or by "...an old flask with memory, From whence gushes forth full of life a soul that is returning", now of the "exotic perfume of the green tamarinds", now of "scents fresh as a child's skin..." or "...of others, corrupt, rich and triumphant, With the expansiveness of things infinite, such as amber, musk, benzoin and frankincense, Which sing of the transports of spirit and senses."

Alternately mystical: "My soul is transported on scent like the soul of other men on music" or sensual: "From her hair springy and heavy, a living sachet, a censer in the alcove, a fragrance arose, wild and musky...", he celebrates still and forever the scents of love: "O promises!

O perfumes, O never-ending kisses!"

Let us conclude by returning to ancient Rome and quoting Catullus, expansive and heady with "heavenly" fragrances, dreaming of existing only to inhale them more fully: "I will tell you of a perfume which my mistress has from the Graces and the gods of love; when you smell it, you will ask of the deities to make of you only a nose."

Outline of an Aromatic Psychobiology

More prosaically, the sense of smell played and continues to play an essential role in communication, particularly racial, and was a decisive factor in the process of development of the various species; this is a conclusive phenomenon in the plant and animal kingdoms. It was, moreover, one of the charges made against fragrances and one which added to their discredit. Corbin observes in his *Etude sur l'odorat et l'imaginaire social au 18e et 19e siècles* [Study on the sense of smell and social make-believe in the eighteenth and nineteenth centuries]: "One or two stereotypes will give an idea of the paradoxes of smell. As a sense of desire, appetite and instinct, it bears the seal of animal nature. Sniffing is associated with the beasts. The incapacity of language to reflect olfactory sensations would, if this sense were predominant, make man a being rooted in the external world. A victim of its own fleeting nature, olfaction would not be able to fall back on thought in any lasting way. Keenness of smell develops in inverse ratio to intelligence."

Whilst animals always mark their territory and identify one another by the smell of their secretions, especially before mating, the human being no longer possesses this natural and prosaic tendency, although he is still, nevertheless, sensitive to bodily exhalations capable of awakening his primal instincts. Today as ever, the issue of an "authentic perfume" (by which we understand the natural, organic exhalation) persists, as shown by Ruth Winter: "The fear with which human beings have been inculcated with regard to their own smell, in particular the smell of their genitals, might well be utterly incongruous and, from a sexual point of view, destructive."

W. Fliess stresses that sniffing, an act always associated with the sex life of animals only, is just as essential to the love life of humans. Perhaps he agrees with Freud when the latter judged that our attitude towards excrement went beyond the bounds of all rationality and that he saw, in the resulting repression of the sense of smell, one of the principal causes of mental illness. He went one better in his scatopsychoanalysis when writing in *Civilisation and its Discontents*, published in 1930: "When man adopted the vertical position and lessened his sense of smell, it was not only his anal eroticism which almost fell victim to an organic repression, but his whole sexuality."

In our opinion, this type of speculation stems from a fundamental reductionism; our scepticism remains as regards the whim on which this type of demoralising and backward-looking theory feeds. It takes no account of the evolution specific to human nature, nor of the fact that the projection onto the animal kingdom of our fantasies and deviations (whether justified or otherwise is not the question) is not necessarily accurate simply because it satisfies our intellectual complaisance.

We feel that comments of Ruth Winter are more temperate and accurate from the scientific point of view when she writes: "It is becoming increasingly evident that we are profoundly influenced, from a physical and a physiological standpoint, by the volatile secretions of other people. Sexual attraction, which we have intellectualised and diluted by bringing romantic notions into the issue, may fully constitute a response to an invisible, silent stimulus; a primitive animal smell." In passing, let us note two examples, as fruity as they are historical: that of Louis XIV who, it is said, revelled in the "smell of hung meat" and forbade his courtesans to bathe; and that of Henry IV of France writing to Gabrielle d'Estrées: "Madam, do not wash, I am coming to see you in three months."

More generally, however, our current habits, hygienic and deodorised - stemming from the disrepute into which sexual smells and musky perfumes began to fall during the eighteenth century - experience indiscreet, intimate body odour as an affront to social decency and even as an olfactory assault beyond the limit of vulgarity. This is a paradoxical hypocrisy in these times of sexual liberation which is brilliantly played upon by the manufacturers of toilet water and other deodorants.

In order to explain this long march towards the generalised deodorisation of the West, we must, according to Corbin, take our sights back to the nineteenth century and to the victory of bourgeois notions of life in society. It was a matter of respectability on the one hand for the well-to-do classes - good taste and modesty forbidding young girls to use scent and honourable married women to use strong perfume - and the earning capacity of the lower classes on the other, associating cleanliness of the body with that of the soul. "Cleanliness, temperance, work, these are, after breathing fresh air, the main conditions for the well-being of the working classes; the accommodation of an honest worker", writes Corbin in quoting Monfalcon and Polinière, "is devoid of luxury, but contains nothing to offend sight or smell... he enjoys better health and earns more. Content in his home, he has greater respect for propriety and the law, and is more attached to the observance of his duties."

We could also view the supremacy of intellect over feeling as a reason for the olfactory reticence from which our culture suffers; this is a prevalent notion in our technicised, scientific civilisation, which testifies to a massive, linear mobilisation of the brain with a view to winning power and the advantage that ensues as a result; the "feminine" values associated with feeling have too often been reduced to trivial romantic - in any case unproductive - factors, one of the components of which is the sense of smell. It is not out of place to believe in a future not far off in which the role of women, irreplaceable and complementary to that of men, and nothing to do with an entropic pseudo-equality of the sexes, will restore smell to the rank of senses worthy of the human being, without for all that foundering in indelicate and scatalogical Freudian considerations.

Thus Maeterlinck, as far back as the beginning of this century, was questioning: "Is it a mechanism which is evolving or atrophying? A faculty which is dozing off or coming to? Everything leads one to believe that it is evolving in pace with our civilisation... This mysterious sense which at first sight appears almost alien to our organism, might well, on further consideration, be that which penetrates it most intimately. Are we not above all aerial beings? Is air not the element most absolutely and most immediately essential to us, and is not smell precisely the only sense which perceives some parts of it? Scents, which are the jewels of such air that enables us to live, do not adorn it without reason. It would not be surprising if this misunderstood luxury were to respond to something most profound and most essential, and more exactly, as we have just seen, to something which yet is not, than to something which no longer is. It is extremely possible that this sense, the only one directed towards the future, already grasps the most striking manifestations of a happy or benevolent form or state of the substance which has plenty of surprises in store for us."

Rather than deny smell or, on the contrary, wallow with a completely animal feverishness in the pleasures produced by sudorific, genital or excremental emanations, we might seek to approach the olfactory world with a new nose, and, what is more, capable of being educated. Furthermore, between the nauseating organic miasma and the natural fragrance enhanced by irreproachable hygiene, it is now possible to study the bodily olfactory phenomena at the basis of certain behaviours in a rational manner, ever since we became aware of the role of pheromones in human sexual attraction.

Initially studied from the perspective of the plant kingdom and in insects, we know that exocrine secretions change according to the time of day, one's inner state and the menstrual cycle, and induce certain modes of behaviour without our being fully conscious of them. An interesting discovery in this connection has recently been made regarding the truffle; known for its aphrodisiac virtues, it appears that the truffle contains an aromatic steroid *(5 α-androstenol)* found in human sperm, underarm sweat and sow secretions. Some people see in this the explanation for the relish that pigs have for the "black diamond".

We also know that the apocrine glands responsible for human odoriferous secretions are only activated at puberty with the appearance of hair on the body; the hairs found under the arms and around the genitals would have originally served to trap the smell, as these glands in all probability secrete sex pheromones. In corroboration of this theory, a close connection has been discovered between the working of the sense of smell and the sex glands, both in human beings and in animals. It was possible to observe, for example, that an impaired sense of smell in women who do not have periods went hand in hand with an increased risk of sterility, and that the onset of the menopause sometimes coincided with a loss of olfactory keenness, this being accompanied in men by a slowing rate of beard growth.

A close link between the nose and the genitals has been shown since the end of the last century by W. Fliess, who discovered by observing his patients that nose bleeds frequently took the place of menstrual periods (or sometimes preceded or accompanied them); some pregnant women even had nose bleeds each month at the time their periods would normally have been due, whilst spells of sexual difficulties coincided with ailments of the respiratory tract (colds, flu, pneumonia, etc.), this occurring in both sexes. Cocainisation or cauterisation treatments or surgery on the "genital areas of the nose" (sympathicotherapy) enabled him to cure serious cases of dysmenorrhoea with very high rates of success.

Apart from pheromones, several smells unable to be detected at the conscious level of our olfactory perception nevertheless influence and engender in us a number of involuntarily determined reactions. These smells seem to act a little like certain ranges of apparently inaudible ultrasounds, although in a way that is amplified, since olfactory stimuli, even more than sounds, have an effect on the emotions. Even when perceptible, it is difficult to grasp smells rationally, except for those whose job it is to select, process or recognise them. In this connection, we would mention that in some areas a more highly developed sense of smell makes up for shortcomings in scientific techniques and is at the same time recognised by various authorities. For instance, the FDA (Food and Drug Administration) in the United States has called on the exceptional nose of a doctor of chemistry, Albert Weber, to detect bad foodstuffs entering from a number of countries - mainly fish for which, curiously, there seems to exist no other means than the sense of smell for testing its state of fitness for consumption.

Briefly, we can say that we like or do not like such and such a smell, without necessarily being able to justify the nature of our feelings; we only *reason* with difficulty what our sense of smell perceives, whilst our visual or auditory perceptions can be subjected to mental analysis without any problem. At first sight, such and such a perfume attracts or repels, enchants or arouses, excites the affects and invites the emotions to override the rational to the point that our olfactory judgement becomes purely subjective. Even in an essentially thinking individual, the perception of a smell does not arouse intellectual analysis but an affective reaction, whether positive or negative. In fact, smell is, amongst all of our senses, the one most directly connected with the reflex drive areas of the brain; contrary to the messages sent by hearing, sight, taste or touch, the olfactory signal does not travel by way of the thalamus but directly to the behavioural centres situated at the base of the brain (formerly called *rhinencephalus*, which in Greek means *olfactory brain*), and is by this fact less subject to rational control.

There also exists a close and obvious relationship between the senses of smell and taste. The smell-taste affinity has been recognised for thousands of years by traditional Chinese medicine, which considers smells to be aerial emanations of taste and in which subtle taste begins and ends with smell; they are an essential complement to one another as regards acting on the organism, where taste acts on the structures and smell on the energies that contribute to the balance of life force energy, according to stages in life, the seasons of the year and times of the day. With reference to the laws of Chinese energetics and the five elements/processes (moves), the classification of smells is superimposed onto the gradual transformation of foods.

Generally speaking, as far as tastes are concerned:

- Acid, tartish (element wood-spring) corresponds to a fresh, raw food (initially representing the seepage from sucking lamb). It corresponds to the coupled organs of the liver-gall bladder, and governs the psychic process of exteriorisation and the need to create. In excess, it leads to irritability, anger, the failure of these organs, fear and anguish.

- Bitter (element fire-summer) corresponds to a cooked food, grilled (action of fire) like roasted coffee. It acts on the coupled organs of the heart-small intestine, and governs the emotions as well as the extremes from over-excitation and joy to timidity and apathy.

- Sweet, sugary (element earth-end of summer) corresponds to a cooked food preserved with spices, such as aniseed for example. It acts on the coupled organs of the spleen-stomach, and governs reflection, memorising and the extremes from obsession to lack of concern.

- Hot, pungent (element metal-autumn) corresponds to a highly spiced or oxidised food, such as garlic, iodine, horseradish. It acts on the coupled organs of the lungs-large intestine, and governs interiorisation and the extremes from fear and sadness to instability.

- Salty (element water-winter) corresponds to a highly fermented, macerated food; this is the putrid tendency - for example strong cheese, anchovies preserved in salt. It acts on the coupled organs of the kidneys-bladder and governs the survival of the individual, procreation and the extremes from authoritarianism to fear of others.

According to this thousand-year-old tradition, fragrances and perfumes are essentially linked to the cycle of the metal and are in direct relation to respiration and the life force energy.

As early as 1769, Haller noted in his treaty on physiology that "since antiquity, doctors were maintaining that of all the sense organs, the nose is the closest to the brain and therefore to the origin of feelings". This is a somewhat empirical affirmation, but evidence of intuitively based research. In 1819, a period in which a veritable revolution was being brought about in the world of smells, one could read in the *Dictionnaire des Science médicales* [Dictionary of Medical Sciences]: "Smell is the sense of tender memories."

The evocation of the smell of madeleines dunked in tea is very well known, the associated recollection of which was keenly illustrated by Marcel Proust:

"But when nothing remains of a past long gone, after the death of men, after the destruction of things, then alone, more fragile but more enduring, more intangible, more persistent, more true, smell and taste linger for a long time yet, like souls, to be recalled, to wait, to hope, on the ruins of all that went before, to bear without yielding, in their tenuity, scarcely palpable, the immense edifice of memory."[1]

But if a smell, a perfume, can remind us of such and such an event, person, situation or time, we are unable, on the face of it, to summon up at will from within ourselves the scents that we are so fond of - unlike the possibility of recalling the memory of a face or a painting, or of mentally remembering a tune. This phenomenon is due to the fact that our olfactory memory is more reactional than creative.

At the level of reactive behaviour, the hold that the world of scent has over the emotions is significant. As Ruth Winter quite rightly observed: "fragrances are capable of bringing back a recollection and

---

[1] Du côté de chez Swann.

driving us to act one way or another without our even being aware of it".

This being the case, we might consider that the links between smells and feelings offer us a most interesting sphere of activity, up till now little exploited in aromatherapy. We can see that they are both, amongst other things, connected with heat, whether physical or psychic. From a therapeutic point of view, the correlation is of significance. In the plant kingdom, if there is insufficient solar radiation, the enzymatic conversions cannot take place and the production of aromatic molecules is totally obstructed. Similarly, heat is the source of scents from living organisms, the importance of which we know as far as communication and sexuality is concerned. In the same way, lack of human warmth or love is detrimental to exchanges, thwarts development and blocks communication; even if not always noticeable, it is only when exposed to the vibrations of love that a person opens up, blossoms and gives of the best of himself - or at least one would hope so. In the cold, one cannot "feel" anything any more, this being as true in the actual and as in the figurative sense.

But the most interesting thing, it seems to us, is the fact that the smell-emotion connection is mutually interactive. This property amplifies its sphere of activity and prevents the psychosensory effect of smells from being restricted to a sort of entropic determinism. In fact, whilst a perfume awakens in us certain affinities or repulsions, depending on our perception of it or any memories it brings up, the feelings that we experience in turn, according to their nature, generate scents - perceptible or otherwise - the effect of which on our surroundings is not to be ignored. Popular expressions such as *he gets up my nose* uttered about someone unpleasant whom one can also say *stinks* or even that *he's shitty*, express instinctive and irrational reactions which may result in our personal emanations.

Interest in the smell/feeling axis, which is fairly well recognised and, curiously, almost exclusively exploited from a commercial point of view whereas its socio-pedagogic applications would be extremely fascinating, is ten times greater when one considers its correlation, the feeling/smell axis[2]. Be it only with a view to knowing ourselves better, the act of observing our olfactory attractions and repulsions and possibly trying to analyse the reasons for them could lead us to objectify our scents.

Whether these be subtle or coarse, attractive or repellent, they are in any case dependent on our way of life (particularly with regard to food) which expresses our attractions and needs, our emotions, the nature of our thoughts and feelings, our psychic stability, in other words our *states of mind*. Whatever our tendencies - whether spiritual or prosaic, reserved or capricious - the exhalations from our temperamental impulses are no less present through their fragrant vibrations, even if we think they remain secret.

Our many observations in this sphere lead us to consider that subversive feelings such as egoism, hate, jealousy, anger, etc. produce "pernicious vibrations" playing the role of vectors of form waves materialised in the physical by acid, bitter, repellent and pungent smells. Conversely, evolutive and harmonious feelings such as altruism, kindness, tolerance and love generate communicative vibrations leading to form waves materialised by sweet, flowery or fruity smells, which are subtle and uplifting. Between these two extremes stretches an infinite range of subtleties in scents and perfumes, from the hot and sugary to the cold and bitter, from the ethereal to the revulsive, the exciting and piquant to the depressive and insipid, in correspondence with the specific nature of each feeling or affective drive inherent in the expression of the personality.

It is of course possible to arrive at the same conclusions by starting from the principle that a negative psychic disposition brings about metabolic disturbances, manifested by the appearance of nauseating aromatic molecules resulting from biological fermentation and organic decomposition. This physiological approach corroborates the "energetic" interpretation of the matter; all the same, the concept of similar form waves between smells and feelings could perhaps explain the "smell of sainthood" which exceptional beings, such as St Teresa of Avila, sometimes seem to exude around themselves. Her body, exhumed because of the delightful perfume emanating from her tomb, gave off a fragrance which was, according to the remarks of Father Ribera in 1585,

---

[2]In this connection, the theory of interactive morphic fields, as expounded by the biologist Rupert Sheldrake, infers similar form waves making it possible to begin to glimpse a potentially significant psychophysiological influence.

"extremely pleasant. The scent of it was such that once *[the body]* was placed on a mule between two bales of straw ready for the journey, the room where it had been remained most fragrant... The doctors examined the body and decided that this must be something supernatural, if not truly miraculous, since after three years, without ever having been opened or embalmed, it was so preserved that nothing was missing and a wonderful smell was emanating from it." The perfumes given off in this way were of iris and jasmine, according to witnesses. Such was also the case of St Thérèse of Lisieux, who smelled of roses until after her death, therefore keeping the promise she made before dying: "After my death, I will cause rose petals to rain over the earth."

This belief in the sweetness of the scent of saints could well have been supported on the other hand by opinions with the weight of dogma as advanced by St Philip of Neri (who is himself deemed to have exuded the fragrance of pine on his death), maintaining that he could recognise those souls bound for hell from the customary stench given off by most sinners, such as the bitter, winey smell that some recognised later as typical of the drunkard.

In the eighteenth century, Dr J.N. Hallé, who was long interested in the quality of air, was thus able to tell accurately the olfactory environment of the rooms in which men, women or children were crowded together. In Bicêtre, he notes in passing "the insipid smell of worthy poor souls". Far more social still was, throughout the last century, the *aura seminalis* of the chaste priest or the grubby celibate schoolmaster, a recurring theme in romantic literature according to Corbin, and one which the writer J Vallès would still be denouncing in 1879. We might note the remarks in the *Journal des savants* (1684) attributing to the adulterous woman or the one "engaging excessively in coitus" an atrocious smell due to the "spermatic discharge into her body-humours, contaminating her fluids". Thus the French word for prostitute became "putain" (from *putida*, foul-smelling).

From the fragrant emanations of the saint and the heavy stenches of the peripatetic, the quality and nature of our smells reflect the diverse aspects of our personality. This is without doubt one of the reasons why the world of odours disturbs us, for we are rarely what we think we are, either in reality or imagination. In a culture which is so biased towards appearances, our smells often act as traitors, obliging us to camouflage them (rightly so, as a rule) although the subterfuge of artificial perfume cannot entirely conceal what we are.

It would nevertheless be hasty to conclude that perfumes have an intrinsic power since, when they arouse in us feelings of a varied nature - from mystical awakening to the most violent sexual urges - it is less by virtue of their own nature than because they reveal our ego. Musk, for example, typical of sexual stimulation, is used by certain *rishi* in their meditations, whilst rose and frankincense may, depending on the nature of the people inhaling them, point to amorous conquest and Eastern frolics as easily as prayer and contemplation.

Depending on age, social conditions, race and culture, and above all depending on our own mental outlook, perfumes will have multiple and sometimes contradictory effects. If group phenomena can be observed, this is amongst other things due to similarity of behaviour and therefore of mental outlook, at least within a specific area, of the people concerned. It is on these collective olfactory attractions that some commercial companies play, their purpose being to impregnate a striking number of mass consumption products with perfume; from washing powder which must smell fresh to after-shave with a supposedly irresistible male scent, from the bakery which emits synthetic smells of fresh bread and croissants to the bus-stop reeking of noble British tobaccos aimed at pipe smokers, nothing is exempt from aromatic molecules employed to influence and pressurise the docile consumer in his decision-making. Some companies have even launched scented clothes onto the market, the smell of which lasts for a number of washes. From the fruity smell to one of garages (diesel, drain oil), anything went for the T-shirts of the *Smell This Shirt* company, one of whose biggest successes in the 1970s was the *Pot-Shot-Shirt* smelling of marijuana. Another company sold women's underwear scented with fruits and flowers, and also with scotch and popcorn - a relatively reasonable fantasy compared to its lingerie smelling of pizzas and gherkins, intended, perhaps, for those all-consuming love affairs!

If olfactory eccentricities seem to know no bounds, perfumers, more socially speaking, know how to exploit even the grossest traits of our personality artistically through perfumes with evocative names that no doubt reflect a number of our collective tendencies and aspirations: *Poison, Opium, Egoist, Black Magic,* etc.

We can conclude from this that, whilst it is possible to influence an individual by awakening certain hidden tendencies or by stimulating features of his personality through smells and perfumes, the judicial use of natural plant essences is most certainly able to act at the level of his psychic and, consequently, his physical health. It is by taking into consideration the olfactory affinities and the organoleptic action of essences that the characterology of essences, the living dimension of aromatherapy, was formed. This is, in our opinion, as vital to the medical practice of this science as an understanding of the biochemical mechanisms. As a result of this approach, aromatherapy takes on its full force by not restricting itself to aromatic chemistry, a very concrete dimension, with a vast - but nevertheless limited - sphere of activity compared to the extraordinary psychosensory potentialities of essential oils.

In an intellectualised and over-materialistic world, the affective resonance and spiritual dimension of a treatment are the poor relations of modern medicine, which is prone to neglect the psychological aspect of the pathogeneses. We may nevertheless reasonably expect a consequent therapeutic action through a coherent and precise use of essential oils, these being natural substances with remarkable physico-chemical properties but also capable of restoring our psychosomatic stability by energising our emotional, mental and spiritual capacities.

The idea of a characterology seems natural when one applies oneself to objectivising the psychosensory effect of essences by defining the personalities corresponding to them. This human approach to aromatherapy offers some similarities with the principles set out by Hahnemann when he established the bases of homoeopathy at the end of the eighteenth century; although the usefulness of personalised treatments is always disputed, the results obtained in homoeopathy speak out on behalf of a therapy that acts on the patient's predisposition, still often neglected in favour of symptomatic interventions.

However, the personalisation of treatment based on patient/remedy affinities and correlations is not an invention of our times. Ancient Chinese medicine, the Ayurvedic tradition and, closer to home, Paracelsus's theory of "signatures" are based on the correspondences existing between plants or other natural substances with specific characteristics - shapes, colours, symbolism, smells, etc. - and the morphopsychic structure of man.

Our approach to Nature and, in the present case, to aromatic plants, leads us to consider as well not only the biological, but also the subtle, links uniting microcosm and macrocosm, involving each kingdom in the evolution of the others and establishing phenomena of correspondences between them; these, when judiciously exploited, are able to make a very positive contribution to restoring harmony to part or the whole of the natural biotope to which we belong.

Whether by studying in greater depth the morphogenetic fields developed by Sheldrake or by understanding the recent developments in nuclear physics, which overturn the mechanistic and fragmented vision of the universe we have inherited from Newton, the principles of energetic resonance require our attention and are worthy of being investigated more fully. Their field of study must not be kept only to the symbolic sciences whose metaphors, for want of proper interpretation, give rise more to ridicule than they invite reflection as far as the scientific rationalist is concerned.

In drawing up aromatic characterologies, we are not claiming to attribute a specific animistic form to species of plants (although this approach is not irrational but proceeds from a thesis worthy of being properly backed up). We are, rather, emphasising the laws of interactive affinities between the plant and human kingdoms which, when properly understood, make it possible to make up a remedy specific to each person. We do not wish to "humanise" plants because of the respect we have for their intrinsic nature, a respect which protects us from a narcissistic anthropocentrism, the tendency of which is characteristic of a certain state of mind given to creating false relations with nature and the surrounding kingdoms.

It is therefore not the frame of mind of *Laurus, Chamaemelum* or *Cupressus* as plants that we define, but rather the morphological and temperamental typologies corresponding to them. The characterologies presented by *Origanum majorana* or *Lavandula vera* people therefore signify only that the individuals connected with these essences are, typologically speaking, rebellious and impetuous, subject to temperamental and ideological excesses as far as the first are concerned; calm, generous and relatively introverted as regards the second, with particular pathological tendencies associated with their nature and specific character.

The aromatic characterology is in no way a projection of our fantasies, deviations and illnesses of a psychosomatic nature onto the plant kingdom, but simply an analogical approach, a search for affinities between the aromatic remedy and the person who is sick. It makes it possible to understand better the rather complex personality of the patient, which cannot be dissociated from the etiology of his illness, and offers the possibility of a treatment appropriate to him. An aromatherapy prescription made out on the basis of characterologies will be more suited to enabling restoration of the patient's predisposed equilibrium than a general prescription, even one based on natural products.

The aromatherapist treating a case of insomnia, for example, will not indiscriminately prescribe the essences commonly used, such as *Lavandula vera, Ocimum basilicum* and *Citrus aurantium* p.o. leaves, but will assess their specific properties according to the people they represent or who, on the contrary, are hostile towards them. *Lavandula vera*, in fact, is typical for the disturbed sleep of a child troubled by the physical or affective absence of his mother, for nervous and emotional insomnia and fear of the dark; *Ocimum basilicum* deals with the insomnia of people "digesting" their anxieties during the night, insomnia due to stress or over-indulgence in food; whilst *Citrus aurantium* p.o. leaves corresponds to the insomnia of the mature person suffering from emotional worries, thrown off balance by a separation and unable to sleep alone at night.

Thanks to the characterology, the treatment is refined and personalised, involves the patient and makes him psychologically aware of his responsibility by affording him the opportunity of going beyond the limited framework of symptomatic intervention in his curative approach. At a time when there is so much talk about global or holistic medicine, when many therapists wish to take more account of the person who is sick than the illness, it is interesting to discover methods which relate the logical environmental approach (the "terrain") to the patient's psychic frames of mind, if one accepts that the origin of pathogenetic disturbances lies in their inherent imbalance.

Subtleties must nevertheless be respected when attributing a specific characterology to a patient, since no individual remains statically the same and must not be categorised for life within a defined typology. In homoeopathy, the fact that some people present the psychosomatic traits of *Ignatia, Pulsatilla* or *Chamomilla* does not necessarily imply that they retain them without changing or evolving, nor that they only express the tendencies of their predisposition to certain diseases. In the same way, in aromatherapy as we conceive it, a jovial person who is relatively easy-going and sensual, such as *Cupressus sempervirens,* may equally show the arrogant and authoritarian tendencies of *Laurus nobilis* and even, on his bad days, the misogyny characteristic of *Rosmarinus officinalis b.s. camphor.*

The characterology of essences must not be understood as a sort of simplistic classification directory which would lead us to conclude that such and such a patient is a perverted sex maniac under the pretext that *Satureja montana* has proved effective during a treatment to fight infection; or that such and such another is necessarily an idle, sensual oaf just because he is fond of the scent of *Cinnamomum zeylanicum.* The characterology must be seen as a synthetic description which makes it possible to grasp the "aura" of each aromatic typology, and not considered as the description of characteristics acquired to be sanctioned without qualification. In practice, a *Eugenia caryophyllata* is not systematically a midwife, an introverted child of the *Thymus vulgaris b.s. linalool* type will not inevitably be a genius once his turbulent adolescence is over, and *Rosmarinus officinalis b.s. bornyl acetate, verbenone* is more a state of awareness than a person one might meet on a street corner - hence the poetic enthusiasm with which we wrote his presentation.

To conclude, we make no bones about the archetypal and often symbolic approach to characterologies which resorts to a metaphorical, even allegorical, interpretation, since we are convinced that any therapy, besides its technical nature, must be founded on philosophical, humanist and spiritual bases. Animism, when one thinks about it, is more complementary to than opposed to rationalism, and when we objectivise the different personality traits that smells reveal, a certain poetry sits quite naturally with the characterology. But has not the latter always been foreseen in such a way that perfumes and the beings associated with them are celebrated to such an extent in mythologies, tales and traditions, with their mythical procession of florid superlatives and coloured epithets?

It is thus simultaneously towards both the approach of a medical methodology and the study of a journey we would describe as initiatory - the illnesses, cures, rises and falls of which are almost inevitable stages - that we invite you in this work. At all events, unless confounded by an automatic hatred of anything new, everyone will be able to gain something of worth from *Portraits in Oils*, if not therapeutic, then at least cultural.

Monographs
of the Essential Oils

Introduction

The monographs of the aromatic plants are grouped by genus (*Salvia, Thymus, Lavandula,* etc.); each species is looked at botanically and its essential oil analysed from a biochemical point of view, together with any variations in specificities which might become evident. Although the properties and resulting indications are given within a broad and non-exhaustive context, they have the advantage of being clear and verified. No property is speculative and no fact derives from a dry and bookish compilation, an approach which would be vague and in any case inappropriate because of the anomalies shown in the majority of works on aromatherapy today.

These properties and indications are the fruit of experience acquired over long years and research that we are currently carrying on within the framework of the Institut Scientifique d'Aromatologie; it is confirmed in practice by many doctors and therapists.

Despite their accuracy, however, these facts can only be presented in a manner which is, if not succinct, at least limited, since an entire work would be needed for each essential oil if we were to explore all its possibilities and study its viable combinations with the other essences. The combinations are therefore only given as a guide, according to the aromatic affinities of the essences and their complementary properties.

We are not able, in this work, to mention dosages, these requiring numerous details which would detract from its clarity as a whole and burden the text with technical and medical data that would be off-putting to some readers. We refuse to accept cook-book formulae or "grandmother's recipe" type descriptions as far as simplifying the indications and dosages is concerned. We know from experience that rough estimates are detrimental to quality and that incomplete information is fully liable to be misunderstood or wrongly interpreted, which would make its use risky and even dangerous in the case of medical practice*.

To end, we would stress the preventative nature of aromatherapy and the fact that it is above all a matter of a "terrain" medicine, in other words, one that works on predisposing factors. In cases of diabetes, urine retention, cardiovascular pathologies, cancers and other serious illnesses, the aromatherapy treatment does not obviate the need for a medical examination and a clear medical strategy.

---

*Refer to this matter in the second volume of this work: *La Nouvelle Aromathérapie; formules et prescriptions* to be published by Editions JAKIN. We recommend that the general public wishing to use essential oils within a family context of prevention and vital hygiene, and needing practical information and essential warnings on the method of action of the essences, should read: *L'Aromathérapie pratique et familiale. Comment utiliser 33 huiles essentielles majeures sans risque et avec un maximum d'efficacité* [Practical and Family Therapy. How to use 33 major essential oils safely and to maximum effect] (Editions JAKIN).

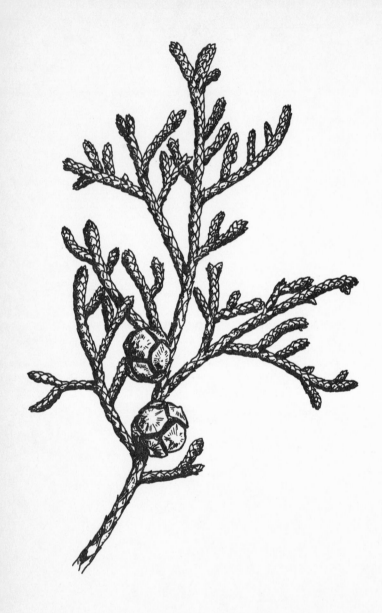

Cupressus Sempervirens

When I walk amongst you, trees of these great woods,
In everything that at once surrounds and conceals me,
In your solitude where I return to my centre,
I sense some higher power that hears me and loves me.
Victor Hugo

Origin and botanical profile

Cupressus sempervirens, which means "Evergreen Cypress", has given its name to the family of the *Cupressaceae*. This is a tree which commonly grows in different areas, sometimes very far away from its places of origin – the Eastern countries, islands of the Aegean Sea and Asia Minor; it is currently found around the whole perimeter of the Mediterranean basin, in northern India, Afghanistan and even in China. It is an extremely old species of tree dating from the Pliocene (Tertiary era, -5.3 to -1.8 million years) which ancient civilisations must have known about since it is mentioned in an Assyrian text 3,500 years old. Exceptionally long lived, some contemporary Cypresses are believed to be two thousand years old.

Better known in its cultivated form with its dense and slender bearing, *Cupressus sempervirens* is still evolving in its wild form, with a less leafy but just as noble an appearance. As such, it forms an integral part of these dry and arid landscapes, where stone has not yet been overrun by vegetation and where nostalgia and the mark of the past are felt all around.

Strongly aromatic, *Cupressus sempervirens* contains essences in all its parts, from the wood to the cones, as well as the leaves and no doubt the roots. There are some twenty species of *Cupressus*, several of which are "fake Cypresses", some with toxic essences.

The essential oil of *Cupressus sempervirens* has a characteristic scent, "the very fine smell of Cypress", as Origen says, less vehement and disturbing than the essential oil of Blue Arizona Cypress (*Cupressus arizonica Greene*), which is toxic.

It is from its twigs obtained by pruning the trees in autumn that the essential oil is extracted by steam distillation. A pleasant distillation, it invigorates the operator, who experiences a feeling of stable strength and balance through inhaling the powerful but soothing fragrances of this majestic tree.

Properties and indications
HEBBD *Cupressus sempervirens*
p.o. twigs, *b.s.* α-pinene

Cupressus sempervirens is a well-known essential oil, without apparent mystery but one which, like Lavender which everyone thinks they know how to use, must be studied in greater depth to reveal all its properties and exploit its fullest potential.

One of its main characteristics is that of being an excellent venous decongestant, very useful in cases of congestion (haemorrhoids) and venous circulatory stases of the lower limbs (varicose veins, oedemas). It will almost always be necessary in such cases to combine with it an internal treatment of *Rosmarinus officinalis b.s. bornyl acetate, verbenone* as a blood purifier, as well as *Mentha piperita b.s. menthol,* a circulatory toner, and *Pistacia lentiscus,* a venous and lymphatic decongestant; in the event of bleeding or wounds, use *Cistus ladaniferus,* a powerful cicatrisant, as well.

The biochemical composition of *Cupressus* allows it a marked action on the humours and hormones. *Cupressus* is a good immunostimulant as a "terrain" essence, especially when combined with *Laurus nobilis* and *Rosmarinus officinalis b.s. bornyl acetate, verbenone,* but it is not very suited to fighting acute or serious infectious pathologies. It is recommended in cases of chronic ailments – such as pulmonary tuberculosis, for example – particularly with *Myrtus communis,* or for preventing seasonal secondary infections with chronic bronchitis or emphysema.

Because of its anti-inflamatory, antispasmodic and mucolytic properties, *Cupressus sempervirens* is an effective cough mixture in cases of acute and chronic bronchitis, whooping-cough and tracheitis, in combination with *Lavandula spica, Hyssopus officinalis var. decumbens, b.s. linalool, 1.8 cineole* and *Thymus vulgaris b.s. thymol*, being antiviral and an immunostimulant. Where indicated, it is effective in cases of sinusitis and rhinitis with *Rosmarinus officinalis b.s. 1.8 cineole* and *Eucalyptus globulus*.

Cupressus sempervirens is also a good prostatic decongestant with *Pistacia lentiscus* and *Santalum album*. It is a stimulant for the exocrine pancreas with *Rosmarinus officinalis b.s. bornyl acetate, verbenone, Mentha piperita* and *Anethum graveolens*, which are stimulants of the digestive functions.

Slightly emmenagogue, its action is, on the other hand, excellent in cases of difficult menopause with hot flushes, combined with *Salvia officinalis* and *Rosmarinus officinalis b.s. bornyl acetate, verbenone*, an endocrinal rebalancer.

It is active in cases of infantile enuresis, with *Thymus vulgaris b.s. linalool*, a nerve tonic, and *Ravensara aromatica*, a balancer of the nerves and emotions, but it is essential to treat relational problems between parents and child.

A "terrain"* essential oil, *Cupressus* is rebalancing and nervine; it is suitable for people who are unbalanced, weary from nerves due to a lack of stability and exhausted as a result of a poor diet. It is also a sweat regulator when perspiration is due to over-excitability.

Cupressus sempervirens is a very versatile essential oil, easy to combine, and with a deep action helpful to people of all ages. One cannot say that it possesses particularly original specific properties, but is, on the contrary, appropriate in a large number of cases. A guarantee of equilibrium and sure serenity, this essence is suitable for those who lack these qualities as well as for those who have lost touch with them. Its highest spiritual action will be enhanced in combination with *Cedrus atlantica* and *Santalum album*. *Cupressus* and *Rosmarinus officinalis b.s. bornyl acetate, verbenone* together prove a very judicious combination, both at the physical and psychic level. *Juniperus communis* p.o. twigs, which, like the ancient Cypress, grows in wild and arid countryside, will be a very good complementary essence in cases of rheumatism or osteoarthritis.

Its combination with *Myrtus communis b.s. pinene, 1.8 cineole* enables the effective treatment of deep-seated broncho-pulmonary pathologies, whilst encouraging the interiorisation of individuals with too flighty a spirit.

As a general rule, one must avoid combining it with the *Asteraceae* and the other *Cupressaceae* – and with *Helichrysum italicum* in particular, despite its affinities with the latter for circulatory pathologies – as well as with *Origanum majorana,* which lacks a certain maturity for coping with the quiet but imposing influence of *Cupressus.*

The characterology allows us to define its nature and its sphere of activity more effectively. It is an essential oil that is almost never used alone and is easy to combine. At the very most, in too great a quantity, it risks detracting from some over-fragile essences, but, for its part, never takes umbrage in any combination. All absorption routes may be used, although there is a preference for it to be administered orally.

Characterology

The splendour of the Cypress, a fine slender tree rising like a flame towards the starry, endless sky, represents the sacred flame of life, the unchangeable, eternal essence, and powerfully evokes the spiritual archetype of *Cupressus sempervirens,* a tall, fine-looking old man with the wisdom granted by a thousand years of intense, disciplined life.

Thus *Cupressus,* the evergreen tree with legendary long life, is associated with the idea of the immortality of the soul, and is the willing companion to the afflicted, survivors of the dead. It is also the wood of sublimation of the sex force, a sign of incorruptibility and purity of soul, of assistance to those who, through transmuting the raw vigour in their roots – the instinctual sex energy – into a refined vigour, a spiritual energy, seek to experience eternal life.

The symbolism of *Cupressus* is found wherever the tree was able to grow and flourish. In archaic Shintoism, the *shaku* (priests' sceptre) was made from Cypress, like the wand of certain magicians. In Rome, the arrow from the bow of Cupid, god of love, and the sceptre of Jupiter, both phallic symbols, were also made from Cypress wood. Still in Rome,

---

*See footnote on page ix of the Introduction.

Cypress trees encircled the house of the sages and the temple of Aesculapius as their fragrance kept away the uninitiated and guarded against evil influences. Aesculapius, the Greek Asclepins (which means *of inexhaustible goodness*), served as a vehicle for the same symbol of life and healing as his father Apollo. Having died and been resuscitated in the form of a serpent, Asclepius brought the dead back to life with the blood taken from Medusa's right side, whilst the blood from her left side had the power to kill. We find here again symbols of sexual sublimation.

Through its salutary nature and spiritual powers, *Cupressus sempervirens* tempers the human passions, masters the reactions of the ego and calms emotional and sexual excesses. It renders men philosophical and wise, sustains their will and helps them to come through romantic upheavals. Thus, a Byzantine account relates that three trees grow at the gate of the "Symbolic Garden": the Cypress, the Cedar and the Pine, which teach us moderation.

The meeting of the Cedar and the Cypress brings us back to the biblical trilogy of the three sacred trees, Cypress, Cedar and Sandalwood: "Solomon sent word to Hiram the king of Tyre:... Behold, I am about to build a house for the name of the Lord my God and dedicate it to him... Send me also cedar, cypress and algum timber from Lebanon... And my servants will be with your servants, to prepare timber for me in abundance, for the house I am to build will be great and wonderful." *(Chronicles 2:2)*

Thus *Cupressus*, hovering serenely beyond existence and death, remains the last loyal and silent companion of the dead, and keeps watch over cemeteries with its familiar, reassuring outline.

Its properties are carried over from the tree to the person, albeit in humanised form; connected with the immortality that it symbolises, *Cupressus's* youthfulness of spirit seems to defy time and makes stability one of its principal qualities. Thanks to this virtue and its equilibrium, the spirit of *Cupressus sempervirens* is rooted in the lands of wisdom and erects its dwelling place upon the highest peaks of patience and serenity.

Even so, its youthfulness is not that, impetuous and rebellious, of *Origanum majorana*, but of the confident soul who lights up the features of an old man. *Cupressus sempervirens* is old but with no defined age, for time, his ally, allows him to enjoy inner peace and the serenity of the golden age, the fruits of patience which are harvested at the end of a harmonious and spiritually rich life. Far from emotional turmoils and mental fluctuations, *Cupressus* remains stable and his own master in the face of the turmoil of the world around.

Cupressus is also a protector and, as such, knows how to listen, like Vasudeva, the ferryman across the river which guides Siddhartha[5]- in his quest for the divine – to the discovery of himself. Always smiling and laconic, the old man knew how to listen to those he took across to the other side of their being, and comforted them with his listening, his patience and peace. "Vasudeva listened with great attention. He heard all about his origin and his childhood, his studies and his seekings, his pleasures and needs. It was one of the ferryman's greatest virtues that, like few people, he knew how to listen."

Cupressus, by its salutary presence, supports the lonely mother whom time turns upside down by etching her face with the furrows of old age. Confronting the depression, the weariness, the silent and concealed tears which are sometimes the companions of the menopause, *Cupressus sempervirens* is there to restore vigour, equilibrium and faith and knows how to comfort, as Orpheus sang:

"- I am parched with thirst and dying.
- Come, drink of the ever-running source, to the right where stands a white cypress.
- Who are you? And whence do you come?
- I am son of the Earth and the starry Sky, and my lineage is celestial."

Aged in body but not heart, of a good and generous nature, receptive and patient, standing calmly and serenely awaiting the end of its existence, *Cupressus* at its best is part of those people whose company is beneficial and whose advice, as discreet as it is wise, is most often worth following.

Generosity, depth, patience and listening to others are the essential qualities of this nature, whose essence will beneficially be prescribed to people who are unbalanced and seeking a form of stability, being rather isolated and going through a phase in which they more strongly feel the

---

[5]The hero in Hermann Hesse's novel of the same name.

need for attention and for someone to listen to them.

This essence is also needed by those souls who, though indicated by the *Cupressus* characterology, evoke the Cypress transplanted far from its land of origin to decorate our homes and gardens and which, in line and over-pruned, displays, instead of its lofty peak, a fatal vacuum in the expression of its deep nature.

Middle-aged men, these *Cupressus* people who always love life but no longer look at it with the eyes of the sage, prove more common. They are nevertheless driven by a certain generosity and, as satisfied sensualists, food lovers and epicureans, lay on wedding feasts and banquets for all around them.

Somewhat distanced from the noble soul of the original *Cupressus*, they suffer as a consequence the physical effects of old age and degeneration, such as thick blood, varicose veins, haemorrhoids, prostatis, diabetes and chronic bronchitis.

Nevertheless, the *Cupressus* archetype remains what he is: a source of peace through his kindly listening, and of elevation through his self-possession and stability which, when the land is again favourable, sows once more the grains of the sacred in the hearts of those in tune with the respect for life and Nature.

Origanum Majorana

O Pan! and you, deities of these waves,
Bestow on me the inner beauty of the soul!
Plato

Origin and botanical profile

Commonly called Knotted Marjoram (or Oregano), *Origanum majorana* belongs to a family as rich in aromatic plants as are the *Lamiaceae*. Its name comes from the old French *maiorana,* from *Marion,* diminutive of Mary, or from *mariol,* a sort of marionette by allusion to the shape of its flowers; thus Matthiole, in 1650, calls it *mariolaine.* The term *Origanum* comes from the Greek *oros* (mountain) and *ganos* (radiance); it is the "adornment of the mountains". Wild Oregano, with which Marjoram is often confused and which grows in its natural state in Europe, has gradually usurped its name.

A hardy perennial in the wild state in hot Eastern areas such as Egypt, for example, it fears the cold of our winter; thus, it is very rarely found in the wild state in France but more in its cultivated version as an annual plant. This has earned it its other name, *Majorana hortensis Moench* or Garden Marjoram, because it needs the attentive hand of man to prosper in our climates.

This little sub-shrub scarcely more than 50 cm high emanates an extremely sweet, warm smell. Its delicate and harmonious contours make it truly delightful to the eye.

Botanically associated with the genus *Origanum,* Knotted Marjoram in no way resembles its Oregano cousins with their piquant, phenol-like smell, and has long suffered the unjustified reputation of being a stimulant due to the confusion with the latter. It is a plant that needs to be rediscovered, with a gentle, fine, warm aroma which gives it the advantage as a spice over Oregano, or Wild Marjoram, with its hotter aroma.

Origanum majorana yields one of the gentlest essential oils of all the *Lamiaceae*, together with *Lavandula vera*. Each of its parts contains essence, its leaves especially so.

It is at present quite difficult to find a good essential oil of *Origanum majorana*, hence its high price. Most of those found on sale are either a substitute through the usurpation of the common name "Marjoram" (thus we have essential oil of *Thymus mastichina* sold under the incorrect name of Spanish Marjoram or Wood Marjoram (Marjolaine sylvestre), very different in composition and at a clearly lower price, which contains above all 1.8 cineole and linalool), or an essential oil which is poorly distilled or heavily blended with essence of *Origanum compactum*.

The laboratories producing genuine essential oil of *Origanum majorana* in France are extremely few and far between. Furthermore, its problematic and costly production excludes practically all large-scale distribution.

Properties and indications
HEBBD *Origanum majorana*
p.o. flowering plant, *b.s. terpineol-4*

Origanum majorana is an essential oil whose action is as formidable as it is unrecognised. Up against competition from the Oreganos, its properties have been belittled and poorly assessed. The doubtful quality of the retailed essences and its high price have also worked against the popularity of the therapeutic use of this nevertheless most beneficial essential oil.

A product of the strong summer sunshine, *Origanum majorana* brings real heat – not that which burns and assaults like *Origanum compactum*, but rather the warmth which arouses and fills the individual with elation for life. As far back as the first century, Dioscorides was recommending *Origanum majorana* to fortify and warm the nerves; it is in fact an excellent nerve tonic and a remarkable general rebalancer. Its action and indications result from these two properties.

Origanum majorana awakens in the person the desire to act, gives him a boost and is far from soporific (unlike infusion of Marjoram). It is a good gastric stimulant and an effective appetite regulator; in this sense, it is suitable for both bulimics and anorexics. It should be combined with *Mentha piperita* and *Anethum graveolens* in cases of stomach pains, and supplemented by *Ocimum basilicum.*

Origanum majorana works to its fullest potential and greatest effectiveness in young people. It combats nervous depression, neurasthenia, claustrophobia and minor psychoses, calms epileptic fits, particularly in children or adolescents who are prey to mistaken feelings of persecution – *Thymus vulgaris b.s. linalool*-types who are excessively introverted; it clarifies ideas and draws them towards the concrete reality of existence. It should in all cases be combined with *Ravensara aromatica,* if necessary with *Laurus nobilis* and *Rosmarinus officinalis b.s. 1.8 cineole* and its action supplemented by the external application of *Lavandula vera.*

It helps to treat illnesses whose deep-rooted cause lies in relational problems: juvenile and nervous asthma, as well as a number of bronchopulmonary and otorhinolaryngological pathologies – rhinitis, sinusitis, bronchitis, whooping cough. *Origanum majorana* is also one of the essences most used in endonasal sympathicotherapy.

Origanum majorana in combination with *Salvia sclarea* is very good for young girls and women, depending on their characterology, who live in a state of perpetual disquiet due to unpleasant apprehension about their menstrual cycle, and who experience uterine and nerve spasms during the cycle, pains and distress (it is recommended in this case that it be supplemented with *Laurus nobilis* and *Mentha piperita*). It stimulates the blood circulation in young girls (with *Helichrysum italicum* and *Rosmarinus officinalis b.s. 1.8 cineole*). It straightens out and improves relationships and calms precocious sexual urges (in combination with *Melissa officinalis,* provided the genuine essence is used).

Origanum majorana encourages the young but also restores the enthusiasm of youth and spontaneity to those who have aged before their time. It soothes rheumatic pains and neuralgias in combination with *Lavandula vera,* and osteoarthritis by external massage with *Rosmarinus officinalis b.s. 1.8 cineole, Ravensara aromatica* and *Gaultheria procumbens.*

Origanum majorana is an excellent "terrain" essential oil whose action can work miracles when its use is based on characterology. Its organoleptic action is indisputable. Do not confuse it with the other types of *Origanum (compactum, vulgaris,* etc.) which are rich in phenols.

Care must be taken not to blend it with the most powerful woods such as *Cupressus sempervirens, Cedrus atlantica,* etc. An extremely subtle essential oil, it cannot bear mediocrity. It is better to do without it if one cannot get essential oils bearing the HEBBD seal.

Characterology

Courage and nobility of heart, love for life and people and beauty of soul and body are the threads with which the luminous aura of *Origanum majorana* is woven; its radiant archetype is based upon the myth connected with Marjoram. A sacred plant for the ancient Greeks, Marjoram was associated with Aphrodite. She picked a few twigs of it to apply them to the wounds of her injured son, Aeneas, when he took refuge on Mount Ida, in Crete, where she had given birth to him after making love with his father, Anchises. The loyal and noble Trojan hero, a model of filial piety who carried his old father on his shoulders away from Troy as it fell in flames and was not afraid of going back into the blazing city to look for his lost wife, was a perfect *Origanum majorana* type, pure of heart, a worthy son of the goddess of love. In ancient Egypt, Marjoram was one of the flowers of Osiris, and the purity of essence from its flower-heads symbolised the state of mind needed to be inititated into the Mysteries. In India, it is apparently dedicated to Vishnu.

Origanum majorana is easily recognised – a harmonious profile of a young Greek shepherd with a philosophy tinged with mythology, such as Telemachus, with his penetrating look putting to sea to find his father: "In his cradle of fog, scarcely had Eos with her rosy fingers appeared, than the beloved son of Ulysses pulled on his clothes and, leaping from his bed, slung his pointed double-edged sword over his shoulder, slipped his glistening feet into his fine sandals and departed from his chamber; to see him, one would have taken him for one of the Immortals... In his hand he had a bronze spear and, so as not to be alone, had taken with him two of his greyhounds. Athena clothed to him with celestial grace. When he entered, all eyes turned towards him and the elders amongst them made room that he should be seated at his father's place." (Homer, *The Odyssey*).

In order to discover and appreciate the *Origanum majorana* person, we must become imbued with the enthusiastic, spring-like vitality of those spirited adolescents, full of energy, their hearts overflowing with the desire for action inherent in their youth that seeks to free itself from the family cocoon, and who prove fully determined to fly as quickly as possible using their own wings.

Origanum majorana, self-assured, wants to conquer the world, set it on fire and transform it, inspire it with that radiant force which his love of life has so intensely awoken in him.

A great idealist, full of potential for the most part as yet unrealised, he wants to manifest his dreams without delay and is not afraid, in so doing, to displease earlier generations more inclined to live on memories and accompany their actions with the requisite caution. Such caution seems not to occur to our impetuous conqueror who, very often and with noble intention, wants to fling open to the world the doors of another dimension which, for the time being, is none other than his own.

Faced with the slowness of matter and existential inconsistencies, *Origanum majorana* rebels; sometimes he makes a statement of this character trait and his hotheadedness then wildly takes on the established social values, family habits and customs, entropic routine and, since they have not been dispensed with, the political and religious dogmas and conformities. "I was born to know you, to name you, Liberty",[6] he proclaims in the face of the hierarchies and authorities he finds unbearable; but like Don Quixote and his windmills, *Origanum majorana* sometimes misses his target, sinks into excesses alien to his loving nature and expends his energies on causes which are not always worth it.

Easily influenced, although he is convinced to the contrary, the hold of a negative *Laurus nobilis* can rouse him to fanaticism, a *Mentha piperita* recruit him into battles with noble appearance but perverse intention. At worst, he may go so far as to get mixed up in terrorism, so much are his whole nature and his lack of wisdom able to lead him into a paradox: to impose non-violence, by force if necessary! When properly guided, he will learn to overcome his ardour and put into practice the words of Gandhi: "There are many causes worth dying for; there are none worth killing for."

---

[6]Paul Eluard

An encounter with a true *Ravensara aromatica* channels his outbursts by putting his bravery to the test through skilful mastery of his impetuosity. One of the lessons he will learn from such a master is that in wanting to prove too much, one fails to convince anyone and in wanting to convince too much, one fails to prove anything.

In fact, *Origanum majorana* experiences a certain vulnerability like an inner drama due to his lack of confidence in himself, clumsily compensated for by an excessive assurance when faced with others. His strength comes from his sense of being on the right path, even if, in reality, he is teetering. He thus deems himself capable of directing his existence and if necessary those of others. Endowed with some power of conviction, sometimes driven by an astonishing charisma, he carries himself like a prince, without, however, possessing either crown or sceptre.

"Your son has gone to Delphi to take part in those celebrated games which are Greece's honour. At the call of the herald announcing the foot-race, with which the competitions opened, his strength seemed quite outstanding before the dazzled crowd. Equal to the hope he engendered, he reached the goal and left the arena laden with victory... Thus it went, but when a god tries to pick a quarrel with you, no matter if you are strong, you will never sidestep his blows." (Sophocles, *Electra*).

His impetuosity thus drives him to believe too soon that victory is his whereas a war is won by a strategy, a plan, highly ordered conduct and a good deal of patience. It is through the spirit of discipline that *Origanum majorana* will win the day, and he senses it but this bothers him because he is in a hurry. Again, it is *Ravensara* who will teach him and show him that his real enemies are within himself. In your inner battle, purity must be your armour, peace your shield and goodness your weapon, he tells him. Taking up Corneille's aphorism in a mystical sense: "To vanquish without peril is to triumph without glory", he complements it by explaining to *Origanum majorana* that a victory without nobility is worse than a defeat.

A handsome young man, without a doubt, he is asked by his spiritual archetype to remain upright, pure and motivated by noble feelings. His undeniable qualities grant him an inner beauty often reflected in a stately bearing and a charm to which the young ladies, genus *Salvia sclarea* or *Helichrysum italicum,* are not insensitive.

Under the supervision of a spiritual father, *Rosmarinus officinalis b.s. bornyl acetate, verbenone* or *Ravensara aromatica, Origanum majorana* is able to excude great warmth from his heart and radiate the light through the crystal of his inner being.

A symbol of eternal youth, the warm and delightful scent of *Origanum majorana,* by its intrinsic purity, invites us to revive ourselves at the primordial source of the Garden of Eden whence spring forth the sweet-smelling particles emanating from the Divine Mother, *Rosa damascena.*

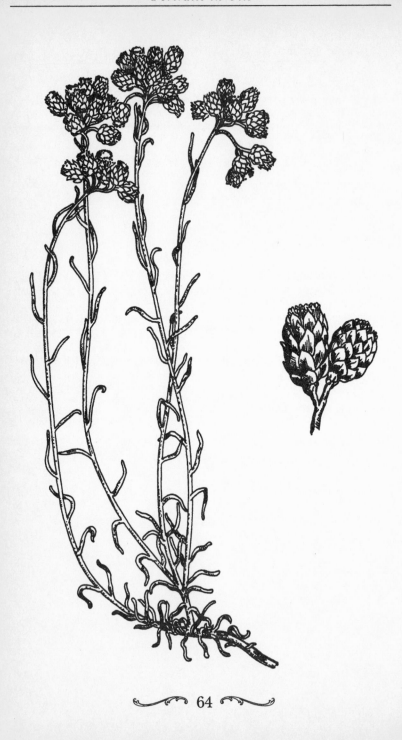

Helichrysum Italicum var. serotinum

Cast a bunch of flowers to the wind, harvested on your blossoming face, and I shall inhale the fragrance of the paths that you tread.
Hafiz

Origin and botanical profile

This little *Asteraceae* with delicate yellow, bobble-shaped flower-heads, better known by the name of Immortelle or Everlasting Flower, grows around the Mediterranean. It is found in former Yugoslavia on the Dalmatian coast and the neighbouring islands, and on the Italian coasts. In France, it grows in the Carmargue, in Corsica, the Landes region and on the Atlantic coastal islands – in particular the isle of Noirmoutier. Helichrysum is very fond of sandy soils because of their silica content.

It would seem there are about five hundred species of Helichrysum, but they do not all have an essence. These different species are very polymorphous and it is difficult to distinguish them from one another.

Very few of them are employed for therapeutic use as they are still not well known. Extraction of the essence by distillation is uncommon and mainly concerns the following species:

Helichrysum italicum G. Don or *Helichrysum angustifolium D.C* (native of Corsica and former Yugoslavia);

Helichrysum stoechas D.C (France);

Helichrysum gymnocephalum H. Humb (Madagascar);

Helichrysum patulum (South Africa).

Helichrysum comes from the Greek *helios* (sun) and *chrysos* (gold), because the way these plants bloom gives the impression of little golden suns. The flowers do not wither, hence their common name, Immortelle.

The most commonly used of these various species is *Helichrysum italicum var. serotinum* or Italian *Helichrysum*, which grows in Corsica. As its yield is lower than the Italian *Helichrysum* from former Yugoslavia and its biochemical composition less useful in therapy, it is not very often picked and distilled.

The colour of the essential oil varies quite a bit, depending on the region where the flowers are gathered – light emerald green for Italian *Helichrysum* due to the microtraces of azulene; light yellow for *Helichrysum stoechade* and bare-headed *Helichrysum*; orangey-red for the Italian **Helichrysum** from former Yugoslavia, which has a different biochemical specificity to that from Corsica.

Helichrysum italicum is a very precious essential oil and extremely seldom found on sale. It has a particular smell – strong like *Chamaemelum nobile* – with a hint of the ethereal and fluid. It burns easily in distillation and then loses its delicacy. Few distillers undertake to extract from it, so difficult is it to produce a very high quality essential oil. It is nevertheless indispensable in aromatherapy for its specific properties.

Properties and indications
HEBBD *Helichrysum italicum var. serotinum*
p.o. flowering tops, *b.s. neryl acetate, diones*

On inhaling essence of *Helichrysum italicum*, one gets the pleasant sensation that the blood circulation is coming alive and that the blood is fluidifying and purifying itself. *Helichrysum italicum* is, in fact, an anticoagulant and fluidifier, and must be prescribed in cases of circulatory pathologies – rosacea, violaceous acne and varicosities. Take care, however, not to use it for problems of the venous circulation which are the province of *Cupressus sempervirens*; one must also guard against mixing them.

Its vasocoronarodilatory and antispasmodic properties are worthy of consideration in cases of pre-infarction and cardiovascular spasms. It is helpful, for serious cardiovascular pathologies and in combination with the medicines prescribed by the cardiologist, to blend it with *Artemisia dracunculus, Lavandula vera* and *Rosmarinus officinalis b.s. bornyl acetate, verbenone*, depending on the case in question.

It is anti-inflammatory and therefore effective in cases of phlebitis and arteritis (internal and external routes); mucolytic due to its oxides, it is recommended for rhinopathies and cases of sinusitis in Helichrysum people, with *Rosmarinus officinalis b.s. 1.8 cineole* and *Origanum majorana.* Blend it with *Chamaemelum nobile* for allergic problems.

Together with *Rosmarinus officinalis b.s. bornyl acetate, verbenone* and *Citrus limonum,* it compensates for certain hepatic inadequacies and sometimes enables diabetics to reduce their insulin intake, in this case blended with *Pelargonium graveolens* and *Eucalyptus citriodora.*

It is a good antiviral supplement, depending on the person's predisposing factors – for example, with *Melaleuca quinquenervia, Ravensara aromatica* and *Salvia officinalis* in cases of herpes.

Blended with *Lavandula vera,* it is an excellent cicatrisant and painkiller, mainly where blows, traumatisms and bruises are involved.

An essential oil that needs to be discovered in order to be properly used, *Helichrysum italicum* is effective both orally and through the skin; it is very active even in low doses, and blending it with the *Asteraceae* and *Lamiaceae* strengthens its action. Avoid combining it with the woods or phenolic essences, however, as these prevent it from fully expressing its personality. In particular, it has affinities with *Chamaemelum nobile, Lavandula vera, Ocimum basilicum, Rosmarinus officinalis b.s. 1.8 cineole* and *Origanum majorana.* A gentle, fragile essence which is difficult to obtain, it proves to be exceptionally effective in many cases and is one of the fundamental keys in one's stock of aromatherapeutic products.

Characterology

The sea nymph, Galatea, "white as milk", "whiter than the snowy petal of the privet", as Ovid describes her, undoubtedly embodied the broad outlines of the character and physical identity of the *Helichrysum italicum* archetype. Galatea, in her innocent youthfulness, loved a young shepherd by the name of Acis – probably an *Origanum majorana* with a heart as pure as hers; tenderly entwined, they wandered all over the meadows of Sicily. But their love aroused the jealousy of Polyphemus, the cyclops, who was also in love with the gentle Galatea, though she fled from his monstrous ugliness. One day when the two young people were sleeping beside the sea, the giant threw a rock at Acis and crushed him fatally. Inconsolable, the sea nymph caused a spring to gush from the stone and turned Acis into the river god.

Helichrysum, with its time-defying golden yellow corolla and its name and appearance, evoking as much the life-giving sun as the incorruptible metal, had in earlier times – no doubt for this reason – a reputation as a very beneficial magical plant. Known as *herba* or *barba Jovis* (Jove's herb or beard) – which confirms the high esteem in which it was held and the notion of divine energy connected with the spirit for which it served as a vehicle – *Helichrysum* even today retains, in its name, this symbol of immortality which characterised Galatea's love for Acis; she still brightens up funeral wreaths and tombstones.

This little flower, from which crowns were made for the gods – "a custom observed most meticulously by Ptolemy, the King of Egypt", remarks Pliny – is still today included in Midsummer Day bouquets and symbolises eternal love in the language of flowers, which corroborates the idea of an evolved being with a profoundly spiritual nature.

Another portrait of the *Helichrysum* archetype is shown in the adventures of the knight, Lancelot of the Lake: "The snow atop of the ice, the fleur-de-lis, the drop of milk, were never as white as her complexion, not even the just-budding flower. Her body was graceful, delicate, her beauty perfect, to the point that even a painter could not have made her more lovely – lovely was her mouth, as much as her eyes and her nose; on her tender face, in the middle of the white, Nature had cast a fresh blush of pink, which made one think of a rose. She was a fine creature – thus was she given the name of Flower of Desire." Such was the account of the white, pure beauty of the gentle Ingle in *Les Merveilles de Rigomer*.

Today, *Helichrysum* – whether as an adolescent or young woman – is still easily identifiable (though sometimes she is seen in an older form), being generally blonde and blue-eyed, with a skin so white it seems

---

[1] Here, as in the rest of the work, the term "Ego" does not relate to the ego as "little me" but to the Kantian Ego – in other words, to the most spiritual element of Man, his Spirit. We are deliberately not retaining the latter term because of its exclusively mystical connotation and the personal interpretations that it may suggest. The sense remains, nevertheless.

The interactions between the Ego and the existential being are dealt with in the chapter in the unabridged version devoted to methodology.

translucent, almost transparent. She is not necessarily as beautiful as her archetypes would suggest but often quite pretty, and a youthful charm tinged with a certain vulnerability emanates from her.

Helichrysum seems to have some trouble incarnating – her delicate structure has to confront various troubles inherent in her ephemeral, vulnerable nature. She suffers from minor circulatory problems, the sort of pathologies typical of her character. With a red nose, almost permanent blotches, her hands alternating between a whiteness which is clammy and pale and bluish red, *Helichrysum* seems to be perpetually frozen stiff. She continually has cold hands and feet, obviously suffers from chilblains in winter, and nothing seems to be able to warm her up. On the other hand, incapable of giving her a tan, the slightest exposure to the summer sun turns her into a lobster. It would appear as though she must be well in spring and autumn, but it is at these times that she has allergy attacks.

Helichrysum evidently has a delicate constitution, although she is not inclined to complain overmuch about it. Her liver is vulnerable and she suffers the consequences of any divergence from her normal eating routine or from a steady temperature; prey to the least germ, she alternates between having sinusitis, styes and cystitis. But this picture, when all is said and done, detracts little from the charm of her company.

These numerous health problems, though relatively disabling, at least have the advantage of forcing her to look after herself. *Helichrysum italicum* actually has a tendency to be detached and often acts as if she were more to one side of the world around her than in it. Her circulatory troubles are, in any case, revealing: the blood is the vehicle of the self, an existential reflection of the Ego,[1] which gives each of us our own identity. *Helichrysum* evidently has problems with her inner identity stemming from a poorly established relationship with her self, of which she is not truly aware, that can lead her to adopt behaviour contrary to her nature or to get mixed up in company which violates her intrinsic sensitivity.

If she fails to resolve this identity problem, establish her boundaries and determine her own choices, she may, through her slackness in acting and indecision, allow herself to be easily deceived and betray her deep, spiritual nature through contact, for example, with a womaniser of the *Mentha piperita* type who will take advantage of her innocence.

Whilst her most promising future is a *Chamaemelum nobile*, another very evolved member of the *Asteraceae*, she can just as easily arrive there by way of the alternative, *Citrus aurantium* p.o. leaves.

In this sense, the combination with *Rosmarinus officinalis b.s. bornyl acetate, verbenone* is saving; this essence – which helps to incarnate the self within the being – aids and stabilises it but does not, for all that, wrench it down too brutally from its ethereal spheres, which seem to be its favourite mental residence.

Helichrysum commonly, and despite everything, remains a dreamer, a gentle emotional person, whose actions, it seems, take place within a continual timelag. The combination with *Ocimum basilicum* does not make her more down-to-earth – on the contrary – and it is necessary to take care to provide her with company and partnerships which are more earth-bound and encourage greater responsibility, without necessarily giving way to the archaism of Cinnamon or the biological violence of *Satureja montana*.

Fairly idealistic, she gets on well with *Rosmarinus officinalis b.s. 1.8 cineole*, who admirably plays the role of Prince Charming, although his very particular sense of humour sometimes escapes *Helichrysum*, who is generally the butt of it. Connected by friendship with another young woman poles apart from her being, *Salvia sclarea*, who displays a shadowy, emotional temperament, she is distinguished from her by her student-like behaviour – whereas *Salvia sclarea* seems much more sure of herself than *Helichrysum*, who, for her part, doubts her abilities, the latter will face the test with courage whilst *Salvia sclarea* will tend to founder. *Salvia officinalis* will give her the basics of wisdom for her to cross over into womanhood, and open her eyes to the risks she is running through her naivety and lack of determination.

Helichrysum italicum, Immortelle, belongs to this noble family of *Asteraceae* whose particularly subtle essences are directed towards the higher mind; rare and precious, in order to be properly used, they ask to be discovered, respected and, above all, loved.

"Your soul takes flight and I follow it with my eyes;
it fades into a white cloud
whilst its tender memory

remains, eternal.
How to hold you, beautiful child of the sun,
who came like a ray of light, one spring morning,
to touch our hearts with the dew from the flowers..."
Bashistya Shivânanta

Salvia Officinalis

*Use no perfume
unless it be the charm of thoughts.*
Buddhist maxim

Origin and botanical profile

Salvia officinalis, Common Sage – also known as True Sage – a sacred herb, tea of Europe, Provence and Greece, is one of those numerous so-called officinal plants (from the Latin *officina*, twelfth century: *workshop*) much used by the apothecaries of the Middle Ages for making up remedies. *Sage* comes from the Latin *salvia*, itself from *salvus* (safe and sound), an etymology which tells us to what extent this plant has enjoyed a reputation as a panacea to cure the most diverse ills. Considered to be an all-powerful herb in the Middle Ages, it was cultivated in monasteries from the ninth century onwards and its reputation lasted until the eighteenth century.

A native of Dalmatia, Common Sage finds its most representative natural habitat there – on the chalky, practically bare and very stony lands overhanging the Adriatic. It probably crossed the Alps thanks to the monks.

There are more than five hundred species of Sage, not all of which contain an essence. Many varieties have been created by horticulturists.

Salvia officinalis is an aromatic sub-shrub belonging to the rich family of the *Lamiaceae*, 50 to 80 cm high, which grows in clumps. The flower produced by Common Sage is much frequented by bees and butterflies; when these insects enter it, they knock against the sterile anther, trip the lever and the other anther sprinkles their backs with pollen. In Sages, the style is shorter than the stamens but grows as soon as the stamens have distributed their pollen; thus, as soon as a visitor enters, the stigmas act like a stiff broom and gather the pollen accumulated on its back. It is extraordinary to discover to what extent the Sages have perfected their reproductive organs for entomophilous pollination.

Salvia officinalis seldom grows at an altitude of more than 800 m; it is a perennial but shrinks from the cold. There are few wild habitats for Common Sage in France, so it is always a product of cultivation.

With a powerful, heavy smell, *Salvia officinalis* commands admiration in consideration of its hardiness and longevity. Preferring very stony, chalky soil, it is capable of making lush ground hard. Moreover, wherever it thrives practically no other herb grows – it acts as a natural herbicide. It likes aerated, very sunny ground.

There are two varieties of *Salvia officinalis*, commonly called "small-leaved" – which must not be confused with nutmeg clone Sage – and "large-leaved". Small-leaved Common Sage is generally preferred as its essential oil is finer, which does not prevent large-leaved Sage from being the most cultivated variety. The greater the plant matter, the lower the yield – thus, the large-leaved variety has a yield twice as low as the small-leaved, which gives a comparatively large quantity of essential oil in relation to the amount of plant matter.

Properties and indications
HEBBD *Salvia officinalis*
p.o. flowering tops, *b.s. thujones*

Cur moriatur homo, cui Salvia crescit in horto? Contra vim non est medicamen in hortis! "Why would a man die, whose garden is host to Sage, unless it be that there is no remedy against the power of Death?" This axiom, extolled by the Salernitan School, says much about the reputation enjoyed by Common Sage. According to Paracelsus, Common Sage was – together with St John's Wort – consecrated by St John the Evangelist who, shortly before his death, conferred upon them properties unchanging until the end of time. This eloquent calling card has undoubtedly not been usurped. Common Sage, whose saving effect no longer needs to be demonstrated but, rather, clarified in regard to its use, possesses numerous properties that contribute to make of it a remedy of prime importance not only in herbal medicine, but in aromatherapy as well.

Salvia officinalis is the "saving" herb. It is a typically feminine essential oil, thanks to which many women will encounter in it the solution to their gynaecological problems. Its effect on the genital area is completely remarkable, both at the physiological and psychological level. It brings rapid relief in the case of painful periods, and in amenorrhoea and dysmennorrhoea; its emmenagogue power is very active and supplemented by a pain-killing effect.

Its effectiveness is commensurate with its toxicity as it becomes abortifacient in excessive doses. It is therefore not recommended for pregnant women except as a "terrain" treatment or in certain specific cases, with many precautions concerning the dosage (blended with *Cistus ladaniferus* if there is a loss of blood). Nursing mothers should also use it with care, as it suppresses lactation; drying-up occurs painlessly, and this can be an excellent way of stopping milk coming in if there is a real need to do so. In such cases, the menstrual cycle is also quickly restored.

In addition, it has expectorant and mucolytic properties which will act in cases of leucorrhoea or respiratory disorders; it will very much help a *Salvia sclarea* person to get over her respiratory and gynaecological problems, especially if these are emotional or relational in origin. *Salvia officinalis* reassures and stabilises women in their genital and emotional vulnerability. Thus it allays anxiety, mental excitation, spasms due to a lack of stability, and hot flushes, as well as tempering hyper-emotional states.

Blended with *Ravensara aromatica* and *Melaleuca quinquenervia*, diluted with a vegetable oil – generally *Corylus avellana* (Hazelnut) or a lipidic extract of *Hypericum perforatum* (red oil of St John's Wort) – it effectively fights against genital herpes (the diet must obviously be changed as well).

It regulates sweating, whether this is excessive or insufficient (*Cupressus sempervirens* acts in the same way in men). It also has an effect on foul-smelling sweat; in such cases, the psychosensory effect is evident since the general equilibrium of the person and her types of reaction to the outside world are greatly altered and improved.

We encounter here the living properties of essential oils, which do not act mechanically but as regulators and general rebalancers; *Salvia officinalis* is a characteristic case in point, notably for genital problems since it is as much able to work in cases of amenorrhoea as in those of very heavy periods and dysmenorrhoea. These actions on predisposing factors must be considered first and foremost, especially with an essence such as this.

It improves the blood circulation, which is inefficient in many women; in cases of venous problems, particularly varicose veins, it needs to be blended with *Cupressus sempervirens* and *Rosmarinus officinalis b.s. bornyl acetate, verbenone*. In cases of arterial disorders, it is more effective to blend it with *Helichrysum italicum* and *Rosmarinus officinalis b.s. 1.8 cineole.*

Thanks to its ketones, it counteracts excess cholesterol; in this case, add to it *Rosmarinus officinalis b.s. bornyl acetate, verbenone, Cupressus sempervirens, Citrus limonum* and *Mentha piperita b.s. menthone.*

Salvia officinalis is also effective for rheumatisms and arthritis, blended with *Eucalyptus citriodora* and *Lavandula spica,* and possibly *Ravensara aromatica* and *Thymus vulgaris b.s. linalool,* if there is a risk of infection. Its anti-inflammatory properties, when used advisedly, make it possible to obtain quite remarkable results.

Salvia officinalis fights intestinal sepsis, necrosis, bedsores (sclerotic tendency), blended in such cases with *Laurus nobilis* and *Rosmarinus officinalis b.s. bornyl acetate, verbenone* internally and *Melaleuca quinquenervia* externally.

It is also a good cicatrisant, blended with *Lavandula vera* and *Cistus ladaniferus* where cuts are involved.

With a reputation that has not been usurped, *Salvia officinalis* fully confirms its many potential uses, mainly as far as women are concerned; we do not generally recommend it in aromatherapy for men, because of its hormonal properties and the facts relating to its characterology. *Cupressus sempervirens, Laurus nobilis* or *Hyssopus officinalis b.s. pinocamphone* would, depending on the case in question, be the masculine essences most closely corresponding to it.

Let us recall that essential oil of *Salvia officinalis* is a ketonic essence – there is therefore a rapid reversal of its effects in scanty doses; hypotensive, it can become hypertensive, neurotonic, and even capable of inducing epilepsy in very high doses. Furthermore, its use must be extremely controlled where pregnant women are concerned, since it quickly becomes abortifacient. An indispensable essential oil, it can become as dangerous as it is effective when incorrectly prescribed.

Characterology

Salvia officinalis evokes the huntress, Artemis, the lunar goddess and eternal virgin. A symbol of the feminine principle, of the soul of the world which the solar spirit, the creator Logos, brought forth from himself, Artemis is his energy materialised, the matter in which he contemplates himself, the life which animates and gives form to every earth-bound creature.

"You were for a moment beside me, and you made me sense the great mystery of woman which beats in the very heart of Creation", sang Rabindranath Tagore in homage to the eternal woman.

Protector of women, children, wild animals and births, Artemis saves her protégés; but like any lunar principle, she wears a double face and although she controls the art of healing as holding the might to protect her own, she also possesses the power to spread diseases and bring death. As Durga, the *shakti* of Shiva – personification of the Divine Mother and protector of the humble, who arms herself with a thousand flames to destroy the corrupt person but whose darkest face is the terrible goddess, Kali, adorned with a necklace of skulls and thirsty for blood – the archetype of *Salvia officinalis* could make her own these words of the Apocalypse: "For my part, I will reprimand and punish those that I love; be zealous, then, and repent."

Artemis combines with her uncompromising sense of justice – which unremittingly punishes the guilty – an unconditional love of life, a divine connection, which drives her to wipe out anything that obstructs free expression. "Opinion", says Ovid, "hesitates to pronounce a verdict – to some, the goddess has seemed, in her cruelty, to exceed all fairness; others praise her and declare that she was worthy of her austere virginity."

Sister of Apollo, the sun god who gives life and light (corresponding to *Laurus nobilis*), Artemis is his complement and his nocturnal reflection, who redistributes this very life over the earth and within women, but also takes it from them. In the universe of duality, everything has a beginning and an end; thus, as the moon, an image of existence, is born, waxes, wanes and dies to be reborn in the light of the sun, everything that is born of matter is inexorably destined to die one day. Such are also the unchangeable cycles that woman carries within her.

The powers of life and death contained within the archetype of *Salvia officinalis* no doubt result from its reputation as a panacea, which has never failed over the centuries, and the veneration in which it was held. "It is a plant endowed with properties so numerous and so magnificent that it even, they say, grants immortality to those who make much use of it", says John Evelyn. Perhaps this is one of the reasons why, in England, it is sometimes strewn over graves whilst Cypresses stand guard over the cemetery enclosure. Common Sage was also felt to safeguard against storms: "To protect the house from thunder, Sage is kept there which was blessed on Assumption Day. To protect the crops, it is placed at the four corners of the field", recommended an old Walloon adage. Sage was also used during religious rituals, and these days the American Indians still use it for smudging before a number of sacred ceremonies.

Salvia officinalis – *Salvia salvatrix* as the Salernitan School calls it – is the essence which saves; from its characterology, therefore, it appears more under the traits of a woman assisting than assisted. Mature in age, which does not necessarily signify advanced in years, prompted by a certain wisdom and authority, she addresses women, appealing more to their intelligence than their hearts. *Salvia officinalis* exerts her rigour against the tide in these times of emotional crisis where sexuality triumphs over conscience and love; she herself was earlier able to go beyond her troubles and sufferings, her crises and emotional illusions, which she has skilfully turned to account to build up her exceptional character.

Associated more with inner than outer beauty, she affords women balance in their sex life by leading them towards a better understanding of their gynaecological functions and what the feminine nature implies from the physical, as well as the psychic, point of view.

Tenacious, persistent, concise and efficient, she is socially a capable woman who is not afraid to impose her authority and strictness. *Salvia officinalis* knows what she wants and what she can do. She knows how to appear without weakness in order to reach her goals, ruthlessly combating indolence, lameness and laxity in her fellow creatures. Uncompromising and just by nature, she sometimes falls into an excess of intolerance and shows signs of an outpouring which is scarcely feminine and the combativity of an Amazon. She then takes on the traits of

Hecate, the chthonic goddess who wears the three faces of Heaven, Earth and Hell.

Uncompromising in the sphere of both good and evil, she does not tolerate mistakes, either her own or those of others whom she reproaches for not having her qualities as well as for their own faults. A tireless worker, she achieves anything she undertakes since she channels all her strength into her will to succeed, which almost inexorably leads her to moral, if not physical, solitude.

Whilst not all play the "male" role, *Salvia officinalis* women, by virtue of their temperament, are generally more appreciable than appreciated.

Capable women, business women, they are found amongst those women who have managed, by dint of will and work, to haul themselves up to take the reins of power within an organisation or government. History provides the example of Elizabeth I of England, the "Virgin Queen", austere, intelligent, protector of the arts and literature, but hard and ferocious with her enemies, and not afraid to behead her rival, Mary Stuart; closer to our times, we think of Margaret Thatcher, the "Iron Lady", Golda Meir and Indira Gandhi, who all faced violent opposition due to their strong personality and their measures – which were energetic, to say the least.

When she is not in politics, she is frequently busy improving the position of women in society, not through questionable liberation movements since she defies anyone to prevent her from being free, but rather by imposing upon women a quality of life which, although extreme, restabilises her sisters in many areas. Emotional imbalance, hypersensitivity, fear, weakness and depression are, in fact, the targets of this high-powered woman who motivates *Salvia sclarea*, *Helichrysum italicum* and the other *Citrus aurantium* p.o. leaves types to walk alongside men rather than one step or one word behind.

In the image of the plant which makes the ground stony simply by its aura, this essence has a difficult manner, with a harsh rather than an engaging smell. Whilst unquestionably indispensable, it is nevertheless a cold, uncompromising essence, a ketone essence which is tricky to use. Associated with justice and efficiency, one would imagine reading within the indigo (a Saturnian colour) fabric of *Salvia officinalis*: "Ignorance of the law is no excuse."

The might of *Salvia officinalis* must be appreciated for it to be used wisely, since it can go from being a saving to a destructive essence, changing from an emmenagogue and regulator of the hormonal functions into a haemorrhagic, abortifacient product. Combining it with *Salvia sclarea* complements it wonderfully, and *Rosmarinus officinalis b.s. bornyl acetate, verbenone* is almost essential in many cases. At the level of characterology, blending it with *Laurus nobilis*, the corresponding masculine oil, however orthodox this may be, suggests their relationship might experience rather fresh winter evenings, but consequent achievements.

It is wise to avoid unsound combinations with *Cinnamomum zeylanicum*, or other bewitching and over-sweet essential oils such as *Cananga odorata*, unless one consciously wishes to play with extremes.

Salvia officinalis is an essence and a character needing to be discovered, and it can give a glimpse of a wondrous nature when one has got past one's initial fear in the face of Cerberus, the guardian of the threshhold, who is sure to be there, with such a treasure.

Salvia Sclarea

Loving is not looking at one another,
but both looking in the same direction.
Antoine de Saint-Exupéry

Origin and botanical profile

Salvia sclarea, Clary Sage (or clary, wild spinach, clary wort) is a very beautiful self-sown plant from the south of France. With its pretty bilabiate pinkish white flower, it belongs to the *Lamiaceae* family. A plant that likes the sun, it is widespread in southern Europe, North Africa and the Crimean peninsula (south of Russia). The beauty of its flowering branches and the gentle warmth of its fragrance very quickly seduced men, and consequently it is heavily cultivated. The natural sites for this Sage (the arid, chalky hills of Provence and the Alpes-Maritimes) have become rare and it is above all found in its uncultivated, sub-self-sown state on the edge of roads, in gardens or growing at the foot of walls.

Sclarea comes from the Latin *clarus*, meaning clear or luminous, characteristic of the appearance of its flowering stems, which seems to confirm its various dialectic names: *Luminare majus, erva de santa Lucia, clarea*, etc., all of which express the notion of clarity. In English, Clary Sage is called "Clary", in other words "clear eye"; a French sixteenth-century saying states in effect that "a clary seed placed in the eye takes away the grains of dust". Ever since antiquity, its reputation has been as great as that of its close relation, Common Sage. It is quoted in 795 under the name of *Sclareiam* by the Capitulary of Villis (Carolingian royal edict).

A perennial as a result of its taproot, it grows to barely more than s.o. (one metre) in its wild state. This Sage is very characteristic due to its broad wrinkled leaves, the mosaic appearance of its lamina (like *Salvia officinalis*) with veins jutting out on the underside, and its superb ramified inflorescence of pinkish-white flowers streaked with violet. Seen from afar, fields of this plant attract the eye by their clarity because of the pink colour; close up, the multitude of flowers holds one's astonished gaze due to the rough, hairy appearance of the base of the plant.

Cultivated *Salvia sclarea* has become a biennial plant reaching a height of between 1 m and 1.50 m. As a result of cultivation, it has spread more or less all over Europe (Germany, Romania, England) and the United States. In the south of France, especially in the Alps of the Upper Provence region, it is frequently cultivated at an altitude of between 400 and 900 m. *Salvia sclarea* is, nevertheless, a fragile plant which is difficult to grow, and this has discouraged many French producers. The nature of the soil and the climatic conditions (cold, wind, rain), particularly at harvest time, are detrimental to the yield of essential oil, which can sometimes be as low as 0.05 to 0.3-0.4%. It is practically impossible to anticipate the yield since many factors lead to significant losses. Due to its unpredictable character, growers call it "Night Beauty" – "incubating" at night, it slips away from them the next day.

Essential oil of *Salvia sclarea*, because of the predominance of its two aromatic molecules, is very similar to *Lavandula vera*, but their smells are different. That of *Salvia sclarea* is green and strong, whilst *Lavandula vera* has a very gentle fragrance.

It should be noted that the perfume industry is a major consumer of Clary Sage extracts, which make excellent perfume fixatives (in addition, they have a pleasant, musky smell). Consequently, the Clary Sage concrete contains more than 50% *sclareol* (a compound too heavy to be properly drawn off during distillation).

Clary Sage is doubly useful to aromatherapy and perfumery due to:
- its essential oil, obtained by steam distillation,
- its concrete and absolute, obtained by hexanic extraction of the distilled plants.

Salvia sclarea has a fairly unremarkable biochemical composition, the principal constituents of which are found in a large number of essential oils. It is the components found in low quantity, or even in trace form, that give it its most original properties.

Properties and indications
HEBBD *Salvia sclarea*
p.o. flowering plant, b.*s.* linalyl acetate, sclareol

Salvia sclarea is a very useful essential oil in aromatherapy, where it has, for some years, had pride of place beside the thujone-rich *Salvia officinalis* and *Salvia lavandulaefolia*, Spanish Sage, which is used less. It is distinguished from these two Sages by the fact that it does not contain any toxic bio-chemical compound – neither α *and β-thujones* nor *borneone*. Nevertheless, this Sage – as a result of legislation which is somewhat uninformed about the subtle differences between the various species – suffers from the hapless shadow hanging over its relation, *Salvia officinalis*, and finds itself classified amongst the ranks of toxic substances strictly reserved for medical prescriptions. This is as much a nonsense for Clary as it is justified for Common Sage. To say that "Sage is toxic" is an aberration because it comes in more than five hundred species – the term "Sage" indicates a genus, not a species.

One big difference from *Salvia officinalis* is its fragrance; the smell of *Salvia sclarea* is very particular and leaves behind a feeling of something unfinished, like fruit that is still green, whilst the second time round it reveals a greater smoothness.

Its properties also differ from those of *Salvia officinalis*, of course. Devoid of ketones but, on the contrary, rich in esters in which the former is lacking, one of the essential qualities of *Salvia sclarea* is that it is rebalancing and antispasmodic. It fights depressive manifestations, and over-excitability in young girls or sensitive women, in keeping with its characterology.

It is an essential oil which works on a deep level, and is therefore an excellent "terrain" essence.

Its predilection is for gynaecological pathologies and ailments, the source of numerous troubles and disturbances to the general equilibrium in women, particularly young girls. *Salvia sclarea* blended with *Salvia officinalis* regulates dysmenorrhoea, activates periods that have ceased (amenorrhoea), tempers and regulates heavy, painful periods, and clears up and stops the vaginal discharges (leucorrhoea) which are characteristic of adolescence. It is often more effective to blend it with *Salvia officinalis* with a predominance of one or the other, depending on the age of the person, her psychological predisposition and characterology.

Salvia sclarea, capable of either slowing down or encouraging the flow of periods depending on the predisposition of the patient, confirms the intelligence and eubiotic role of essential oils. Its action, strengthened by the support of *Salvia officinalis*, is also enhanced by bringing in a "masculine", rather paternal, essence of the *Rosmarinus officinalis b.s. bornyl acetate, verbenone* type, all the more so since immuno- and liver deficiencies can appear at the same time as gynaecological imbalances.

Salvia sclarea helps young girls to come to terms with their sensitivity and often enables them to cross into womanhood with as few problems as possible. The characteristic age of *Salvia sclarea* is between about twelve and twenty to twenty-five years, in other words from puberty to the end of adolescence. It is, moreover, interesting to note that if the passage from initial barrenness to fertility is inwardly experienced as problematic and consequently brings with it a number of psychophysiological disturbances typical of *Salvia sclarea*, these difficulties will reappear with the menopause, when passing from fertility to the second period of barrenness.

Depressions and physical troubles with the perimenopause will then be treated with *Salvia sclarea* before using *Cupressus sempervirens* or *Chamaemelum nobile*, according to the characterology. The barrenness-fertility-barrenness rotation recurs with each menstrual cycle; regularisation and restoration of the cycle's balance will have very positive effects on sexuality and transform any traumas at puberty which will not come up again, so to speak, during the menopause.

Salvia sclarea therefore has a strong psychological effect on young girls and must be used to that end, blended, in that case, with *Origanum majorana*, a young man with a character very much in line with our young lady's ideal boyfriend. She finds in *Lavandula vera*, absorbed through the skin by massaging the stomach, a remarkable ally which refines and reinforces its action. Blended with *Helichrysum italicum* and *Rosmarinus officinalis b.s. 1.8 cineole*, she improves arterial circulation. With *Anethum graveolens* and *Ocimum basilicum*, she is a powerful antispasmodic for the strong back pains that may occur during menstruation.

She can also be used as a sedative at times of sleep disturbances connected with heartache; in that case, she should be blended with *Citrus aurantium* p.o. leaves, *Origanum majorana* and *Chamaemelum nobile* (refer to the characterology of the essences).

As a general rule, we avoid blending her with the woods and prefer the flowers and leaves of the *Lamiaceae, Asteraceae, Rutaceae*, etc.

Salvia sclarea is fundamentally a "terrain" essence and her intrinsic properties stem from her characterology. Thanks to her, the aromatherapist possesses a remarkable means of regulating deep-seated gynaecological problems and the psychological consequences ensuing as a result of these.

Characterology

In aromatic characterology, it represents two typical young girls with affirmed personalities, antagonistic towards one another but complementary: *Salvia sclarea*, like the dawn of the step into womanhood, and her inseparable friend, *Helichrysum italicum*, the little golden sun.

Ronsard seems to have written these lines for them:

"Watching you sitting by your cousin
Lovely like the Dawn and you like a Sun,
I thought of two flowers of the same shade,
Growing in beauty, one beside the other."

Although the physical descriptions are not rigid, *Helichrysum* types, as we saw earlier, are generally blue-eyed blondes, diaphanous of skin and fragile in appearance. *Salvia sclarea*, on the other hand, is more brunette, with dark eyes and a matt complexion. We must not forget, however, that the characterology defines more a state of mind – a general psychophysiological disposition – than a stereotypical person.

Salvia sclarea is indeed a young girl, as its properties and directions suggest, but it corresponds above all to a state that many adolescents go through who, having become women, will either remain in that state or relive it through quite specific situations. *Salvia sclarea* experiences adolescence – an essential transition period – torn between childhood, which she has not completely left behind, and adulthood, which she has still not quite entered and towards which she hesitatingly makes her way. If there is, therefore, a typical *Salvia sclarea* person, there is also and above all the *Salvia sclarea* state which relates to almost all adolescent girls. This subtle difference is found in several characterologies, particularly that of *Citrus aurantium* (leaves), a potential development of our Clary type.

Who, then, is this young *Salvia* girl – camouflaged and protected in relative anonymity by the powerful aura of her spiritual mother, *Salvia officinalis* – whose veil only a few well-informed aromatherapists are able to lift in order to present, in broad daylight, the marvellous qualities of this meadow flower?

Like the young, green perfume of the essential oil which will never, it seems, come to full maturity – in the image of the plant from the base of which grow heavy, rough stalks and thick, wide leaves, hard and saturated with water, dragging on the ground, dirtied by the earth, yellowed by the lack of sun, but whose flowering stem with soft colours and fragile lips blooms with exquisite delicacy – the young *Salvia sclarea* is full of paradoxes.

Made awkward by her Venusian sensitivity and the natural vulnerability of a young person prey to existential torments and fluctuations, disturbed by the transient clarity of emotional impulses, sparkling like bonfires but ephemeral as fireflies, *Salvia sclarea* seeks her mirror and travels the world still not knowing herself. Creating her personality from day to day, changing at the whim of influences, fashions, needs of the moment and yearning for identification, *Salvia sclarea* compensates for the fears she will not admit with an artificial emissivity, and masks her vulnerability beneath false self-confidence and an almost systematic tendency towards conflict and negativity.

Dishonest towards herself as much as others, she does her best to appear other than her view of herself and her deep nature, like the plant, solid and proud from afar, but quite obviously so fragile to the person who approaches it.

Despite the attitudes she adopts and the tricks she employs, *Salvia sclarea* is driven by an undoubted inner femininity which she is unable, or does not know how, to assert in her daily life.

The social environment, the precocious development of sexuality, virilisation of women and destruction of poetry and romanticism have reduced many young girls to viewing their femininity with uncertainty and indiscriminately sacrificing their dreams and their hopes.

Deprived of sure values, lacking objective judgement, *Salvia sclarea*, without wishing to admit it, gets lost in constant relational difficulties. Considering herself emancipated, not really knowing what attracts her to men, most of the time she experiences a premature, troubled sexuality, devoid of beauty, harmony and any real happiness. The gynaecological problems she cannot prevent (leucorrhoea, irregular cycles, period pains) reveal the failure of her emotional life to blossom, but are not enough to bring her inner dilemmas to light.

And yet, deep inside, she dreams, she loves and wants to believe that life will offer her love, the only value – for the moment – that is still worth something in her young eyes.

The young Katherine Mansfield, pouring out her feelings in her *Journal*, reveals herself to be a *Salvia sclarea*: "Beloved, even though I don't see you, know that I belong to you, that each thought I have and all of my feelings are yours. This morning I awoke, I'd seen you in a dream; all day long, whilst my outer life carries on, regular, tedious, monotonous, I enjoy inside, with you, a life that is heady and full of excitement. My love acquaints me with all the emotions imaginable. For me, you are man, lover, artist, husband, friend, you give me everything and I return everything to you... One day, we will be reunited once more, and only then shall I become myself and blossom, for I sense, I know that in your hands you hold the few final notes, without which the song of my life remains incomplete."

But her heart, bedazzled and impatient, feeds on illusions and the nature of *Salvia sclarea*, more inclined to have an engaging youth murmur sweet nothings to her than to allow herself to envision and be worthy of a Prince Charming, leads her into short-lived adventures that run counter to her need for genuine love which only an *Origanum majorana* with a noble heart might be able to fulfil.

Salvia sclarea is like Eos, the young goddess of the dawn "with rosy fingers", condemned by Aphrodite to perpetual heartache for having been the lover of Ares, the beloved of the goddess of love. For her misfortune, the charming Eos "in the saffron gown" is successively taken with many handsome young mortals in her vain quest for solar love, for failing to wait for the one who followed her.

Thus, often led astray and then let down by the life that she leads, she may, in revolt, sink into the worst excesses; she swings from momentary joy to dark bitterness and renounces her true aspirations for the most illusory of desires, until sometimes coming to reappraise the very meaning of her life:

> "There was once a time that I cannot hide
> There was once a time when it was a bitter thing
> When my soul in distress forgot its pride
> In its ardent desire to find love in this world."[2]

The remedy, depending on the case, is found in *Salvia officinalis*, the authoritarian; or *Lavandula vera*, the gentle, psychologist-confidante; or in a paternal equilibrium provided by *Rosmarinus officinalis b.s. bornyl acetate, verbenone* or *Ravensara aromatica* b.s. eugenol; or even in the hope of true and delightful love embodied by *Origanum majorana* or *Rosmarinus b.s. 1.8 cineole.*

Alone, the young *Salvia sclarea* prepares the way very early on for the disillusions of *Citrus aurantium* p.o. leaves; one can support her by helping her to develop in herself the intelligence of the heart, confidence in her deeply held feelings and pride in her sensitivity.

Salvia sclarea is someone who is easily influenced, whatever she may claim to the contrary, whose blossoming and growth depend to a large extent on the environment in which she lives, and especially on the good or bad standards one manages to instil into her. But her impetuous nature often leads her to prefer a day's illusion to earned experience, and the lesson of life – bitter as it may be – to wise counsel, even if it were to promise a radiant future.

Salvia sclarea is an impending woman who already demands the title and rights of such without, however, possessing the maturity for them, nor the awareness of what the status implies, and whose uncertain future rests essentially on the courageous recognition of her sensitive and spiritual nature.

---

[2] *Emily Brontë*

Rosmarinus Officinalis

The air was calm, and the strong scents of the hill, like invisible smoke, filled the bottom of the ravine. Thyme, aspic and rosemary turned green the golden fragrance of the resin, whose long, motionless tears shone in the clear shade on the black bark.
Marcel Pagnol

Origin and botanical profile

Rosmarinus officinalis, also known as Sea Rose, Incensier, Herb of Crowns (*R. coronarium*), Compass Plant and Mary's Tree, is a sub-shrub of the *Lamiaceae* family, very branchy, with evergreen foliage and a warm aroma which stimulates, stabilises and fortifies those who inhale it. Rosemary has been praised and even venerated since earliest antiquity, and branches of it have been found in Egyptian tombs dating back to the First Dynasty (about 3000 BC). As years went by, the therapeutic reputation of Rosemary continued to grow until it became legendary. It was Arab doctors who first managed to extract its essential oil, which was later very much valued by the spagyrists of the Renaissance.

"Rosemary" comes from the Latin *ros* (dew) and *marinus* (sea). "Sea dew" alludes to its scent and its present habitat on sea coasts. Rosemary has the particular characteristic of flowering practically all year, its floral buds blooming continuously or sporadically, depending on the region and climate. An undemanding plant, *Rosmarinus officinalis* grows all over the areas around the Mediterranean. It is particularly fond of very sunny places with a pronounced summer drought and soil which is chalky or quite clayey, but not water-saturated. It forms vast masses in Provence on the uncultivated hills and is also very common in Spain, Morocco, Tunisia, former Yugoslavia, Italy, Greece and Corsica. Rosemary bears great branches pointing up towards the sky, and the brightness of its numerous flowers softens the green of its foliage.

Rosemary is gathered from May to September, depending on the region. It is pleasant to pick, requiring, nonetheless, all one's physical might and a good pair of secateurs to cut its thick, tough branches. It brings strength and stability to the picker, whose hands and skin become hard on contact with it. It is preferably the flowering branches that are picked, whilst the old branches are cut back to encourage the clump to grow. Picking constitutes a real ecological operation, for the biotopes of Rosemary, far from all habitation, are left in their wild state and the plant tends to grow old. The picking-maintenance operation allow its vigour to be restored, enabling uniform distribution in the growth of its branches and a new vegetative spurt, which is very advantageous and prolific with the next harvest in mind.

Essential oil of *Rosmarinus officinalis* contains three basic compounds: *α-pinene* (bicyclic monoterpene), *1.8 cineole* (bicyclic oxide) and *camphor* (bicyclic ketone). The smell of Rosemary varies according to its habitat, however, depending on the percentage of its three basic compounds and the appearance of specific compounds associated with its biotope. In France, it is strong and rather camphorous (high ketone percentage); it is gentler in Corsica (presence of an ester, less *camphor*); whilst in North Africa, it is more cineoleic (higher oxide proportion), which gives it a peppier, fresher aroma.

We will look at these three biochemical specificities, each having identical basic properties but their own particular therapeutic colouring and, above all, very different characterologies.

Rosmarinus Officinalis b.s. 1.8 cineole

*They are most tempting
these pretty Tarasconian hilltops,
all scented with myrtle, lavender and rosemary.*
Alphonse Daudet

Properties and indications
HEBBD *Rosmarinus officinalis*
p.o. flowering branches, b.s. *1.8 cineole*

This biochemical specificity is the most common, and is found especially in Morocco and Tunisia. The *1.8 cineole* gives this biochemical specificity very marked properties as far as the respiratory area is concerned.

Although it is difficult to ascertain which specificity was being referred to in the ancient recipes that have been handed down to us, we may imagine that the Rosemary which went – with sage, wormwood, cinnamon and garlic, in particular – into making up the famous *Four Thieves' Vinegar* might be rich in *1.8 cineole* since it was intended to prevent epidemics. Rosemary *b.s. 1.8 cineole* was also perhaps included in the no-less-famous Hungary Water (named after Queen Elizabeth of Hungary), although the properties of this water of youth relate equally to the other two specificities. It was, amongst its other virtues, good for toothache and for strengthening the limbs. We might note that these recipes used the whole plant and not just its essence, and that the biochemical specificity is less significant since Rosemary contains other active principles apart from its aromatic molecules.

As far as aromatherapy itself is concerned, *Rosmarinus officinalis b.s. 1.8 cineole* is the specific essence for lung and respiratory ailments: bronchitis, asthma and sinusitis. It is also a good expectorant for coughing fits in combination with *Cupressus sempervirens b.s. pinene*. *Rosmarinus officinalis b.s. 1.8 cineole* is also mucolytic, which complements its expectorant properties.

Less specific on the hepatobiliary area than *Rosmarinus officinalis b.s. bornyl acetate, verbenone*, it nevertheless acts as a decongestant and liver tonic in combination with *Citrus limonum*, particularly in young children whose liver weakness shows up in continual rhinopharyngeal ailments.

It is an excellent essential oil for the ENT (ear-nose-throat) pathologies of youth; it is very efficient – through external massaging of the ear – against ear infections, especially when blended with *Melaleuca quinquenervia* and *Lavandula vera*.

Rosmarinus officinalis b.s. 1.8 cineole is above all effective when absorbed through the skin, most often when blended, but the pulmonary and oral routes should not be overlooked. It is a very good complement to the *Myrtaceae* (*Eucalyptus, Myrtus communis* and *Melaleuca quinquenervia*). It is a good pain-killer for use with problems of rheumatoid arthritis; if there is infection, it should be supplemented with *Thymus vulgaris b.s. linalool*.

It does not possess marked infection-fighting properties, but goes into making up an excellent antiflu remedy, in equal parts with *Ravensara aromatica, Eucalyptus radiata* and *Melaleuca quinquenervia*.

Alone or blended with *Lavandula spica*, it acts remarkably, when massaged in externally, on the toothache problems of all young children. We also recommend *Rosmarinus officinalis b.s. camphor* for this type of ailment, but this last essence must be exclusively reserved for adults; the *1.8 cineole* specificity proves more effective, and is, moreover, harmless, for young children, all the more so for teething infants.

Blended with *Mentha piperita b.s. menthol* and *Lavandula officinalis*, it can stop headaches when massaged on the brow and temples. Nevertheless, an in-depth treatment is called for since headaches are only a symptomatic manifestation which may have multiple causes.

It is an excellent circulatory tonic in combination with *Cupressus sempervirens b.s. pinene* for the veinous circulation or *Helichrysum italicum* for the arterial circulation.

With *Lavandula hybrida, abrialis* clone and *Pelargonium graveolens*, it is also a good muscular tonic and antiparasitic for the skin.

Neither toxic nor caustic, *Rosmarinus officinalis b.s. 1.8 cineole* blends readily with many essential oils, complementing their specific properties. It is administered more externally than orally, and can supplement the Eucalyptus essences for the complex compounds intended for air diffusers. More specific on the respiratory tract, it is nevertheless a good regulator and general tonic, and particularly easy to use.

Rosmarinus officinalis b.s. 1.8 cineole is a fresh, young and fluid essential oil; pleasant to smell, easy to use, it strengthens the mind and may be a very good antidepressant, particularly for people who are psychologically inhibited. Its effect is not to be disregarded in this capacity.

It blends very readily, both with woods and flowers, makes a treatment more dynamic and lends a characteristic freshness.

Its characterology makes it possible to determine its sphere of activity more accurately and to understand its easy, jovial and associative nature. It is far more active at the psychic level than it would lead one to think and than it would think, too.

Characterology

Rosemary, which some Latin authors[3] call *herba salutaris*, is a beneficial, sacred plant used since antiquity, whose reputation has in no way been blunted by the centuries. The Greek and Latin races wore it in wreathes to sharpen their memory and invigorate their spirit, hence its name of Herb of Crowns. A symbol of sincerity, frankness and good faith, Rosemary has from time immemorial been associated with love between engaged couples and marriage ceremonies. The statues of the lares, protective Roman household gods, were decorated with this plant, and as it symbolised stability (although this property relates more to *Rosmarinus b.s. bornyl acetate, verbenone*), young newly-weds used to plant a branch of it on their wedding day – if it grew, it was a good omen for the family. "The fiancé and the wedding guests each wear a sprig of Rosemary... the bride wore a Rosemary headpiece", notes a sixteenth-century chronicler.

In one region of Germany, engaged couples used to give the minister a candle, a mug of beer and a sprig of Rosemary decorated with a thread of red silk on the day of their wedding. In the department of Ain

---

[3] Apuleius and Isidore of Seville, in particular.

and the Burgundy region, on a boy's saint's day, his close relations used to put a sprig of Rosemary by his window and that of his girlfriend to show that they knew of their feelings for one another. For that matter, we see Juliet's nurse saying to Romeo: "Doth not Rosemary and Romeo begin both with the same letter?... My mistress hath the prettiest sententious of it, of you and Rosemary, that it would do you good to hear it."

Rosemary makes you cheery if you put its flowers on your heart, says a Bolognese custom, whilst the Englishman, Banckes, asserts that simply inhaling its pungent leaves, enjoyed on holidays, keeps one in a "youthful frame of mind".

Sincerity, cheerfulness, youth – these are the qualities of *Rosmarinus b.s. 1.8 cineole*, a colourful character, very likeable, with an infectious spirit, the image of its peppy, fresh scent. The life of this eternal adolescent evokes Phaeton, the son of Helios, a handsome, carefree young man, who wanted – at any cost – to show his sisters what he was capable of; he begged his father, the Sun, to let him drive his chariot across the heavens. Once in the sky, however, Phaeton had not the strength to hold the four white horses and lost control of the reins. He was pulled so high that all the earth froze, then so low that drought was rife everywhere and the whole world suffocated. Zeus threw a thunderbolt at Phaeton that brought him down to earth in flames, whereupon he fell into the Po and was drowned.

Generally quite a tall, good-looking boy, with naive charm and a bit of a joker, he saunters about as if he had the body of a wader, with an enormous head overflowing with imagination and little commonsense. *Rosmarinus b.s. 1.8 cineole* is a person with a rather eccentric mind, like Phaeton, who evolves at leisure in a world made up of his own thoughts and dreams he would like to belong to everyone.

Endowed with some vivacity of spirit, though sometimes – due to his nonchalance – slow in reacting, Rosemary *1.8* fluctuates in his ideals and focuses of interest, and his problem – or rather that of everyone around him – is the distance that seems to exist between the creativity of his fertile mind and his capacity for materialising it.

His head is in the sun of his illusions, he being one of those people who consider their extravagances as brilliant and their sense of values as an example, not out of foolish self-conceit but rather from carefree naivety. He is certainly someone full of good intentions but who, from a rational point of view, seems to find as many reasons for not doing what one asks of him as to do what one would particularly like him not to do.

A bit lazy by nature, with a carelessness that can sometimes be as wearing as his kindness is obvious, he baulks at physical effort unless he enjoys an activity; his concentration cannot last, however, his focus of interest being too mobile and his lack of attention too habitual for one to hope to see him successfully carry through his project.

A blunderer, whose arms and feet are as disproportionate as his imagination, he knocks over, breaks or inadvertently steps on anything not safely out of range, and seems – through his non-existent sense of restraint – to make clumsiness his trademark.

Seeming to have stepped out of a cartoon, with his tactless speech and over-expansive gestures, Rosemary *1.8* wears people out with the stupid things he does as he goes along as much as he cheers them up with his kind-heartedness, artless and unaffected mentality, spontaneity and joy of life. In fact, he is a charming boy who needs not to grow old but to grow up.

Mixing him with *Helichrysum italicum* and *Thymus b.s. linalool* is excellent for bringing them out. Almost as much of an idealist as *Origanum majorana*, he nevertheless takes the injustices of life with more of a sense of fun than revolt. With his breezy nature and vivacity, he can be mixed with essences that are cold or full of contradictions, like *Citrus aurantium* p.o. leaves, which he perks up and dusts off.

His masters, *Ravensara aromatica* and *Rosmarinus b.s. bornyl acetate, verbenone,* contribute greatly to him, and there is no doubt that one day he will be able to extract the quintessence of their example and manage to transcend his clownish spirit with a good humour full of common-sense. In the meantime, the word "spiritual" for him is still synonymous with joking and laughter. The two are not incompatible, far from it, and if it were not to be feared that he might be snuffed out under over-harsh conditions, he would be a blessing in many a monastery.

Rosmarinus Officinalis b.s. bornyl acetate, verbenone

*Sage is the master of he who is not
and he is the matter on which he acts.
Thus do they have need of one another.*
Lao Tzu

This particular biochemical specificity has a very limited area of production. As far as we know, *Rosmarinus officinalis b.s. bornyl acetate, verbenone* is only found in Corsica. It is nevertheless probable that it also grows on the nearby Italian coast and Sardinia. However, in some regions of Provence, one does find Rosemary bushes producing an essential oil containing not too much *camphor* and, ultimately, quite close to the Corsican biochemical specifity; *verbenone*, already found only in low quantity in the latter, is, on the other hand, absent. A consequent ester content allows us to compare their properties and, above all, their characterology, the essential difference relating to the ratio of *borneone (camphor)*, which then defines a completely different character.

Far rarer than the *1.8 cineole* sprecificity, *Rosmarinus officinalis b.s. bornyl acetate, verbenone* is nevertheless a basic essential oil. Its biochemical composition is particularly full and very balanced and gives it a high degree of therapeutic effectiveness, enabling it to be used frequently in aromatherapy.

Properties and indications
HEBBD *Rosmarinus officinalis*
p.o. flowering branches, *b.s. bornyl acetate, verbenone*

Rosemary was known in the past for its gastro-intestinal, depurative and regenerative properties, a rather precise assertion, and since it is in no way certain that our food is better and less rotten that than of former times, this enables us to predict the good use we might make of this essence.

Rosmarinus officinalis b.s. bornyl acetate, verbenone is in fact – and perhaps above all – a remarkable regulator of the liver.

Choleretic and cholagogue, it can be taken alone or blended with a little *Mentha piperita* and *Citrus limonum*. As we noted earlier, essential oils, despite their specific properties, cause one another to become more dynamic when blended – provided, of course, that they are not combined to produce incongruous, absurd compounds. Essential oil of *Rosmarinus officinalis b.s. bornyl acetate, verbenone*, included in most internal complex compounds and preparations, is even more expressive as a result of the synergy that operates precisely when congenial blends are created. Furthermore, it is one of the rare essences able to blend harmoniously with all others, and we would even go so far as to say that two essential oils – not antagonistic, although without any real affinity – can get on with one another thanks to *Rosmarinus officinalis b.s. bornyl acetate, verbenone*, which complements and balances them. We encounter this property in *Lavandula vera*, but for external use.

Rosmarinus officinalis b.s. bornyl acetate, verbenone, which, for simplicity's sake, we will call "Rosemary *bav*", is a basic essential oil for beginning a treatment because it encourages the work of clearing excretory ducts and organs, draining the hepato-biliary area and strengthening the natural immunity.

For people with a very tired, over-loaded liver, fetid breath and a grey complexion, who naturally have problems with digestion and assimilation, a dietary régime must be imposed and, in addition, Rosemary *bav* should be blended with *Ocimum basilicum b.s. methyl chavicol* (especially if there are digestive spasms), *Mentha piperita* (only a little), *Anethum graveolens* and *Thymus vulgaris b.s. linalool*. This preparation is also suitable for poisoning, especially when this is drug-related.

It is very useful for overworked intestines, with *Satureja montana, Carum carvi* and *Laurus nobilis*.

Rosemary *bav* will almost systematically be prescribed in an initial oral complex compound, as it makes the body more receptive and frees it from symptomatic obstacles in the way of effective, rapid action at the level of predisposing factors. It may also cause some unresolved problems to re-emerge and bring up a number of old symptoms that had been masked; the therapist must therefore know how to use this faculty and exploit its effects.

It is, moreover, a good lipolytic, indicated in the event of excess cholesterol, with *Salvia officinalis* for women and *Cupressus sempervirens b.s pinene* for men.

Its esters and ketones gently stimulate the cardiac function which has been disturbed by bad eating habits. It is blended, for arteriosclerosis, with *Helichrysum italicum* (be careful, however, if there is a venous weakness because the *diones* in Helichrysum are very fluidifying, which can lead to some distress in *Cupressus* temperaments); *Artemesia dracunculus* (orally) and *Lavandula vera* (through the skin) will be added for tachycardia.

Rosemary *bav* balances the physiological functioning of the body, draining it on the one hand, and stimulating it on the other. It is, in addition, an immunostimulant and essential where there are infectious pathologies; not only will it help eliminate mucus, but it will enable the phenols in *Satureja montana* and *Thymus b.s. thymol* to be assimilated more easily. We find some theories advocating the use of pure phenolic essential oils senseless – with an infectious pathology, there is, more often than not, a reduction in the hepato-biliary balance and the toxicity of phenols proves inappropriate. On the other hand, thanks to Rosemary *bav*, phenol essences are well accepted, enabling more energetic action on the pathogenic germs.

It must certainly be an endocrinal stimulant, although we have not been able to assure ourselves of this property through precise clinical studies – this property therefore remains at the level of probability.

Due to its rebalancing power and its physicochemical properties – combined with its "metaphysical" virtues which made its reputation thousands of years ago – it very effectively combats nervous depression and anguish in people subject to serious problems of identification or who are completely out of sync with themselves. Rudolf Steiner said that "the etheric oil of Rosemary allows the self to be incorporated into the being", a theory we credit and which leads us to say that *Rosmarinus bav* is one of the best essences for restoring the supremacy of the Ego within the individual and thus calming the instinctive drives and reactions of the personality. It is a very good psychic rebalancer, which works gently and is appropriate for everyone. Clearly, blending it with *Ravensara aromatica* or *Laurus nobilis* could prove advantageous. In such cases, the characterology takes on its full meaning.

Rosemary *bav* also proves very useful for post-natal depression, together with *Eugenia caryophyllata*, all the more so as it will lessen any psychic and physical traumas and assist in eliminating any metabolic waste, for the greater good of mother and child.

Rosemary *bav* acts as a diuretic with *Daucus carota* and *Anethum graveolens*; add *Levisticum officinalis* if there is urine retention. Mucolytic, it is indicated for respiratory and genital ailments (particularly leucorrhoea or foul-smelling discharges), in combination with *Salvia officinalis* in the latter case; in addition, it is helpful with *Satureja montana* for cystitis and salpingitis.

Rosmarinus officinalis b.s. bornyl acetate, verbenone is a multi-purpose essential oil and non-toxic, something one needs to count on when treating with aromatherapy. It has an exceptional action. It is absorbed orally, and seldom through the skin, which is the preserve of Rosemary *b.s. 1.8 cineole*. Although more specific on the hepato-biliary area, it is most effective for cardiovascular and broncho-pulmonary pathologies.

The description of Rosemary *bav* shows that this essence is one of the most versatile and indispensable of all. It is a considerable asset for the aromatherapist, not only for its effectiveness but also due to its ease of assimilation and great faculty for blending. Its universalism, moreover, corresponds to its characterology – infinitely more mature than Rosemary *b.s. 1.8 cineole* and more social than Rosemary *b.s. camphor*.

After many years of practice, Rosemary *bav* will still come up with many surprises for the watchful and respectful therapist, particularly the one who observes results at minimal and infinitesimal doses.

Characterology

There is no doubt that the veneration which men have shown from time immemorial towards this bush with its branches pointing skywards like bouquets offered up to the gods – a veneration which is found in a great many rituals, customs and legends associated with it – is directed towards Rosemary's highest and purest spiritual archetype.

A sacred plant, it often takes the place of incense in purification rites and rites for dispelling evil spirits, hence its name, Incensier. Thus Jean de Rupescissa, a sixteenth-century alchemist-doctor, recommended the use of Rosemary to chase away the "black wrath of melancholics": "Such are those of whom Saturn is the dispositor in their generation, and likewise if he is afflicted. And, indeed, the devils willingly reside with such people, and minister to them secret thoughts and abundant imagination, of which they, being thus tormented, are constrained to speak with them, argue with them, struggle with and thwart one another, so much do those who are around them hear them. These are such people who, being heavily tormented with melancholy and evil spirits, sometimes despair and kill themselves..." These remedies "take away the machinations of the spirits and prevent their venture". The exorcising properties resulting from the constructive authority of Rosemary *bav* are expressed in somewhat sulphurated language.

The Ancients also used Rosemary in funeral ceremonies because of its evergreen foliage, the scent of which used to preserve the body of the deceased. Thus Rosemary, like *Cupressus sempervirens*, became a symbol of immortality. In Nordic countries, the deceased were accompanied to their last resting-place by their close relations who carried a sprig of Rosemary in their hands. "Dry up your tears, and stick your rosemary On this fair corse; and as the custom is, In all her best array bear her to church",[4] Friar Lawrence advises Juliet's parents in their distress at her apparent death. It is doubtless for this reason that Rosemary is also the plant of remembrance; "the Arabs and other doctors think that Rosemary encourages the exercising of the mind", notes the Englishman, Gerard. "There's rosemary, that's for remembrance; pray, love, remember", says Ophelia to Laertes.[5] But the memory that Rosemary brings is not only earthly; it also calls on us to remember our celestial home and our divine origins, and the smoke from burning it accompanies our souls to the gates of Heaven to taste there divine ambrosia.

That is why Rosemary is naturally reputed to bring good luck. A

---

[4] Shakespeare
[5] Shakespeare

German custom used to advocate adorning one's home with it on Christmas Eve, whilst in England in olden days, people used to gild sprigs of Rosemary to make garlands of them when celebrating the birth of the infant Jesus. Is it because of its name – St Mary's Tree (*Rosemary* in English) – or because it is still flowering at that time of the year that Rosemary was associated with this festival and the Virgin Mary? In any case, a legend tells us that the Virgin, during the flight into Egypt, covered the then white flowers of Rosemary with her blue cloak, and from then on they adopted this colour in remembrance of the honour accorded to them. A variant narrates that, again during the flight into Egypt, the Rosemary bush served to shelter the Virgin, and that it flowered on the day of the Passion because, during her journey, she spread her clothes and those of the Child over its branches.

A Sicilian tale says that a queen, being barren, envied the Rosemary in her garden for its many branches; she finally became pregnant and gave birth to a Rosemary bush which she watered four times a day with her milk. Her nephew, the King of Spain, stole the plant and watered it with goat's milk; while he was playing the flute one day, he saw a beautiful princess emerge from the Rosemary bush and immediately fell in love with her. But, having to depart for war, he entrusted the Rosemary to his gardener; his sisters, who had found his flute, played it, and the princess emerged from the bush but they beat her out of jealousy; the princess disappeared and the Rosemary withered away. The gardener fled, full of fear, but at midnight he heard a dragon tell his mate the story of the Rosemary bush and thus learned that the plant would recover if it were sprayed with dragon fat. The gardener therefore killed the two dragons, sprinkled the Rosemary with their fat and broke the spell. The King returned and married the princess, the beautiful Sea Rose.

This initiatory tale presents a barren queen, matter, who loves the Rosemary bush, a symbol of the spirit that impregnates her and gives her a son in its likeness, incarnated in an earthly body (the number four and the goat both symbolise the physical world). The king, the human ego, takes over this body – the Rosemary bush – and works to sublimate its sexual force, the flute, an image of the spinal column; he thus comes into contact with the princess, his celestial soul, born out of the Tree of Life symbolised by the Rosemary, but his sisters, a manifestation of the lower personality, stifle his soul. The male and female dragons – like the serpents on Hermes's caduceus – represent the two polarised currents which operate in the world of existential duality and which the king must transmute into a force of universal life in order to reach the Tree of Life and espouse his soul, the celestial Rose, Mary. The Holy Virgin is a representation of the universal Mother, the *prima materia*, the raw stuff, reflected by the sea – the water of love which gives life to the earth – in the material world. Rosemary, the tree of immortality and eternal youth, which Paracelsus made the symbol of the quintessence and elixir of life, is, in all these myths, that of the fruit of the Tree of Life, the Philosopher's Stone, the divine spirit embodied in the perfect man.

We again find the spirit and the work of *Rosmarinus bav* in mythology in the characteristics of Hercules cleaning the Augean stables. King Augeas owned the finest herds of oxen in all the world, but their stables had never been cleaned and the surrounding pastures were covered with a layer of dung so thick that it was impossible to cultivate them; a pestilential stink spread throughout the kingdom. Hercules agreed to clean them in exchange for a tenth of Augeas's herd. He diverted two neighbouring rivers and caused them to run through the two openings he made in the wall; the water washed out the stables, and then the pastures onto which it then flowed.

The herds of Augeas represent humanity sunk in its negative thoughts and feelings, spreading foul smells, and whose unjust actions, in the form of the mountain of waste, are the result. The stables are, symbolically, the different bodies – physical, emotional and mental – congested with impurities. Hercules drove two breaches through the egoistic wall of the separativeness that cuts human beings off from the higher worlds in order to open them up to the currents of the Age of Aquarius, the sign of brotherhood and universality. In astrology, the planet ruling Aquarius is Uranus, the divine sun, symbol of the spirit of truth, which corresponds to the archetype of *Rosmarinus bav*.

Equal to its mythical reputation, Rosemary *bav* is one of the essences that are, at one and the same time, both the most exceptional and the most uncomplicated, and it is precisely this special character which enables it to be universal, and thus prescribed and used by everyone.

The description of Rosemary *bav* is certainly more that of an ideal state – of a principle to aim towards – than a character one might come into contact with every day. A symbol of the perfect person, the hero or demi-god who saves humanity from the hell of its downward slide, he imposes by his vital presence an authority recognised by the gods themselves. There is no problem that cannot be brought to Rosemary *bav*, no person he cannot help, no shadowy situation to which he cannot bring light. He is at the very heart of the spiritual sun to which our soul aspires, whilst plunging into the torments of our distress and sickness to purify our earth (the physical body) of the miasmas that haunt it.

A superhuman being whose stability, strength and equilibrium have no equal but love, justice and light, he exceeds *Laurus nobilis* in power and *Ravensara aromatica* in wisdom, so much has his control forged him an irreproachable character. There is no risk of his sinking into pride, for humility is one of the keys that determine his action; despite his strength and boldness, Rosemary *bav* is more a servant of Heaven than ruler of earth and, master of his ego, he does not claim to hold the truth but bows before Truth, which holds him.

He guides people along the path that leads to Atman, and assists them to be reborn from water and spirit, love and wisdom, to allow the perfect child of Truth to grow in them. As "the wise man", of whom Gautama the Buddha said that "he spreads the scent of his virtue in all directions", Rosemary *bav* encourages Man to develop within his purified heart a boundless love for all Creation and, through it, towards the Creator; he teaches him that the greatest wisdom is undoubtedly to know that love is above everything, for life is born of love and, without life, all wisdom is useless.

A sacred flame shining bright on the altar of our soul, he purifies it until it is immaculate, to make of our body the ideal temple for the heart to which the *Dvir*, the Holy of Holies, reveals himself as the pure essence of the life of the spirit.

If, one day, we happen to meet a being displaying the archetypal traits of Rosemary *bav*, we will not be able to forget it; an exorcising fragrance seems to radiate from his presence, an aura of shimmering, iridescent colours, and one imagines one can hear, almost as if unreal, melodious sounds from the music of the spheres, and heavenly voices singing this prayer:

> Where my gaze rests, let hope be reborn
> and awareness develop,
> Where my hand rests, let abundant and
> harmonious life flow once more,
> Where I pass by, let bliss run freely,
> Where I rest, let there be light,
> Where I reside,
> let Truth shine through.
> *Bashistya Shivânanta*

Rosmarinus Officinalis b.s. camphor

I must tell you that in Provence, it is the custom,
when the hot weather comes,
to send the livestock up into the Alps...
then, with the first quiver of autumn,
they are brought down again to the farmhouse,
and comfortably return to graze
on the grey little hills fragrant with Rosemary...
Alphonse Daudet

In Provence and Languedoc, some habitats of *Rosmarinus officinalis* – often old standing trees whose branches are distilled at the end of the season – produce an essential oil very rich in *camphor*; it is not vital, but we mention it nevertheless since it shows, in comparison with the essences of *Rosmarinus officinalis b.s. 1.8 cineole* and *bornyl acetate, verbenone*, to what extent the biochemical specificity modifies not only the properties but also the characterology. This once again stresses the fact that a proper understanding of aromatherapy is dependent upon a rigorously defined aromatic material.

Properties and indications
HEBBD *Rosmarinus officinalis*
p.o. flowering branches, *b.s. camphor*

Rosmarinus officinalis b.s. camphor is an essential oil which is more difficult to use than the *bornyl acetate, verbenone* specificity. It contains a large proportion of ketones and one must be careful with the dosage, as it can produce a rapid reversal of effects.

Rosemary *b.s. camphor* works essentially on the illnesses of old age. It is the most specific heart tonic of all the essential oils of *Rosmarinus offic-*

inalis, but in low doses, especially with respect to people susceptible to hypertension. It is naturally a hypotensor due to its ketones but, we must stress, in low doses, for it otherwise becomes a hypertensor. Personally, we prefer to use *Rosmarinus b.s. 1.8 cineole,* blended with *Helichrysum italicum b.s. neryl acetate, diones,* and *Lavandula vera* to achieve a hypotensive action.

Rosmarinus officinalis b.s. camphor is a good muscular decontractant in cases of rheumatic pain or cramps, externally for the striated muscles, internally for the smooth muscles. It blends well for internal treatment with *Cupressus sempervirens b.s. pinene,* but once again we are not convinced of the advantage of this over Rosemary *bav.*

When blended with the lipidic extract of *Hypericum perforatum* (the red oil of St John's Wort), it has a good effect on the rheumatic complaints and, more specifically, spinal arthritis. It is in this kind of situation that we recognise its intrinsic value.

It has a pain-killing effect on toothache in adults (through massaging the cheek). *Lavandula officinalis* may be added in this case.

Rosmarinus officinalis b.s. camphor is not much used orally, but more through the skin, although care must always be taken. The pulmonary route (by aerosol) is not recommended because of its strongly camphorous smell. In any case, the absence of Rosemary *b.s. camphor* is not too much of a nuisance, since one can readily treat the illnesses that it deals with by using the other two biochemical specificities. We consider that its drawbacks are not compensated for by a convincing advantage, and unless one is a well-informed aromatherapist for whom its use is interesting from the point of view of characterology, it is preferable to opt for the other specificities. If it were not part of the large family of Rosemarys, we would not have thought it worthwhile to make out a monograph especially for it. However, its characterology may be interesting in some respects.

Characterology

"An old maid, it is said,[6] in the past set up the *festival of youth.* From then on, the members of that society visited her grave each year to burn a sprig of Rosemary decorated with ribbons after sprinkling it with three glasses of wine." This Rosemary, like the one that cured the Queen of Hungary's rheumatism and ailments of old age without inspiring in her the desire to remarry, has some features in common with our *camphor* specificity, a model of which is found amongst the Knights of the Round Table in the person of Sir Keu. King Arthur's seneschal was a Saturnian, ever sombre of mood, bellicose and choleric, "spiteful, most foolish and malicious of tongue",[7] and a rather miserly household steward. Although Keu was a valiant knight, he was little given to gallantry. On the day that a young maid, who had not laughed for six years, burst out laughing at the sight of Percival turning up for the first time at Court, the seneschal furiously slapped her face so hard that she fainted.

Rosmarinus b.s. camphor has little to do with the peppy Rosemary *b.s. 1.8 cineole*, nor with the wise and mythical Rosemary *bav*. That a simple modification to the biochemical specificity can result in temperaments so different may, on the face of it, be surprising, but one need only think of the case of *Thymus vulgaris*, where the rustic, peasant force of the *thymol* specificity has few characteristics in common with the fragility and sensitive interiority of that of *linalool*. Certain molecules present in large quantity throw a character off-balance and alter the effects of the plant, as may also be noticed with *Origanum majorana*. Thujanol specificities have been discovered at the same time devoid of all olfactory delicacy; these features transform the idealist character of a positive *Origanum* into an unpleasant aspect of revolt, sometimes nasty and violent, able to manifest in acts as crazy as terrorism and which thus run counter to the altruistic, generous nature of our young *Origanum b.s. terpineol*. Thus the old standing trees of camphorated Rosemary are clearly differentiated from the other specificities, and we must take this into account in our aromatherapeutic prescriptions.

Rosemary *b.s. camphor* is an elderly man, essentially characterised by the temperament of an old moaner. Old he is indeed, but more in heart than body. Basing his existence on a narrow, personal creed, consoling himself with outdated, overturned values, he refuses any adjustment in relationship to those around him and rejects, on principle, anything that might in any way modify his entropic existence.

---

[6] *Yearbook of the Royal Court of Grenoble, 1841.*
[7] *Chrétien de Troyes.* Perceval le Gallois.

Even when married, he retains the temperament of a confirmed old bachelor, combined, in the most radical cases, with an extreme misogyny. One imagines him, in full caricature, as a retired old service-man with a bugle round his neck, brandishing the flag of simple-minded patriotism and proclaiming – for the information of "this government full of incompetents" – that what's needed is a good war to bring this whole band of good-for-nothings and unemployed people into line.

Fortunately, not all *Rosmarinus b.s. camphor* types go to that extreme and the authoritarianism that conceals their old complexes is rarely combined with any genuine nastiness.

One of the problems of Rosemary *camphor* is that he is as rigid at the physical as the moral level; thus, in his eyes, the rheumatic ailments that cripple him are solely due to the bad weather or to the maid who left the window open. In addition, his hypertension and cholesterol level do not contribute to a joyous mood, but he would, in any case, always find a reason – even where there is none – to express his discontent continually: "Thus, rightly or wrongly and as is his wont, Sir Keu unleashes his tongue..."

- "Oh, Sir Keu, you might speak more gently. Will you thus take your anger and bad humour out on me?" cries the good knight Gawain in exasperation.

In short, it requires the patience of *Lavandula vera* to put up with his company and get to know him, in spite of all his excuses.

But the most annoying thing about the characterology of Rosemary *b.s. camphor* is the fact that it is more a matter of temperament than an effect of age. Thus, one sees Rosemary *camphor* types of thirty carrying in them the seeds of eternal dissatisfaction, displaying an insulting contempt for women, reproaching the sun for creating shade because they turn their back on it, and poisoning the life of those around them with their unhealthy egocentricity.

Obviously, this is the gloomiest picture of this character, but where there is discontent, the door is open to a stream of ingratitude and rancour which end up, like a cancer, eating away, damaging and destroying.

One may maintain the hope of improving some of them or of tempering their excesses, particularly by stressing the other extreme,

Rosmarinus b.s. 1.8 cineole, or the goodness of *Lavandula vera*. As for the others, the irascible, hopeless cases, they can only look forward to eternal rest to allow their wives to become merry widows.

Thymus Vulgaris

> *Sometimes she embraces the lovely narcissus, and sometimes*
> *The rosy hyacinch, and following no particular path*
> *Wanders from meadow to meadow, from garden to garden,*
> *Collecting up a sweet load of melissa or thyme.*
> Ronsard

Origin and botanical portrait

A little sub-shrub with a stunted, greyish appearance, *Thymus vulgaris* is amongst those well-known aromatic species living wild in the areas surrounding the Mediterranean. Further north, it is commonly planted in gardens. The etymology of Thyme probably dates back to the Greek name *this*, meaning *force* or *I perfume*. *Tham*, the Egyptian term for an aromatic plant used to embalm the dead, seems also to be at the origin of its name. This aromatic, stimulating plant is one of the major ingredients of the Provençal *bouquet garni*, a mixture of well-known aromatics used for scenting the kitchen. To those living in the south of France, Thyme is called "farigoule" and is forever associated with the landscapes of Marcel Pagnol.

The genus *Thymus*, which belongs to the *Lamiaceae* family, includes more than fifty species spread throughout Europe, of which only about fifteen are native to France. This is the case with *Thymus serpyllum*, Mother of Thyme (or Wild Thyme), a little creeping plant with a very wide area of distribution extending far to the north.

The southern French who pick Thyme in its wild state do not do so at random, for its fragrance varies from one place to another. They were the first to sense the differences in growths depending on the site where the plants were picked. Their empirical observations have been under research since the 1960s. This has highlighted the uniformity of wild populations of Common Thyme. The essence from the distillation of various individual plants growing within a limited area shows a very different biochemical composition. This study – far from completed – raises more problems for the researchers than it has provided solutions, but it has the merit of demonstrating once again the living, evolving aspect of Nature. This biochemical polymorphism would seem to be due to variations in the expression of the genes of the species, since the plant, despite its fixity, learns to adapt to its surrounding conditions over time.

To date, at least six quite different biochemical specificities have been discovered, and others undoubtedly exist. The high incidence of their distribution seems to be associated with ecological – mainly climatic – and genetic factors. The phenol (*thymol, carvacrol*) and *linalool* specificities are the most usual in Nature within Common Thyme's area of distribution. The *carvacrol* specificity is the most widespread one in the dry southern scrublands at around sea level; that of *thymol* is fairly widespread on the plateaux at an altitude of between 300 and 500 m. The *linalool* specificity is one of the most surprising; it is fairly widespread at mean altitude (between 500 and 1,300 m). Little known and not much used in therapy, it is still not recognised in the pharmacopoeia or by the standardisation bodies despite its remarkable properties (described more fully in the monograph on *Thymus vulgaris b.s. linalool*). The other specificities (*geraniol, thujanol* and *α-terpinyl acetate*) are far less common and rarely used.

As far as the names are concerned – "Spanish Thyme"; "Red Thyme", which owes its colour to the fact that it is distilled in iron stills; and "White Thyme", which is Spanish Thyme rectified to suppress its red colour or drawn out by essential oil of turpentine – these mean nothing at all and their ambiguity conceals an uncertain origin. The colour of the essential oil varies according to the place where the mother plant was picked; it is therefore possible to have essential oils of *Thymus vulgaris b.s. thymol* which are dark red in colour, and also yellow ones.

Most of the specificities that are well known today led to the business of cultivation. Analysed, transplanted and then cloned, these different specificities of Thyme are currently found in the cultivated state. In this way, it is possible to have plants that yield a stable, well-defined essence, thereby avoiding mixtures of specificities as well as non-uniformity of composition in the essential oils obtained by distilling wild plants. However, some of these Thyme clones undergo a phenomenon of gradual die back under cultivation. A good example of this is the *thujanol* biochemical specificity; fragile, it is prone to all sorts of diseases. Too rare in its natural state, one cannot therefore rely on this biochemical specificity in aromatherapy for the time being; furthermore, we find it smells unpleasant, a disadvantage which is not compensated for by any genuine therapeutic usefulness.

In our opinion, wild plants are still the best raw materials for extracting essences. Common Thyme, very widespread in its natural state, can be picked at a large number of sites and three natural biochemical specificities are worthy of consideration (phenolic: *thymol* or *carvacrol* being predominant; and alcoholic: *linalool*).

The *thymol* biochemical specificity is especially extensive on low plateaux, often interspersed with the *carvacrol* specificity (on the plains). The *linalool* specificity is found at higher altitude, as we have seen; its mildness contrasts so greatly with the piquant smell of the phenols that it is impossible to mistake them. Relatively well delimited in space, there is no risk of confusing Thyme *b.s. linalool* with the other specificities – it is a matter of knowledge and experience in the field.

Thymus vulgaris grows in clumps surrounded by stones. Greatly prolific, it is fond of dry, very sunny soil. Stocky and greyish in appearance, *Thymus vulgaris* stands the test of weather and the intense summer heat.

It is extraordinary to observe how, within a given habitat, each clump of Thyme is different when compared with another – tiny flowers, white or pinkish white flowers, small leaves, larger leaves, clumps that are thick or spaced out...

Thymus vulgaris is a very interesting plant with a lot of character and nothing of the commonness that its name would suggest. A study of its two main biochemical specificities, *thymol* and *linalool*, highlights their subtle differences not only insofar as their properties are concerned, but above all as regards their characterology.

Thymus Vulgaris b.s. thymol

From dawn to dusk, I stand by my door;
I know that suddenly the happy moment will come when I will see.
Meanwhile, all alone, I smile and sing.
Meanwhile, the air is filled with the scent of promise.
Rabindranath Tagore

Thyme *b.s. thymol* is picked in May in the south of France; it is already summer in that region then and the plant is covered with pretty little pinkish white flowers. Picking is preferably done with secateurs rather than a sickle in order to respect the integrity of the plant more. The fact that the sparse clumps of Wild Thyme are small makes harvesting long and difficult, and the pleasure that one gets from picking it comes from the stimulating sense of well-being and the warmth – simultaneously gentle and piquant – that Thyme exudes around itself. The branches with the most flowers are naturally preferred to the others and, as is the case with Wild Lavender, pickers and bees learn to get along together.

Thyme holds its essence well and, when dry, keeps its smell for a long time. The essence-secreting glands are almost visible to the naked eye, hidden in the whitish down of the underside of the leaves with their curled edges; end-of-season Thyme *b.s. thymol* thus has dark red glands due to the high phenol concentration of its essence.

The two biochemical specificities of phenolic *Thymus vulgaris* are found most especially in the low Mediterranean scrublands on a level with the low altitude plains and stony plateaux. The *carvacrol* specificity seems, in Nature, to form a fairly uniform, dense population. The *thymol* specificity, on the other hand, is more widespread but less uniformly distributed. The *thymol* populations are invaded by the other specificities (*linalool, terpineol-4*), as well as by the *carvacrol* specificity, which is always present. Are we to conclude from this that the *thymol* specificity will gradually disappear as the species evolves? Certain cloning experiments could suggest this.

It is knowledge of the terrain and of the places noted for picking and the fact of being used to seeing Thyme in Nature that enable the distiller to target a dominant feature of such and such a specificity in a given place. This specificity is not always uniform, however, and there is frequently a discrepancy between the overall, general assessment of the picker-distiller and the analytic results of laboratory research.

The presence of alcohols affords *Thymus vulgaris b.s. thymol* a gradual, gentle action. Many minor compounds balance this essential oil and make it less aggressive than other phenolic essences such as *Satureja montana b.s. carvacrol* or *Origanum compactum.*

Properties and indications
HEBBD *Thymus vulgaris*
p.o. flowering plant, *b.s. thymol*

Essential oil of *Thymus vulgaris b.s. thymol* is simple, and its action deep, long-lasting, very consistent and helpful in a number of cases. Its major quality is that it is an infection-fighting agent almost as powerful as, but less violent and aggressive than, *Satureja montana.* These essential oils both act on the infectious manifestation, but in different ways.

Thymus vulgaris b.s. thymol will be used for deep-seated, even chronic, infections that alter the individual's "terrain" or predisposition to disease and directly affect his psychic and physical identity. Very much an immunostimulant but much less toxic to the liver than *Satureja montana* due to its low level of *carvacrol, Thymus b.s. thymol* acts in depth and restabilises the "terrain", particularly where there are repeated infectious pathologies.

Its action is essentially physical. It fights debility with *Mentha piperita* and *Daucus carota,* and cleanses the gastro-intestinal area, especially when blended with *Rosmarinus officinalis b.s. bornyl acetate, verbenone,* blended with *Lavandula spica* for external treatment and diluted with a vegetable oil, *Thymus vulgaris b.s. thymol* releases joints and restores their faulty mobility; it acts on rheumatism and tranquillises osteoarthritic pains, but must not be used on the skin as it burns and is an irritant.

It is a gastric stimulant and a good depurative which, blended with

Mentha piperita b.s. menthol, Laurus nobilis and *Cupressus sempervirens*, forestalls degeneration.

Its great significance is, above all, in its infection-fighting and immunostimulant properties and the fact that it can be used for a longer period of time than *Satureja montana*. Relatively easy to blend, it tolerates powerful woods and does not, by too marked a character, wipe out the effect of subtler essences.

Thymus vulgaris b.s. thymol nevertheless remains a phenolic essential oil requiring care and appropriate directions for use. In high doses, it becomes toxic to the liver and, in any case, irritant and dermocaustic. When using it externally, blend it systematically with gentle essential oils and a vegetable oil. It is best administered orally. *Thymus vulgaris b.s. thymol* also proves very effective in suppositories and, when a large dose is given, is better tolerated in this way than by the oral route. Never put essence of *Thymus vulgaris b.s. thymol* in a bath or inhale it with a microdiffuser – as with all phenolic essential oils, there is a risk of serious irritation. An excellent "terrain" essential oil, it is powerful without being violent.

Characterology

"It is there that I saw for the first time clumps of dark green emerging out of that "baouco"[1] and looking like miniature olive trees. I left the path and ran to touch their little leaves. A strong scent rose up like a cloud and enveloped me completely.

It was a smell I didn't know, sombre and sustained, that spread out in my head and penetrated to my very heart. It was thyme, which grows on the gravel of the scrublands – those few plants had come down to meet me, to tell the little schoolboy about the future scent of Virgil. I pulled off a few sprigs of it and went back to the cart, holding them under my nose...

It's fresh thyme, said my mother. It will make a wonderful stew..."
(Marcel Pagnol)

The evocation of simple, genuine pleasures, the reminiscence of a clear relationship with a nature as welcoming as it is wild, the feeling of

---

[1] Uncultivated land covered with dry, yellow grass.

eternity in a Provençal summer which seems as if it must go on for ever, whilst the shrubs on the scrublands tremor in the light, warm breeze heavy with a thousand scents under the southern sun – the aura of *Thymus* touches without disturbing, fortifies without inflaming, calms without inducing sleep and emanates a perfume of authenticity and sound values which were once known and appreciated.

Thymus b.s. thymol, the simple, honest man of the soil, with no trace of cunning and somewhat outside his time, evokes in its archetype Philemon and Baucis, that elderly peasant couple in Ancient Greece who were living peacefully in their humble earth-built cottage, united by a love made only stronger with the passing years.

Zeus and Hermes arrived one day in disguise to ask them for hospitality. The gods had resolved to punish humanity for its maliciousness and to wipe it out in a flood, but were looking beforehand to see if they could find a few men worthy of being saved. Everywhere, they found the door closed.

Only the two old people welcomed them, and bent over backwards to serve their unknown guests, apologising for their poverty and the meagreness of the meal, made from delicious fruits they had grown themselves. "They [Zeus and Hermes] had not to wait long, and from the hearth came hot dishes. The wine, which is better drunk fresh, was then in turn removed; a little space was made and the second course served – nuts, figs mixed with wrinkled dates, plums and, in splay-topped baskets, sweet-smelling apples and bunches of grapes with purple leaves, picked straight from the vine. In the middle was a white honeycomb. To all this was added, more precious still, the kindness that could be read on their faces, a look of sincere eagerness and generosity." *(Ovid)*.

Just when they were about to kill their only goose in honour of their guests, the gods stopped them and revealed their identity. They took Philemon and Baucis to the top of a mountain before flooding the earth. The old couple were later allowed to turn into trees at the moment of their death in order not to have to bear the sorrow of one of them continuing alone, having outlived the other.

The Greeks, who held Thyme in high esteem, sometimes included it in the rites practised in honour of the goddess Hecate, mistress of the three worlds – heaven, earth and the underworld – and identified sometimes with Artemis, sometimes with Demeter. Placed at crossroads, her statue received offerings of food which the poor ate on her behalf; the leftovers were thrown away with sprigs of Thyme, hence the name *oxythymia*, the Greek word for "crossroads".

In northern Europe where its close relation, Mother of Thyme, replaces Thyme, it is to Freya, the Nordic Venus, that this plant was dedicated before being consecrated to Mary (hence its names of Herb of Our Lady or Women's Herb). These various divinities, symbols of the feminine principle that builds matter, are vehicles for the life force that animates the earthly world; perhaps this is one of the reasons why Thyme, a plant with a physically very active essence, is associated with them.

A squat little plant stuck in arid soil, one is obliged by its size to focus on the earth, by the picking of it to bear the torrid heat of the sun and by its habitat to merge silently with the song of the cicadas and the buzzing of the bees. One does not speak whilst picking *Thymus vulgaris b.s. thymol* and the harvesting of it is like the life of the character – arduous, patient labour for meagre recompense.

The terrain is flat, the altitude mean, the plant constant and omnipresent, without surprises and always true to itself; everything is reminiscent of the stability and permanence of the cycles and of beings who seem to defy time, far from the life of essences that are more civilised or capricious, sometimes more evolved, but not necessarily more spiritual.

Such is the plant and such is the character. A man of the soil, solid and squat, with tanned skin and a leathered complexion, the smile of simplicity and kindness lights up his face, which is burned by the sun and etched by the furrows of age. *Thymus vulgaris b.s. thymol* carries about him the mark of his laborious life – simple, prosaic but truthful; not much given to speaking, he experiences things more than he rationalises them, and only rarely and discreetly reveals what he experiences. His intelligence is intuitive, his knowledge spontaneous and his kindness natural and modest.

This man of basic needs is subject to a world he does not understand and which does not seek to understand him. A hard worker, he makes up for his expenditure in energy by an over-rich and – these days

– unnatural diet; *Thymus vulgaris b.s. thymol* still lives in the era when one liked to believe that one could eat anything, and despite the solidity of his person and the rustic nature of his life, he suffers from deficiency diseases (osteoarthritis, high cholesterol, varicose veins, hypertension, rheumatism) which gradually condemn him to restrictive handicap which, for the most part, he bears without saying a word. It is very difficult, not to say impossible, to change *Thymus b.s. thymol*, because he cannot conceive of what "living better" means, not imagining that he could live badly, which in a sense is not inexact.

Very much "in the body", essentially physical and earthly, *Thymus vulgaris b.s. thymol* helps ethereal beings of the *Ocimum basilicum* type to stabilise within matter, and *Rosmarinus officinalis b.s. 1.8 cineole* types to talk less and do more.

The very ancient essence of *Thymus vulgaris b.s. thymol* is doubtless bound to disappear in its current form or at least evolve. This character with a clear and wholesome spirit, devoid of sterile intellectualism, who lives in tune with the rhythm of the earth and its seasons, must therefore resolve – at the risk of otherwise falling asleep forever – to gain a foothold in socio-cultural advancement, even if it means giving up a part of his wild and autarkical existence. Love of the earth demands that he should firstly take proper care of his own earth – the physical body – his needs being those of a particular time, the present, albeit imperfect and often incomprehensible.

Philemon and Baucis were able to open themselves up to the messengers of a new era; their old cottage – the image of a run-down body – was transformed into a temple for their souls, and they themselves changed into trees, symbols of ever-renewing life. The soul also follows cycles in its evolution and requires the body to change. What is worthwhile one day is consequently not able to serve as an eternal reference.

Thymus Vulgaris b.s. linalool

> My share of wealth in this world
> must come to me from your hands: this was the promise.
> That is why your light
> shines through my tears.
> I hesitate to follow the others, for fear of missing you,
> there where you wait to be my guide,
> at some turn in the road.
> Rabindranath Tagore

Thymus vulgaris b.s. linalool is a much less common specificity than the phenolic ones. Whilst some people manage to leave their footprints dotted around the habitats of phenolic *Thymus vulgaris*, one must climb to an altitude of between 500 and 1,300 m in the Alps of Upper Provence to find it in any quantity. *Thymus vulgaris b.s. linalool* prefers the sun and south-exposed slopes.

It is possible, in a reasonably mountainous landscape, to find *Thymus vulgaris b.s. thymol* at considerable altitude; these two types can even alternate the more one ascends in altitude, all the more so since the area for Thyme in France includes other species that have not yet been studied. The matter of Thyme and its various essences is complex – the combination of climatic and genetic factors must play a dominant role in their genesis.

Thymus vulgaris b.s. linalool is branchier and denser than *Thymus vulgaris b.s. thymol* which, for its part, is more hirsute, but also smaller and squatter, as if it wanted to protect itself. Scattered about, caught in pebbly slopes, picking it is a laborious task, but gentle and ethereal – more liberating than stimulating – as well. Its essence glands remain a light colour.

Thymus vulgaris b.s. linalool has a mild, delicate smell similar to its cousin in altitude, *Lavandula vera*. It is distilled later in the season than the phenolic Thymes. Its yield is lower, less than 0.2%, and it is consequently a precious essence.

Transplanted under cultivation and cloned, it is more robust than the *thujanol* biochemical specificity and less subject to die back.

Properties and indications
HEBBD *Thymus vulgaris*
p.o. flowering plant, *b.s. linalool*

Very different from *Thymus vulgaris b.s. thymol*, both from the olfactory point of view and that of its therapeutic action, *Thymus vulgaris b.s. linalool* is nevertheless an essential oil with infection-fighting properties, but one that works gently; it will therefore be favoured for use with children. It is a vital, major essential oil for treating childhood illnesses – broncho-pulmonary infections, rhinitis and otitis, on which it has a remarkable action.

It is a good renal drainer for children worn out by a long course of antibiotherapy; it drains these products of metabolic degradation (blended with *Citrus limonum* p.o. expressed zest, *Anethum graveolens* and *Mentha piperita b.s. menthol*).

It fights intestinal worms, tapeworm and amoebae due to its antiparasitic, non-toxic action.

It calms spasmodic coughing fits in whooping-cough. Blended with *Myrtus communis b.s. pinene, 1.8 cineole*, it relieves "tuberculin syndromes" in children with a hollow, violent cough.

Thymus vulgaris b.s. linalool is an excellent general tonic, being neither stimulating nor aggressive due to its low phenol content. In cases of anaemia, it should be blended with *Daucus carota* p.o. seeds. It is an effective immunostimulant in cases of repeated bronchitis and angina, thereby avoiding the automatic or provisional removal of the adenoids and tonsils in children.

All children at some time or another need the beneficent action of *Thymus b.s. linalool.*

It is a nerve tonic, and an intellectual and mental stimulant, which acts in cases of nervous depression, mental fatigue, mental deficiency and claustrophobia, blended with *Origanum majorana b.s. terpineol-4* and *Rosmarinus officinalis b.s. 1.8 cineole*. These properties and directions take on their full sense and value in association with the characterology.

Thymus b.s. linalool is very helpful for children suffering psychic problems due to parental lack of understanding and conflicts and who are unbalanced by family disharmony, due to its strong antidepressive and stimulating effect on the psyche.

Thymus b.s. linalool, blended with *Lavandula spica* (massaged in with lipidic extract of *Hypericum perforatum*), is also a good pain-killer and local infection-fighting agent for acute rheumatoid arthritis in children, the result of a ß-haemolytic streptococcus throat infection which has not healed properly.

It regulates the appetite, slowing it down in cases of bulimia and stimulating it in cases of anorexia.

Blended with *Origanum majorana b.s. terpineol-4* and *Melissa officinalis*, it tempers instinctive reactions, violence, fears and uncontrolled sexuality. It can also help to remedy late genital development (other than where there is an organic pathology).

Essential oil of *Thymus b.s. linalool* is therefore quite exceptional – rare, precious and very slightly phenolic, it is easy to use and replaces the phenolic essential oils for infectious problems in children. Its impact – psychically speaking – must not be disregarded, all the more so since many children go through crises typical of its characterology.

It must under no circumstances be confused with the *thymol* biochemical specificity, which has very different properties. Blending it is a more delicate matter – like *Origanum majorana*, it shrinks from being blended with the heaviest woods and very strong essences, such as *Satureja montana* or *Cinnamomum zeylanicum*, which prevent it from expressing itself in all its glory. It blends very well, on the other hand, with the *Asteraceae*, mainly *Helichrysum italicum*. Unlike the *thymol* biochemical specificities, *Thymus b.s. linalool* can readily be used externally. It is very popular with young people, who easily tolerate it, particularly through the rectal route if large doses need to be used.

Characterology

In its archetype, *Thymus b.s. linalool* rather conjures up Percival the Gaul, the Knight of the Round Table pledged to find the Holy Grail. In his early years, however – fatherless and raised in a manor house isolated from the world by a possessive, anxious mother whose death he caused when he left on his quest – Percival is rather like a simpleton, so much are his virtues interiorised for want of a properly structured education. Simple-minded and rustic, he compounds his mistakes but retains his candour and purity. The confidence of King Arthur, the symbol of his Ego, begins to free him from his inner blockages; he undertakes to demonstrate his worth, but will need years to erase the remnants of his childhood.

Just as *Thymus vulgaris b.s. thymol*, which grows on the plateaux, is an ancient, relatively stagnant essence, so *Thymus vulgaris b.s. linalool*, an upland plant that grows sparsely, is an essence of recent appearance and one in the process of evolving. The person corresponding to it is young, a new character who reveals himself gradually under the impetus of the era that is unfolding.

Thyme *b.s. linalool* is a reserved person, an introvert; he has neither the exuberance nor the carefree attitude of *Rosmarinus officinalis b.s. 1.8 cineole*, nor the assurance and force of character – arrogance, even – of *Origanum majorana*; neither does he have their obvious luck or charm, but his depth is worthy of our full attention.

Endowed with a character which is difficult and hard to make out, *Thymus vulgaris b.s. linalool* is generally intelligent, but his relatively unassuming nature sometimes leads us to think otherwise. Like Einstein, whose parents feared he was suffering from mental retardation because he did not speak until he was three, *Thymus b.s. linalool* seems to seek to distance himself slightly before developing his potentialities, and to delay the inexorable onset of maturity when he will no longer be entitled to be young. He may be exceptionally gifted, which causes problems because his vivacity of spirit and intellectual maturity collide with his too great sensitivity and his emotional needs.

A dualistic person, driven by an inner force to surpass himself by accepting the notion that his faculties are still latent, he has no idea where life is leading him, but is not sufficiently nonchalant not to worry about it.

A troubled, misunderstood child, inhabited by a fear he never speaks about, he is – without knowing it – as solid in his profound being as he is fragile in his body. Often weak, even puny, generally suffering from growth problems, he seems to be prey to all sorts of diseases –

normal, permitted or unacceptable. In extreme cases, it is sometimes onto him that accrued family ordeals and accidents are projected. Like a frail craft about to flounder, he nevertheless weathers these storms without any upheaval managing to destroy him. Seeing him, these words of Zend Avesta come to mind: "Oh, great saint, I am a fragrant seed of light sown in a thick forest amongst the thorns."

Thymus b.s. linalool is, above all, a highly strung person who rationalises things more than he experiences them, contrary to *Thymus vulgaris b.s. thymol*; however, his hypersensitivity cruelly makes him sense his aloneness and the lack of understanding of others. *Thymus vulgaris b.s. linalool* in general says nothing, apparently acquiesces without rebellion until the day when, over something minor – no doubt the last straw – this deceptively calm child has a real fit of hysterics; with uncommon violence, he exteriorises his fear through anger and his distress through sobs which nothing seems able to stop. Finally, he sinks into a troubled sleep, prey to nightmares and a despair that only genuine maternal understanding and consoling warmth can soothe – not the paradox it seems, for it is logical that a strong intellectual power should go hand in hand with too fragile a heart in a being in the process of radical transformation – all the more so since he cannot bear injustice, whether real or imagined, towards him.

A characteristic trait of *Thymus b.s. linalool* is that he manages to synthesise illnesses that are serious in appearance (fever, tremors, anorexia, delirium) but the cause of which is difficult to determine. This child of delicate appearance nevertheless recovers from it all since, through these crises, he seeks only, in fact, to retreat into total silence – a means of shutting himself off and expressing the paradox of the introvert, who wants people to leave him in peace whilst ardently wishing they would take notice of him. If stifled and made to feel insecure by a mother of the *Citrus aurantium* p.o. leaves type, *Thymus b.s. linalool* suffers and takes it upon himself – and sometimes manages, in his extreme instability – to express his suicidal tendencies.

The parents of a child showing this characterology need to adapt to his apparent eccentricities and his mood swings, his needs to behave childishly and his interminable silences. Whilst not falling into a laxness of which he could take advantage, it is necessary to give him time to blossom and to respect his inner sensitivity by channelling it, helping him to retain it in order to prevent him from eventually becoming hardened.

Thymus b.s. linalool does not have the nonchalance of *Rosmarinus officinalis b.s. 1.8 cineole* or the impatience of *Origanum majorana*, and seems to march towards a destiny which will lead him to a sudden awakening that will reveal his numerous abilities. The fragile *Thymus b.s. linalool* then becomes a strong person who, at his best, does not confuse love and weakness; in general honest and motivated by a profound sense of justice, he will be able – once his troubled adolescence is over – to act in a composed, thoughtful and efficient manner.

Thymus b.s. linalool must live at his own pace; he needs to be loved as he is and one must guard against committing injustices towards him for, just as *Rosmarinus officinalis b.s. 1.8 cineole* is inclined to forget and *Origanum majorana* to explode, so *Thymus b.s. linalool* stores in the depths of his memory those unfortunate lapses that wound and gnaw away at him like a cancer until he can take no more. He then risks becoming hard and a holder of grudges, like an ill-aspected *Laurus nobilis* type, and making people pay dearly for his suffering.

Associating with a *Rosmarinus officinalis b.s. 1.8 cineole* is very beneficial to him for it teaches him to laugh, as is the company of an *Anethum graveolens*, who opens him up to the simple joys of Nature and communication with its different kingdoms. The psychology of a *Ravensara aromatica* enables him to flourish wonderfully, as, of course, does the depth of a *Rosmarinus officinalis b.s. bornyl acetate, verbenone*. Generally of an incorruptible nature, *Thymus vulgaris b.s. linalool* fairly effectively resists a dominant *Mentha piperita*, and hereditary influence, whilst a burden in tender youth, leaves practically no indelible mark on him. The behaviour of those closest to him strongly influences his direction but will not determine his life, and whilst *Thymus b.s. linalool* needs to be loved, supported and guided, one must not turn him into a "welfare case" but allow him to retain his free will. Percival thus had to let his mother die, she being a symbol of his earthly heritage and restricted personality, in order to embark upon the path in search of his soul.

Thymus b.s. linalool is someone who needs to be assisted, understood and above all loved, but without ever sinking into any sort of weakness which might keep him stuck in his fears and limitations.

Citrus Aurantium var. amara

I recall a little grove of orange trees,
at the gates of Blidah, it is there that they were beautiful!
In the dark, shiny, glossy foliage,
the fruits were brilliant as coloured glass
and gilded the air about with that halo of splendour
which surrounds the radiant flowers.
Alphonse Daudet

Citrus aurantium
var. amara p.o. leaves
Origin and botanical portrait

The Citruses are little trees originating in oriental Asia (China, India, the Asiatic South-East) belonging to the family of *Rutaceae*. Shrubs with evergreen foliage and a straight, very branchy trunk forming a dense, rounded top, they have simple, semi-persistent leaves (the old ones fall after the new ones have grown). The flowers are white, open for most of the year and full of scent; the petals contain essence glands. The fruit is a cortical berry called "agrume" in French (from the Latin *acrumen*, meaning bitter) because of its acidity, or "hesperidium" (from the Greek *hesperos*, meaning evening star) in allusion to the mythical garden of the Hesperides in which, it was said, grew a tree with golden fruit.

The Seville Orange tree or Bitter Orange tree grows spontaneously in the mountainous parts of north-east India and southern China (the Sweet Orange tree is also found there and would seem to be a variation on the Seville Orange). It is the Citrus most resistant to our latitudes and makes excellent grafting stock for the other species.

The word "orange" comes from the Arabic *narandj*, meaning

"orange". It was, in fact, the Arabs who introduced the Orange tree to Europe, and from the eleventh century they were distilling products from the Seville Orange to make perfumes in Spain, which they then occupied. Restricted under cultivation to a height of 3 to 5 m, the Orange tree could – under natural conditions – reach 15 m and live for several centuries.

"Bigaradier", the French word for the Seville Orange tree, comes from the Provençal *bigarrado*, meaning mottled, a term commonly applied to the bitter orange fruit. The Seville Orange tree contains essences in each organ – leaves, flowers, fruits, bark and branches. The main essences extracted and used are from the zest of the fruit, an essence obtained by expression, and from the leaves and flowers, extracted by distillation. The leaves of the Seville Orange come from the annual pruning of the shrubs; the branches bearing leaves and very recently formed fruits called "petit grains" ("little grains") are distilled, hence the common name of the essential oil of *Citrus aurantium* p.o. leaves: Petitgrain Bigarade. The essential oil has a warm smell and a very bitter taste.

The flowers of the Seville Orange are picked by hand, from April to June and in the mornings, just before they open. The essential oil then obtained, which is very precious, is called "Neroli Bigarade", a name which comes from the Duchess of Trémoille (seventeenth century), known as "la Nerola", who used it to scent her gloves.

Properties and indications
HEBBD *Citrus aurantium*
p.o. leaves, *b.s. linalyl acetate, linalool*

The biochemical composition of Petitgrain Bigarade grants it a spasmolytic action, which is very helpful for highly strung, tense people suffering from all kinds of spasms which are essentially emotional in origin. In fact, *Citrus aurantium* p.o. leaves is an essential oil with a most helpful action at the psychic level, as its characterology will show, and it assists in resolving a number of relational problems mainly affecting the respiratory, nervous and circulatory systems.

It is a mainly rhythmic essence, by which we mean that it regulates the respiratory flow (blended, in that case, with essential oils rich in *1.8 cineole* and bearing a strong psychological, masculine-type impact, like *Ravensara aromatica, Laurus nobilis* and *Rosmarinus officinalis*), the rate of heart beat (with gentle, antispasmodic essences such as *Ocimum basilicum* internally and *Lavandula officinalis* externally), and in general all sorts of tensions able to act on other systems, depending on the psycho-physiological tendencies of the person – genital, gastro-intestinal, cutaneous, etc.

More generally, however, its action is in the nature of a nerve regulator. In this sense, *Citrus aurantium* p.o. leaves is sedative, but for the type of insomnia stemming from anguish due to solitude, from a refusal of celibacy and from emotional shortcomings that generate increasing troubles. Different from the insomnia of *Lavandula vera*, which essentially concerns young children troubled by a mother who is not there, whether mentally or physically; different, also, from *Ocimum basilicum*, which treats the insomnia of the man who is stressed out and broods on his worries during the night, as well as digestive insomnia, *Citrus aurantium* p.o. leaves, again, acts mainly on problems of an emotional origin, and it is in this sense that we must comprehend its action and to which we must direct its use. With its sweet smell and despite its bitterness, it suits people whose nerves are off-balance and who cannot find a proper rhythm that allows them to blossom in life, who have cyclothymic tendencies and are perpetually moody.

Citrus aurantium p.o. leaves can also temper nervous asthma in people with a difficult, irritable character, which sometimes goes with a certain depressive, de-structuring anxiety. The composure of *Eucalyptus globulus*, the strength of *Laurus nobilis*, the psychology of *Ravensara aromatica* and the laughter of *Rosmarinus officinalis b.s. 1.8 cineole* will then restore the situation. *Citrus aurantium* p.o. leaves noticeably improves the arterial circulation, particularly according to its impact on the person's "terrain" or predisposing factors, and mainly by internal administration with *Helichrysum italicum*; moreover, both treat tachycardia.

Citrus aurantium p.o. leaves is a good anti-inflammatory; it is also the essential oil for the neuro-arthritic, the person who is "stuck" and lacks flexibility in confronting daily problems and who has a tendency towards cervico-dorsal arthritis.

It has minor infection-fighting properties; in cases of complaints involving the respiratory tract due to stress, it complements *Rosmarinus officinalis b.s. 1.8 cineole* and, where there is acute rheumatoid arthritis in children, *Thymus vulgaris b.s. linalool* as well.

Citrus aurantium p.o. leaves has a powerful action on the skin; it is a cellular regenerator and also regenerates skin tissue in cases of acne, boils and patches of scurf. It gives good results in skincare in combination with *Daucus carota* and *Lavandula vera.*

It can assist in regulating certain gynaecological problems with *Salvia sclarea* and *Salvia officinalis,* according to the "terrain" and characterology. Here again, blending it with particularly balanced "masculine" essences can only prove beneficial.

Citrus aurantium p.o. leaves is consequently a very interesting essential oil, not only for its specific properties – only recently recognised and exploited – but also due to the strong psychological impact it can display, which makes it particularly effective in a "terrain" treatment. The characterology makes it possible to determine its mode of action and to refine the treatment. The duality between the sweetness of its smell, almost reminiscent of the flower of the Orange tree, and the bitterness of its taste is telling of the constant dualism of the person to which it is linked.

It has the advantage of being neither toxic nor stimulating despite its alcohols, and is well balanced due to the presence of esters, notably *linalyl acetate,* in which it resembles *Lavandula officinalis* and *Salvia sclarea,* with which it has many affinities. Fairly easy to blend, it can, without difficulty, be combined with the *Lamiaceae* – even the phenolic ones – and with woods and the most fragile essences such as the *Asteraceae.* The blends will be particularly important when used along the lines of its characterology, since the receptivity and nervous sensitivity of the patient will be exacerbated.

Characterology

Citrus aurantium leaves, like all the Citruses, belongs to the branch of the *Rutaceae* also known as *Hesperides,* a name that owes its origin to Greek mythology. The Garden of the Hesperides was a heavenly garden, in the Far East, over the seas, in the place where the sun disappeared on the horizon. In this garden lived the Hesperides, the three daughters of the Titan Atlas and Hesperis (*evening*, which has given the word *vespertine, of the evening*); Hesperis was herself the daughter of Hesperos, the evening star – in other words, the planet Venus, visible as the sun sets.

The Hesperides looked after the golden apple tree – guarded by a dragon – which grew in the garden and gave fruit with wonderful properties. The tree was the present of the Earth Mother, Gaia, to Hera on the occasion of her marriage to Zeus. This tree of life was therefore the symbol of the union between sky and earth, or sun and moon, in other words between spirit (gold) and matter – a divine union which gave birth to the physical world.

One of the twelve Labours of Hercules involved the hero in going to pick the golden apples. Having slain the dragon (an act symbolising mastery over the sexual force), the hero resorted to a ruse and suggested that Atlas – who was carrying the vault of the heavens on his shoulders – should go and pick the fruit for him whilst he took care of his burden. Atlas hurriedly gave him three apples picked by his daughters, then took back his load whilst Hercules returned to Man the golden fruit symbolising divine life, and heavenly love and wisdom.

These golden apples from the tree of the origins of the world became Oranges – *or* (same etymology) is *aur* in Latin, a term one finds in *aurantium*; gold, according to esoteric tradition, is solar light condensed by the earth, which could equally refer to the Hebrew term *aur*, meaning light. We thus see the full solar symbolism associated with the fruit of the Hesperides.

The Orange tree, its branches, flowers and fruit, were associated in all areas with nuptial feasts and finery – young brides used to wear a wreath of new orange blossom sprigs; in Crete, married couples are sprinkled with orange blossom water; in Sardinia, oranges used to be fastened to the horns of the oxen pulling the couple's cart; in Sicily, the images of the Virgin Mary are decorated with sprigs from the Orange tree, whilst at Easter two posts decorated with Orange branches are planted in the earth.

The solar symbol for which the Orange tree serves as a vehicle – likened to a tree of life because of its golden-coloured fruit and sweet-smelling flowers which make one think of the love of young married couples – Petitgrain Bigarade paradoxically carries this love within it like a memory slightly altered by maturity. Its sweet-scented leaves conjure up the memory of a lost love for whom *Citrus aurantium* leaves will, deep-down, ever be nostalgic; its bitter little fruits are like the image of its aborted dreams and the bitter taste left on the lips by its tarnished existence. The unvanquished dragon, the unfound light, the unripe fruit – this is the symbolic lot of *Citrus aurantium* leaves.

A lunar, feminine essence, Petitgrain Bigarade is like a middle-aged woman, about forty years old, generally quite distinguished and elegant, sometimes a little haughty due to the essence's connections with Neroli Bigarade. Her features, for the most part, lack finesse although they are marked by a certain charm, allowing a physical maturity resulting from early experience, suffering and disappointments to show through. *Citrus aurantium* leaves reaches a turning-point in her life and must, with reflection, face up to a maturity she has fought off for too long. Thus, although her age cannot be pinned down, she has symbolically stopped at forty; *forty* is, in fact, the number of a death that must lead every person towards his or her resurrection, according to the precept: "If thou dost not die, thou wilt not live." After forty days, the caterpillar retreats into a cocoon to become a butterfly; and the desert, too, gives us forty days to overcome the three temptations of the body, the emotions and the mind, transcended by the three golden apples.

At one extreme, *Citrus aurantium* leaves makes us think of what Mary Magdalene was able to be, having reached this fateful stage – she, who in her youth, had led a life of decadence but who was able to wake up in time to spiritual love and the light.

Feminine, sensitive, idealist without being fully aware of it, continually searching for true love but without really being prepared to pay the heavy price to merit it, *Citrus aurantium* leaves is constantly disappointed in her quest and well acquainted with the bitterness of tears too often shed.

In order to understand her, one must get into the hearts of those women who dream of impossible romances, those eternal women tugged at and disappointed by love, whose heartache is a constant factor in their lives, for whom the "pervasive pain becomes deeper with amours and desires, suffering and joys in the human dwelling-places of the heart", as Tagore so wonderfully describes it, and which flows at the insistent pace of a life of alternations.

Citrus aurantium leaves has a big heart – too big, no doubt – and whereas she was *Salvia sclarea* or *Helichrysum* in her tender youth, she is laying the ground for a tough old age unless she stops frittering away her emotional potentialities.

She dreams of love, but lacks wisdom and plunges too early into the ocean of life, forgetting the stable heights of her spiritual nature. Against winds and tides, she thinks she can use her sensitivity at all ports of call, which she takes to be havens of peace and happiness and towards which she is led by boats promising enchanting islands and illusory treasures. *Citrus aurantium* suffers and exhausts herself with these endless journeys and on these piers where she lands – full of hope – but from which the moorings slip very quickly, obliging her to sail once more to and fro without respite across the tried and tested sea of emotional turmoil.

For this is precisely the trap of her illusions – *Citrus aurantium* leaves wants to believe in love but seems to choose men simply made to deceive her. A woman who compromises too easily, she betrays her sensitive soul and forces it to drink to the dregs the cup of life filled with her bitter tears.

Exhausted by her incessant search for stability, but tenacious and resistant, she is the very expression of a dualism – an inner division – which Sappho once sang about:
"I know not what I must do,
And I feel two souls within me.
I know not what desire keeps me bound
To die, and to see the banks
Of lotuses, under the dew.
And as for me, you have forgotten me."
Professionally reliable, and sometimes capable of extreme devotion, her ubiquitous lunatic and cyclothymic inclinations can cause her to sink into all the excesses of the unpleasant side of her character – impatience, aggressiveness, depression – until they bring her to the worst: her suicidal tendency. In an astonishing cocktail, she combines weakness and will, whim and rununciation, gaiety and despair. Sometimes

beautiful, sometimes ugly, fragile but resilient of health, her complex, changing nature confuses and exhausts those around her as much as it disturbs her. Consequently, one leaves her one day without ever knowing how one will find her the next.

Her drama springs from her unquenchable need for affection. The deep nature of *Citrus aurantium* leaves is often spiritual but she ignores it, confusing twilight affectivity with shared love. She is often alone – separated, divorced or deceived – and each day experiences the anguish of an imposed solitude which she does not accept but senses, however, is imperative. Sometimes on the edge of paranoia, she greatly wants to give of herself but her hands are almost empty and she is alarmed by those who want to take from her what little is left.

Nevertheless, her altruistic nature, which stems from her archetype of true love, drives her to pursue a social or humanitarian course – as a nurse, social worker, teacher of handicapped children, etc. – so many vocations that are often no more than refuges enabling her to conceal her inner conflicts through service which is for the most part irreproachable.

It would be a good thing for *Citrus aurantium* leaves to meet a *Ravensara aromatica*, not as a lover but a guide who will teach her to become aware – sometimes the hard way – of her true nature; this is bound to make her cry and feel guilty, a prelude essential to any change as far as she is concerned. *Rosmarinus officinalis b.s. bornyl acetate, verbenone* will also afford her the balance of a paternal masculine strength, but will sometimes scare her with his absolute stability in contrast to her own lack of balance, which, at its most extreme, can verge on madness.

In fact, *Citrus aurantium* leaves will suffer so long as she fails to admit that her soul is suffocating and that the love she is seeking, and which would fill her up, cannot ever be found in the all too human, prosaic nature of the men with whom she associates.

"I have two loves, one full of happiness, the other of despair, who are like two spirits tempting me without end. The fairest angel is a man of light, and the darkest a woman of night",[2] weeps *Citrus aurantium*, torn between her twilight affectivity and her need for transcendent light.

---

[2] Shakespeare

Bitter as the life of the person it reflects, but delightful to smell, this essential oil is seldom used alone and is ideal for uncontrollable emotional outbursts. As far as health is concerned, *Citrus aurantium* leaves tends towards inflammatory diseases due to her lack of emotional balance. As she ages, she may display osteoarthritic syndromes due to increasing rigidity; she may also suffer from serious lung problems and her skin is often like her social life – rather unhealthy. Her weakness is rhythmic in nature, and the balanced exchange essential to any existence is constantly disrupted and inharmonious where she is concerned.

The properties of this essence are, as we have seen, clearly linked to its character – skin regeneration, circulatory and respiratory arrhythmia, insomnia in people who cannot sleep alone but who are sometimes unable to put up with others, regret for the past but lack of any real courage to face the future, depression and weariness, dreams and disillusion, as Katherine Mansfield describes it:

"Far, far away,
In the time of the streams of my distant childhood,
So straight the poplars quivering
Beside the lake that once I knew.
The fields where I ran have forgotten my name
And I turn over in vain
On my lonely bed, sleep evading my eyes."

Rosmarinus officinalis b.s. bornyl acetate, verbenone and *Ravensara aromatica* give confidence back to this woman who has too low an opinion of herself. *Rosmarinus officinalis 1.8 cineole*, kind and incredibly scatter-brained, cheers her up and provides her with the dual image of the fiancé she would have liked to have from the time when she was *Helichrysum* or *Salvia sclarea*, and of the son she did not have or whom she rejected, often by having an abortion.

Lavandula vera calms and soothes her, and pulls her out of her psychic torpor which could, at worst, turn her into an alcoholic, drug addict or schizophrenic (she often has psychotherapy, intuitively seeking a *Ravensara* counsellor). She should mistrust *Mentha piperita*, who – for a short time – makes her nervy and then euphoric, like a drug which can do nothing but harm. Conversely, *Ocimum basilicum* can be a good alternative to relax and calm her down, before she manages to face up fully to her responsibilities.

Citrus aurantium leaves can, at her best, perform a sublime metamorphosis and cultivate within her the spiritual flower of *Chamaemelum nobile*, with original purity and universal love. Thus, proud to have found herself, her gaze turned towards the heights of her conscience, she gains through the gift of herself the stability that she has sought so hard and which will help her to become a beautiful, highly thought-of woman.

In conclusion, *Citrus aurantium* leaves is not only a person with a well-defined characterology but also, and perhaps most of all, a stage in the life of many women (and men, in fact), a state of consciousness – or rather unconsciousness – during which affectivity, badly handled and disconcerted by certain experiences, turns into a black tide that snares up the wings of love.

"Sad I am and paying my debt;
But how can I rebel? God did warn me.
My parched soul wanted to believe in you,
My source, my love,
But how can I reproach you for being arid yourself?
God did warn me."
Charles Duke

Lavandula Vera var. fragrans

When my eyes were closed,
at night in my little room,
my favourite hill used to come to me,
and I would sleep under an olive tree,
enveloped in the scent of hidden lavender.
Marcel Pagnol

Origin and botanical portrait

Lavender, *Lavandula*, comes from *lavare*, meaning "to wash" in Latin. "The Ancients used to use the flowers and leaves of the plant to perfume their baths and to give the water in which they washed a pleasant smell – hence its generic name of *lavandula*".[3] Washerwomen also used it in their wash-houses and tucked it into their linen to make it smell fresh.

So-called essence of "Lavender" is probably the most frequently used of all the essential oils. However, there is not one but several Lavenders, and also Lavandins or hybrid lavenders. It is therefore important to place these various plants within their botanical context.

There are three species of genuine Lavender in the wild in France: *Lavandula vera*, *Lavandula stoechas* and *Lavandula spica*, which we will look at in the specific chapter devoted to them in this monograph.

These species, which come from the same genus, belong – like their hybrids, the Lavandins – to the same botanical family of the *Lamiaceae*. They are all sub-shrubs, but their shape and the environment in which

---

[3] Burnett

they live are different and clearly characterise them. They have in common the fact that they are sun-loving plants growing in the south of France. After steam distillation, they yield very different essential oils, each with specific properties, and one needs to know how to distinguish them properly.

Lavandula stoechas L., or French Lavender, is quite different from the other species. Sometimes known under the name of Cotton Lavender, it seems that it owes its name to its origin, the Stoechades or Isles of Hyères. Not used by the perfumery industry because of its rather unattractive smell, it is nevertheless useful in aromatherapy. It grows on the siliceous soil of the hills bordering the sea, in clumps which are sometimes spread out.

At the level where *Lavandula vera* (female Lavender) and *Lavandula spica* (male Lavender) meet at between 700 and 800 m, bees create natural hybrids called Lavandins (*Lavandula hybrida* or *Lavandula longifolia*) by carrying pollen from one species to another. Lavandins possess characteristics that are midway between those of their parent plants and are largely sterile.

Originally, Lavandin plantations began by transplanting wild standing plants, but the technique of propagation by cuttings appeared from 1925 onwards, which led to numerous clones being developed. Selection of these clones is of obvious economic interest, for the essential oil yield is two to five times greater and the cost price three to four times lower than for *Lavandula vera*.

The first cultivated clone was the *abrial* or *abrialis*, followed by the *super* and now the *grosso*. Under cultivation, these clones are subject to the phenomenon of die back, which restricts their growth and makes it difficult. Lavandin *grosso* is currently the most often cultivated; it has a very big yield (three times greater than the *abrial* clone), but its essential oil is very mediocre as far as quality is concerned. In aromatherapy, it is the Lavandins *abrial* or *super* (the Lavandin which is biochemically the closest to Lavender) which are most often used for their fragrant qualities.

The cutting technique was adopted at the same time for *Lavandula vera*, which led to the creation of the clonal Lavenders, these being more and more commonly cultivated today. The *Maillette* clone being the most widespread, especially in eastern countries, this is gradually replacing cultivation of True Lavender in France. There is also another cloned variety, *Matheronne*, which is, however, not used as much.

On seeing the diversity of the species of Lavenders and the economic interest they represent, one can readily understand how True Lavender is one of the most adulterated and tampered with of all essential oils on sale in France; in spite of everything, by virtue of its delicacy, its properties and the psychosensory influence it exerts, it remains – in qualitative aromatherapy and above all in characterology – without equal and irreplaceable by any species of Lavender at all, even a close, good quality relation. The other species need to be appreciated for their intrinsic qualities, but must never be used as the *Vera*, the "True", authentic and unique, one.

Several sub-species have resulted from this wonderful *vera* (also known as *Lavandula officinalis* or *Lavandula angustifolia*: *Lavandula vera DC* or *Lavandula officinalis Chaix*, True or Officinal Lavender (also called female Lavender), is the queen plant of the southern French aromatic flora.

Little affected by the cold, it grows at an altitude of 700 to 1,800 m on the sunny, chalky hills of the Provençal hinterland. The most prized quality comes from flowers picked at over 1,000 m. True Lavender grows in tight little clumps, its leaves at the base of the stalk are linear and narrow, and the floral, non-branching, scape is tall or less so, depending on altitude; the short inflorescence bears three to seven flowers. There are two natural varieties of *Lavandula vera*:

- the *fragrans* variety, which prefers dry, very sunny ground (the south-facing slope of chalky hillsides or "adret"); it has spiky stems, linear leaves and compact inflorescences with violet-blue flowers;
- the *delphinensis*, which prefers fresh, shady valleys (the north-facing side or "ubac"); it has sturdy stems, broader leaves and more open inflorescences with pale violet-blue flowers.

At more accessible altitudes – around 800 to 1,000 m – *Lavandula vera* produces a high quality essence, better than the taller variety (from 40 to 60 cm); it is easier to pick and brings about a pleasant feeling of fusion and harmony with Nature. The burning heat of the sun is softened by the fragrant scent of the Lavender flowers. *Lavandula vera* is one of the most pleasurable aromatic plants to pick, as it frees the mind and fills the heart with joy.

Properties and indications
HEBBD *Lavandula vera*
p.o. flowers, b.s. *linalyl acetate, linalool*

Genuine essential oil of *Lavandula vera* is rare, and mostly replaced by Lavandin or a cultivated clonal Lavender smelling much the same; it is difficult for the layman to distinguish them, as one needs to be accustomed to the difference.

Old recipes and instructions for using Lavender essence did not specify the species, thus one can only suppose that they were referring to True Lavender, all the more likely since it was found only in the wild in former times. Lavender has always enjoyed a good reputation, as much spiritual as therapeutic; in Tuscany, for example, it was supposed to get rid of the "evil eye" in children – a fine sprig of freshly picked Lavender was boiled in water and the child then washed in this brew. If the water became very turbid, the evil eye had been lifted.

Lavandula vera is a basic essential oil in aromatherapy, with numerous and versatile properties. It is one of the rare essential oils able to be used in its pure state, not being toxic in any way, but it also blends very readily with other essences and takes very well to being diluted in vegetable oils (sweet almond, hazelnut, macadamia, etc.). Contrary to what is often written, we would not recommend that *Lavandula vera* be used orally; it is absolutely non-toxic but loses many of its properties and much of its effectiveness when used in this way. *Lavandula vera* is an essential oil for the skin; the transcutaneous route is particularly suited to its action, as is the respiratory tract (inhalation with the aid of an efficient microdiffuser).

It is above all an excellent antispasmodic, decontractant and general harmoniser. Its calming and slightly anticoagulant properties are enhanced by the presence of coumarins. It nevertheless also has a tonifying action – which, to the contrary, is not incompatible – due to its alcohols. *Lavandula vera* does not induce drowsiness, but prepares one for sleep – notably children stressed and disturbed by things going badly within the family environment. At the characterological level, it is the essential oil for childhood insomnia – relating to that age which is earlier than preadolescence – involving restless nights and grumpy, even miserable, awakenings, often due to the mother's absence, at least mentally, if not physically. *Lavandula vera* protects, calms and pacifies, and a gentle ointment of several drops on the solar plexus, its preferred province, or on the soles of the feet, is saving. Completely non-toxic, this essential oil – blended with sweet almond oil and massaged along the spine – is easy to use with young children, even new-born babies and infants.

Lavandula vera acts very well on skin complaints. It is both a cicatrisant and anti-inflammatory (due to its coumarins and ketones) on dermatitis, burns, skin allergies, pruritus, wounds, ulcers, traumatisms and bruises.

Slightly disinfectant – although the Lavandins are more so – it is a remarkable pain-killer where wounds and burns are concerned; it heals and regenerates the skin without leaving a scar. Moreover, it can be used pure on a slight burn as it is very gentle and in no way aggressive to skin tissue. In cases of more acute, localised burns (for any widespread burn is serious and requires specialised treatment), it should be diluted with lipidic extract of *Hypericum perforatum* (St John's Wort) and applied to the wound.

Where the circulation is concerned, it is slightly anticoagulant and blends very well with *Helichrysum italicum* and *Rosmarinus officinalis 1.8 cineole*, which is a remarkable combination for haematomas. It is a valuable aid in cases of phlebitis, coronaritis, arteritis, poor capillary circulation and oedema, in conjunction with traditional treatments. It is also anti-inflammatory and useful for neuritis with *Citrus aurantium* p.o. leaves and *Chamaemelum nobile*.

It is a good heart regulator, and calming in cases of palpitations, tachycardia and arrhythmia.

Lavandula vera also fights respiratory pathologies, particularly those of an asthmatiform type, where these are nervous in origin or result from uncontrolled anxiety. It relaxes the person and enables him to breathe more easily. In this case, blend it with *Ravensara aromatica* for the essential support of *1.8 cineole* and for the assurance it provides at the psychic level.

In cases of mycosis of the skin (where it should be blended with *Ormenis mixta* and *Pelargonium graveolens*) and muscular cramps, it is preferable to use *Lavandula hybrida* (*abrialis* clone), which is a better infection-fighter and muscular decongestant, but less spasmolytic.

To sum up, *Lavandula vera* is an essential oil with an exceptional action if it is of very high quality. Cultivated True Lavender does not possess all the properties of genuine high-altitude wild Lavender, particularly if one wishes to work with it through the characterology, but this comes close to perfectionism because it is still astonishingly effective. Essence of True Lavender is vital in the family pharmacopoeia, and if one does not know which remedy to use, opting for this wonder of Nature is almost an assurance of success, or in any case of an obvious improvement.

Essential oil of *Lavandula vera* is therefore a basic remedy. It is vital to use it via the skin since it loses all virtue through the oral route. Non-toxic, it is readily and regularly used for all sorts of complaints and, we would emphasise, is suitable for young children without any reservation at all, provided, of course, it is absolutely pure and of certified origin.

As far as atmospheric diffusion is concerned, its smell may not suit everyone and could become a little heady. It is compatible with all other essential oils, which is completely exceptional but quite representative of its characterology, as beautiful and profound as it is subtle.

Characterology

If *Rosmarinus officinalis b.s. bornyl acetate, verbenone* is the essence of the spirit – the Ego – and although androgenous in nature, represents the masculine principle, the virile force of the creator-spirit, *Lavandula vera* is its feminine complement, ideal and universal. *Lavandula* is the essence of the soul, magnetic and formative, the perfect symbol of gentleness and maternal love which mythology represented through the traits of the Mother Goddess, Demeter, who is similar to the Egyptian Isis, the Phrygian Cybele and the Roman goddess of agriculture, Ceres, whose name has given us "cereal".

Goddess of fertility, barley and wheat which she gave to humanity, the tender and generous Demeter is associated with the myth of her daughter, Kore. Abducted by Hades, the god of the underworld, who wanted to marry her, Kore disappeared – to the despair of her mother who adored her and travelled all over the earth to find her again. When she learned that her daughter was a prisoner in the subterranean realm of Hades, Demeter – in her distress – caused the earth to become dry and infertile, which prevented the plants from growing, until Zeus agreed to help her. A compromise was found which allowed Hades to keep Kore – who had become Persephone – by his side for three months of the year, whilst Demeter, overflowing with joy, could have her beloved daughter back for nine months.

This allegory of the seasonal cycle of vegetation and the eternal nine-month gestation is also, and above all, that of the human soul, Kore. Daughter of the universal Soul, she leaves it to incarnate on earth but the constant love, concern, tenderness and generosity of her divine Mother never cease to lend her support, consolation and spiritual nourishment. Suffering for her daughter – humanity – and rejoicing with her, the Mother Goddess has imprinted in the feminine soul the memory of a natural inclination towards tenderness, devotion and renunciation – virtues which are at the very heart of *Lavandula vera*.

"Love, tenderness, gentleness – these are the three main elements from which God formed the soul of woman; to love, heal and console – this is her destiny on earth", professed Hendrik Conscience; Balzac, for his part, recognised that "to feel, love, suffer and devote herself will always be the life's work of women".

Essence of *Lavandula vera*, so well known and so abused, however – and more often than not confused with the cultivated Lavandins – nevertheless falls into the category of the most evolved, the purest and most beautiful essences; it synthesises a number of admirable physical and spiritual qualities to which it adds a total gift of itself, manifested at plant level by its abundant production and the generalised use of its scent.

Indispensable and omnipresent, essence of *Lavandula vera* is worthy of our raising ourselves to its level, in order to appreciate fully the value of and benefit from the properties of this plant with its exorcising fragrance, although it willingly and directly brings itself down to the level of even the most ungrateful of us.

Lavandula vera is far from being a common, ordinary essence, and were it to be proferred with the moderation of Neroli Bigarade, no-one would fail to consider it of royal blood and worthy of every homage. But we need not suffer in order to contemplate and profit from its ingenuous freshness, for the greatness of *Lavandula vera* all comes from inside and its beauty is simple, genuine, humble and subtle. When one watches this almost scrawny little plant – covered with bees by day and seemingly on watch by night – produce its flowering top without display or ostentation, bear the most torrid sun and attach itself to the dryest soil, suffer the most violent of storms, never giving way or ceasing to perfume the air with its soothing scent, one comes to consider social existence as vain and terribly pretentious. And is it not right, this little clump of blue spikes, which is content with everything and unceremoniously gives thanks for what life sends its way, whether trial or delight? Yes, Albert Samain understood it precisely: "There are strange evenings when flowers have a soul."

Looking at it, these pretty lines from Tagore come to mind: "Listen, my heart; in this flute sings the music of the scent of wild flowers, sparkling leaves and shining water; the music of shadows, echoing with the sound of wings and bees."

It touches the soul of those who approach it, but so discreetly that it sometimes makes us blush not to have been aware of it. In the same way, the plant gives up its pollen and allows itself to be picked and distilled – no secret, no difficulty, once one has made the effort to lean over to gather it and extract its precious essence. The layman has access to this alchemy and his clumsy hands can, without risk or reprisal, penetrate to the heart of this generous soul.

That is the spiritual archetype of the essence, and – allowing for the universally acknowledged subtle human differences – that is the character. Like the essence, and like a true woman, *Lavandula vera*, with constancy and patience, washes the heart and body of those with whom she comes into contact. Tireless, always even-tempered, with unfailing gentleness and devotion, *Lavandula* cares for and calms, listens to and remedies a thousand ills. She takes care of children, adults and the elderly, animals, plants, the earth and sky. She looks after everyone with equal love and if there is anyone in the world whom she neglects, it is herself.

She makes of her life a constant prayer, and since the term "vera" means "faith" in Slavonic, we see that this interpretation suits her unreservedly. The most striking thing about her is undoubtedly her discretion – not to be confused with the hypocritical modesty imposed by a timorous piety. Her virtues, the outcome of much work on herself, have caused her to set aside her personality.

She gives service and gives thanks; she assures those who bother her that the pleasure is all hers; even when tired, she still always finds a way of supporting her fellow man.

If one were to reproach her for being guilty of anything, it would not be for lack but excess. *Lavandula* is more often than not excessive – excessive in giving of herself, in her devotion, in her constant concern to give everyone, even if they have fallen to the depths of moral degeneration, the best, the essential, the very substance of her being. Consumed with love, she exhausts herself to the very limit of her strength.

Mother Teresa, who chose her name in veneration of St Thérèse of Lisieux and has dedicated her life to the service of the poorest of the poor, is a magnificent representation of *Lavandula vera*. "Love has no message to transmit other than itself", she says simply, expressing her absolute faith in Providence.

Love and giving of herself are her gospel, and before every one of the orphans, beggars, lepers and the dying she takes in, feeds, cares for and comforts, she remembers He who said: "Whatsoever you do for the humblest of my people, you do for me."

"I have taken Jesus at His word", smiles Mother Teresa, adding: "Faith is the fruit of prayer. It is prayer that makes us say: I believe. And the fruit of faith is love. It is faith that makes us say: I love. And the fruit of love is service. It is love that makes us say: I want to serve. And the fruit of service is peace."

Lavandula vera knows all about peace and shares it as one would share the best bread, risen with the warmth of the heart and kneaded with the force of self-sacrifice.

To end, we would add that it appears very difficult to set limits on the virtues of *Lavandula vera*; it seems to act everywhere and on everyone with constancy, patience and efficiency. An exceptional essence, *Lavandula vera* can be blended with all the others – from woods to seeds, and flowers to leaves. It brings its feminine gentleness to powerful characters like *Laurus nobilis* or *Mentha piperita*, listens to the somewhat egoistic tears of *Citrus aurantium* p.o. leaves or *Salvia sclarea*, smiles at and soothes – insofar as it is able – the luscious *Cananga odorata*, eases the troubled soul of *Thymus vulgaris b.s. linalool*, and the rebellious one of *Origanum majorana*, and, last but not least, paves the way for the work of *Rosmarinus officinalis b.s. bornyl acetate, verbenone* and *Ravensara aromatica*.

Whilst acknowledging that we have been full in our lyricism – not in order to surround this essence with an aura of inaccessibility, quite the contrary, but in homage to its virtue, which is the only beauty with which humanity should wish to invest itself – we would express our gratitude and send our blessings to *Lavandula vera*, to all the *Lavandulae verae* throughout the world, good fairies and symbols of the eternal Mother, physical expressions of the prayer of St Francis of Assisi: "Lord, make me an instrument of your peace..."

Lavandula Spica

On the plateaux of the scrubland,
thyme, rosemary, cade and kermes hold
their eternal leaves around the ever-blue aspic,
and it is to the depth of the valleys, that autumn,
furtive, slips.
Marcel Pagnol

Origin and botanical portrait

Lavandula spica DC or *Lavandula latifolia Vill.*, Aspic Lavender or Spike Lavender, is often regarded as a poor substitute for *Lavandula vera* and is less appreciated for its fragrant qualities. Commonly called Aspic, it is considered as the "male Lavender" in contrast to *Lavandula vera*, which serves as an image for "female Lavender" (although people sometimes used the term "female Lavender" or "female Aspic" for *Lavandula latifolia*, in that case deemed a sub-species of *Lavandula spica*). "Aspic" comes from the Greek term meaning "Egyptian cobra"; perhaps it owes this name to the Ancients' use of it against the venom of the asp.

A plant growing much further south than *Lavandula vera*, *Lavandula spica* is commonly found in France in the scrublands and dry, chalky hillsides along the sea; sensitive to the cold – unlike *Lavandula vera* – it is encountered only at up to 800 m. It thrives in Spain, Portugal and North Africa where it is very widespread, but the biochemical specificity of its essence there is different from that in France.

Lavandula spica is not greatly cultivated, on the one hand because there are numerous wild sites of it and, on the other, because its essence – not so valued as that of *Lavandula vera* due to its camphorous smell – is of less interest to the perfumery industry. The Lavandins, whose composition – albeit very roughly – resembles that of True Lavender, are preferred instead. In aromatherapy, however, *Lavandula spica* has its specificities and is of interest in its own right.

Picking *Lavandula spica* is a pleasant task, certainly less heady than with *Lavandula vera*, but nevertheless profound due to its closeness to Nature in the wild, a fact of which the picker is not unaware. The task is carried out during the last hot days of summer and arouses some nostalgia on this count.

One can recognise a population of Aspic plants from its pale violet flowers displayed on loose spikes – hence its name of Spike Lavender – at the top of tall, branchy stems that lean over somewhat. It is a plant with an aerial, diffuse appearance, unassuming and merged into its rocky environment, and one has difficulty distinguishing it from afar unless one is familiar with it. *Lavandula spica* encourages the picker to work in silence in communication with Nature, peaceful although a bit autarkic.

Properties and directions
HEBBD *Lavandula spica*
p.o. flowers, *b.s. linalool, 1.8 cineole*

Not as subtle an essential oil as *Lavandula vera*, *Lavandula spica* is administered above all through the skin but, unlike the *vera*, can also be given orally; however, without being as restrictive as in the case of the *officinalis*, we consider that the properties of *Lavandula spica* are more clearly evident through transcutaneous absorption.

It has valuable expectorant and mucolytic properties but, like many essential oils possessing these, it is necessary to place them within the context of their characterology.

It is useful in cases of lung complaints, in combination with *Rosmarinus officinalis b.s. 1.8 cineole*, *Ravensara aromatica* and *Hyssopus officinalis*, an essence with which it has certain affinities.

It is a gentle infection-fighting agent, rather an immunostimulant due to its high alcohol level, and well suited to in-depth treatments as a supplement to oral complex compounds based on phenolic essences.

It is very good at fighting fungal infections (due to its ketones and alcohols); the body must always be drained when there is mycosis to prevent it from reappearing elsewhere. We would recommend using

Lavandula spica externally with *Ormenis mixta* against mycoses of the feet and hands. As far as skin problems are concerned in any case, blending it with *Citrus aurantium var. amara* p.o. leaves and *Laurus nobilis* will help against oozing acne.

Blended with *Rosmarinus officinalis b.s. 1.8 cineole* – or even *Sassafras albidum* and *Ravensara aromatica b.s. eugenol* – it is also a useful anti-inflammatory and efficient pain-killer in cases of rheumatism.

It has a slightly emmenagogue action when blended with the Sages, in cases of late or painful periods.

As a heart tonic, it beneficially replaces *Rosmarinus officinalis b.s. camphor*, which is trickier to use (its hypotensive tendency quickly turns hypertensive in the wrong dosage).

Massaged on the cheek, *Lavandula spica* can be used to relieve pain in children's toothache (with *Rosmarinus officinalis b.s. 1.8 cineole*), and – blended with *Mentha piperita b.s. menthol* – used to bring abcesses to a head, and in cases of neuritis or headaches in adults.

Blended with *Lavandula vera* and *Melaleuca quinquenervia b.s. viridi-florol*, it has a good healing effect on bedsores, with *Laurus nobilis* and *Salvia officinalis*, if the patient's predisposing factors so permit.

With *Cupressus sempervirens b.s. pinene*, it works very well on varicose ulcers, complemented by blending it with *Cistus ladaniferus* if the ulcer is open (the wound must obviously be drained and the diet changed, because ulcers are often a toxinic emunctory). Depending on where they originate, batches of the essence are more or less camphorous; with a high level of *borneone*, the properties of *Lavandula spica* resemble those of *Rosmarinus officinalis b.s. camphor*, but we would still recommend the Provençal specificity. One must be cautious with specificities rich in *camphor* (more than 50%) since, like all ketonic essences, they can become toxic in high doses.

Spica, whilst it does not have the versatility and reputation of *Lavandula vera*, is worthy of our full attention because it proves very effective in its field, even if its somewhat gruff and offputting side – as its characterology will clearly show – sometimes makes one feel inclined to disregard it. It is an essence to be rediscovered, frank and interesting, and capable of showing that it can be of great help, mostly in an excellent supporting role.

Characterology

Lavandula spica – which has no mythic past, presumably because Nature, however far-sighted, was not able to imagine the extent to which man's outrages against her would reach – has an ancestor: the protagonist of the "return to Nature" and myth of the "noble savage". Delighting in bucolic reveries, plant collecting and "hanging out" in Nature, Jean-Jacques Rousseau was a *Lavandula spica* before it existed. "I used to rise with the sun and was happy; I used to go for walks and was happy... I walked in the woods and over the hillsides, wandered through the valleys, read and was idle; I worked in the garden, picked fruit, helped with the cleaning, and happiness followed me everywhere." An anti-establishmentarian through his writings, in which he challenged the false values and hypocrisies of his time, so was he sometimes also through his deliberately dishevelled appearance: "I was attired on that day in the same sloppy way as I was accustomed to, with a heavy beard and rather a badly combed wig. Taking this lack of decency for an act of courage, I thus entered the very drawing-room into which, shortly thereafter, the King, Queen, the royal family and the whole Court were to be admitted." The author of *Confessions* was a "dreamer who took solitary walks", fairly likeable, all things considered, but not a very sociable character, tinged with Rosemary *b.s. camphor* in his last days, when ideas of persecution poisoned his old age.

His emulator, *Lavandula spica*, is someone characteristic of our time, searching for sound values and a new awareness – though well-anchored in today's world, he wants to materialise his dreams of tomorrow, but uses yesterday's means to do so; in other words, he is constantly out of sync with the world as he is with himself, but this is undoubtedly part of his own equilibrium and his picturesque charm.

Physically, he looks like an old student from May 1968 who has come down from his barricades to go and climb hills – long-haired, bearded, dishevelled, who "away from pollution, is off to shear his sheep"; he carries on his self-sufficient life as a likeable fringe-person and questions – not without reason, in fact – social values and the advanced technologies which, however, he does not shirk from using, sometimes, when the need arises.

A staunch ecologist, protagonist of untreated foods and a return to Nature, he talks of a healthy life whilst rolling his cigarette with "organically made" paper, and although he likes to think of them as totally new, his sometimes ready-made ideas and frequently stereotyped remarks correspond to a creed that has very little originality.

Intelligent, often having had a university education but making little use of his intellectual capabilities – or rather, employing them in a somewhat unconventional way – he opts for an active militantism, the principles of which he applies in a nonetheless personal manner. Although exerting pointless effort and surpassing himself are not amongst his favourite practices, he nevertheless leads a sincere existence, secluded in Nature, contenting himself with little and living accordingly.

Often scruffy in appearance, he has the picturesque quality of Larzac* which he well knew how to defend in times of glory and danger. Even today, he starts and reacts sharply to certain taboo words such as "nuclear power stations", "irradiated foods" or "freon aerosols". Is he wrong for all that, and are his campaigns, however typical, vain and artificial? Indeed not, and if his conception of universality is a little particularist, his full and frank comments – rebellious and often aggressive – reflect the will for necessary changes. What one can undoubtedly reproach *Lavandula spica* for is that he often contents himself with condemning without being capable of proposing an alternative, but perhaps that is not his role, the campaigner seldom being the instigator.

Although saving humanity is not part of his plan, the neighbouring river, the hectare of olive trees or the ash-grey clavaria already monopolising his heroic potential, he has a heart big enough and a respect for life and Nature deep enough to engross himself fully in just causes. Ronsard, lamenting the massacre of his forest of Gastine, would undoubtedly have won every sympathy from our ecologist, *Lavandula spica*:

"Hey, lumberjack, stay your hand a while!

That is not wood you are bringing down;

---

*A large uninhabited region in the South of France which the French government wanted to turn into a military camp but abandoned the attempt in the face of popular protest.

Do you not see the blood, freely dripping,
Of the nymphs who used to live beneath the rough bark?"
More countrified than *Lavandula vera*, without the control of *Rosmarinus officinalis b.s. bornyl acetate, verbenone* and devoid of the psychology and ability to adapt of *Ravensara aromatica*, he occasionally comes out with good ideas and remains assuredly confident in the thought that others will find the means to pay the heavy cost of implementing them.

Of a kindly, albeit sometimes shady, nature, he can also be asocial and retreat into an entropic life, living, in that case, off his goats' milk, chickens' eggs and his own makeshift repairs (he is good with his hands and has some artistic leanings), growing his "organic" vegetables delicately scented with a few standing cannabis plants.

This is a very good essence for bringing people back to the natural life, and whilst its attraction is that of the scrublands of Languedoc, stony and dry, where the wild, warm fragrances of Lavender and Common Thyme, Rue and Hyssop mix wonderfully, it at least has the advantage of an authenticity that is refreshing to encounter, even if it is sometimes accompanied by intransigence and coloured by an objectivity which are, all in all, eccentric. It is a good counterweight to an insane rationalism, which is only unbearable in the eyes of those for whom the earth is the object of fleeting profits.

Lavandula spica is an essence of our era, but does not live in an age ready to take it seriously, since there have always been people of a wild nature, defenders of the land, who are fundamentally good, with sane ideas concealed behind an offputting, voluntarily asocial, appearance – even if one did not speak about ecology in times past, it not yet having become a political issue. *Lavandula spica* will evolve with his time, his era and his social condition, all the more so since he will make them evolve through the collective spirit that he represents in his necessary solitude. At the level of characterology, his destiny appears to be drawn; his best future *Cupressus sempervirens*, his worst *Rosmarinus officinalis b.s. camphor*, and the most likely – himself.

"There you are and you wait,
man of the mountains, of wild nature;
you wait until slowly
the stars light up and pierce the clouds,

whilst the lights of the towns so far away
no longer recollect your bohemian way of life."
Charles Duke

Mentha Piperita var. Franco-Mitcham

There are perfumes as fresh as the skin of children,
Gentle as the oboe, green as the prairie,
And others that are debauched, rich and triumphant.
Charles Baudelaire

Origin and botanical portrait

Mentha piperita – Peppermint, in English – is one of the plants of the *Lamiaceae* family. From the Greek *minthê,* which gave it its Latin name *mentha,* Mint can be compared with low Latin *mentalis* or *mens,* meaning mind or spirit.

There are about twenty species of Mint, but they are very prolific as hybrids and this makes the genus *Mentha* complex and difficult to classify.

Mint has been known since remote times and is mentioned – amongst other plants – in various recipes for liturgical perfumes found on the walls of the Egyptian temple of Horus at Edfou. The Chinese, Jews, Greeks and Latins used it, but it is difficult to know exactly which species were involved.

Five authentic species of Mint are found in France, and these can be classified into two groups:

- the Mints with a verticillate or whorled inflorescence at the axilla of the leaves, right along the stalk:
  - *Mentha arvensis L.*: Wild Mint;
  - *Mentha aquatica L.*: Water Mint;
  - *Mentha pulegium L.*: Pennyroyal;
- the Mints with a spiked inflorescence at the top of the stalk:
  - *Mentha rotundifolia L.*: Roundleaf Mint;
  - *Mentha silvestris L.* (or *Mentha longifolia Huds.*): Longleaf Mint.

These different species crossbreed spontaneously near one another. Amongst their numerous hybrids, the one used most is the Mint originating in China and Vietnam, which comes from the cultivation of *Mentha arvensis L. var. piperascens Malin* (a hybrid of *Mentha arvensis* and *Mentha aquatica,* known as Japanese Mint); its aroma is much harsher than that of *Mentha piperita.* It is mainly from *Mentha arvensis var. piperascens Malin* that *menthol* is extracted, as it contains a lot of this constituent (at least 60%).

Mentha piperita, the Mint most used in aromatherapy, is a hybrid from two crossbreeds:

Mentha rotundifolia L. (piperitenonoxide) x *Mentha silvestris L. (piperitonoxide)* = *Mentha aquatica L.;*

Mentha aquatica L. (menthofuran) x *Mentha spicata Huds.* (or *Mentha viridis L.*) (*carvone*) = *Mentha piperita L.* (*menthol, menthone* and *menthofuran*).

This hybrid was described in 1696 by the English botanist, J. Ray, who discovered it in Mitcham on the outskirts of London. After that, cultivation spread throughout Europe and then to the United States. There are three main types of Peppermint:

White Peppermint or *Mentha piperita L. var. officinalis Sole* (*palescens Camus* shape), with green stalks and leaves, and white flowers. Its smell is very delicate, but the plant is fragile and yields little essence, so it is very rarely cultivated. It is the Mint richest in *menthyl acetate* (7 to 9%).

Black Peppermint or *Mentha piperita L. var. vulgaris Sole* (*rubescens Camus* shape), with crimson stalks and leaves, and pinkish flowers. Its smell is not as delicate, but the plant is more robust and yields a greater amount of essence. It is the most cultivated Mint – many selections of it have been perfected and numerous clones bred throughout the world. Depending on where it is planted, Peppermint *var. Mitcham* will produce different qualities and growths: *Mitcham* or *Italo-Mitcham.*

Black Peppermint or *Mentha piperita L. var. silvestris Sole,* known as Hungarian Peppermint, has similar botanical characteristics to the previous variety, but is sturdier. It contains more *menthone* than *menthol.*

Due to the many clonings and selections practised with Peppermint, it is often difficult to know the origin of the cultivated plants.

Mentha piperita is a little plant about 80 cm high, a perennial and stoloniferous. It is a sturdy plant but infertile, because it is a hybrid, though it sometimes produces seeds which are themselves infertile. A hybrid plant tends to decay, and it is therefore necessary to pull up all the cultivated plants every three to five years and replant with young ones.

Picking is done from the first year onwards, in June, just before flowering. This is the time when the best-quality essence is collected. It is, however, possible to take a second cutting in September, and even a third later on.

Properties and indications
HEBBD *Mentha piperita var. Franco-Mitcham*
p.o. whole plant, *b.s. menthol, menthone*

Being very effective, *Mentha piperita* is one of those essential oils aromatherapy could not do without, so numerous are its properties. Its penetrating smell is perceived as refreshing, piquant or burning; it is, in fact, all of these, depending on the patient's "terrain" and "humours".

Mentha piperita arouses and stimulates the physiological functions of the body. It is a general stimulant and a nerve tonic valued by convalescents exhausted by a long illness. It is also an excellent blood purifier, blended with *Citrus limonum* and *Rosmarinus officinalis b.s. 1.8 cineole*, which drains the blood and fights the debility caused by prolonged allopathic treatments. Cholagogue and choleretic, *Mentha piperita* – with *Rosmarinus officinalis b.s. bornyl acetate, verbenone, Citrus limonum* and *Anethum graveolens* – cleanses and drains a tired liver. Blended with *Daucus carota*, it also builds up the liver cells again; it is effective in improving the comfort of cirrhotic patients, cirrhosis being irreversible. When *Thymus vulgaris b.s. thymol* is added to this blend, it acts favourably against anaemia.

This essence is indispensable – though in low doses – during hepatitis, blended with *Citrus limonum, Ocimum basilicum* and *Rosmarinus officinalis b.s. bornyl acetate, verbenone*, and after the acute phase of hepatitis, with *Daucus carota* and *Anethum graveolens*.

It is an excellent anti-emetic with *Citrus limonum*, particularly in cases of travel sickness.

It may be blended with *Cinnamomum zeylanicum* p.o. bark, *Satureja montana, Pinus pinaster* and *Rosmarinus officinalis b.s. bornyl acetate, verbenone* for constipation, when this is due, in particular, to certain psychological and emotional blockages. In cases of parasitosis, it helps people to tolerate, and also complements, the action of *Santolina chamaecyparissus* and *Chenopodium anthelminticum*. It is effective in combating mycosis with *Ormenis mixta* and *Lavandula spica*.

Mint stimulates the digestive functions with *Thymus vulgaris b.s. thymol, Carum carvi, Pimpinella anisum* and several other essences besides (the characterological action and specification of the ailment are important here, given the number of essences with gastro-regulating properties), particularly in cases of gastro-intestinal atony in the elderly.

Its (slight) anti-inflammatory and ("terrain") infection-fighting action is effective in cases of shingles and cystitis. For shingles, it is blended with *Ravensara aromatica, Eucalyptus citriodora* and *Lavandula vera* in vegetable oil of *Hypericum perforatum*. In cases of infection, *Mentha piperita* must always be blended with other more active essential oils, which it will make more dynamic and the effects of which it will intensify. For cystitis, one must add *Salvia officinalis* and *Satureja montana*.

It is a good pain-killer for violent headaches after any organic pathology has been removed (one drop rubbed on the temples and brow), stomach pains, toothache and muscular pains, in synergy with *Lavandula vera* in vegetable oil of *Hypericum perforatum*; and neuralgia, by external massage with *Lavandula vera* and *Citrus aurantium* p.o. leaves in vegetable oil of *Hypericum perforatum*.

It also has useful expectorant and mucolytic properties as a supplement to essences with marked broncho-pulmonary properties. It is a uterine tonic as a supplement to *Eugenia caryophyllata* and *Cinnamomum zeylanicum*.

Essential oil of *Mentha piperita* is therefore extremely versatile. It is useful in many cases and although it must be handled carefully – since it is, all the same, an essence containing a high level of ketones – it makes a preparation more dynamic and always acts as a general tonic and immunostimulant. It must nevertheless always be used in low doses because of the risk due to an excess of *menthol* and *menthone* which, in high quantities, make it excitostupefying and hypertensive. Its characterology clearly shows the excesses and dangers of the person. Be that as it may, it proves remarkably effective and tolerates almost all the other essences, at the risk of shamelessly supplanting the most fragile ones.

Characterology

Affording a particularly colourful portrait, this exceptional characterology distinguishes itself by a powerful, "over-the-top" personality which draws its resources from the extremes of the human soul, embodying simultaneously Heaven and Earth, Paradise and Hell – the eternal purgatory, the paths of which lead to a thousand conflicting destinies, uncertain karmas and futures wherein meld raptures and wisdom, happiness and suffering, temptations and mastery.

Mint's journey seems to date back to the beginning of the world and its origin gives rise to many a legend. Greek mythology tells that the nymph, Minta, was formerly the lover of Hades (Pluto) and used to live with him in his underground kingdom. When the god of the Underworld abducted Kore and made her his wife, Mintha flew into such a rage that Persephone (Kore's new name) stepped on her with her heel and thus turned her into Mint – that is why Strabo says of her: "Mint exudes so soft a scent when stirred by the foot." According to a variant, it was Hades who, as compensation, allowed Mintha to be reborn in the form of a fragrant flower: *Minthê*, Mint or *Hêduosmos* – "with the sweet smell".

Another tale recounts that Demeter, in mourning for her daughter ravished by Hades, suddenly glanced at Wild Mint and was taken by such an aversion for the plant – no doubt because she recognised in it Hades's lover – that she condemned it to infertility.

There are still a few traces of the link which associated Mint with these divinities – in Elis, in the Peloponnese, stands Mount Minth, at the foot of which is one of the rare temples dedicated to Hades, on the edge of a sacred wood consecrated to Demeter.

The fact that Mint has been used in funeral rites – alongside Myrtle and Rosemary – to conceal the smell of corpses, provides the simplest explanation of this myth; thus, one of the common names for Mint is "Herb of Death" or "Death Herb" since, in the French countryside in days gone by, people used to burn Mint in rooms where the dead were laid out. Moreover, a Sicilian saying used to warn women having their period not to go near Mint at the risk of death. There is as much a physical reason for this – since Mint can as easily stop periods as dangerously increase the blood flow – as an occult one, since menstrual blood was often used for black magic practices, in this case powerfully channelled by the force of Hades.

According to Dioscorides and Pliny, Mint had the property of "killing the fetus and obstructing generation by preventing the sperm from coagulating"; was this an effect of Demeter's curse? For the ancient peoples, sterility used to be seen as punishment for an illegitimate union or as the fault of the husband or wife. When she curses Mint, Demeter – Mother Goddess, the universal Soul – is lamenting the loss of her daughter, the human soul, it being the fault of Eve for tasting the fruit of the tree of knowledge of good and evil.

Mint is mendacious, it is said, (more phonetically, "la Menthe est menteuse" in French) and, because of its engaging smell, it is accused of informing, and of talking too freely and detrimentally. A legend recounts that during the flight into Egypt, some harvesters hid the Holy Virgin and the Baby Jesus – who were being pursued by Herod's men – under a pile of sheaves; Mint, which was growing near a stack of corn, denounced them. But Sage (*Salvia*, saving), a neighbour of Mint, stopped the search by saying to the soldiers: *Escoutez pas la mento, que se flouris noun grano*, "Don't listen to Mint, which flowers but gives no seed." *Mentitur Mentha*, said the Salernitan School as well, which not only again constitutes a ready phonetic connection, but relates to a typical trait of the negative mind, which the *Mentha piperita* character equally illustrates.

These texts are also perhaps ambiguous in the same way as the Latin term *mentha*, which can be compared to *mentula*, in other words "masculine sex". The eroticism of the stories connected with Mint is seen again in the reputation as an aphrodisiac which it used to and continues to enjoy – justly moreover, for Mint signifies "exalted love", "I burn", in the language of flowers; "the girl who drinks Mint falls in love" whilst "bulls that eat Mint immediately become enraged", say ancient French proverbs.

On account of this ambiguity attached to the role of Mint because of the duality of its action, Mint – elevated to the level of a sacred plant in the initiatory rites of Eleusis – also symbolises sexual sublimation by the goddess and is established by her as a model for her initiates. This second constituent of the myths associated with Mint relates to the evolution of the soul whilst the first is reminiscent of human incarnation by means of the sexual force coming down and death which follows. On the other hand, it is in this way that humanity was able to acquire a discriminatory mind, a pledge of its freedom of choice, as a result of which arose the awareness of man's individual self. Here again, we find a relationship between a quality of Mint, with its name so similar to "mind", and the virtues capable of stimulating it.

The dualism of *Mentha*, a character very much "in his mind" and without scruples, is due – amongst other things – to the very nature of the intellect. That essentially masculine function of the human being is sterile unless it is connected with its feminine counterpart – love that comes from the heart, of which Demeter represents the sublimation – and cannot otherwise bring forth a healthy, viable child, in other words a just and true action. Mint is clearly both aphrodisiac and contraceptive, even abortifacient, properties highlighted in the myths. We see in this again one of the reasons for the curse of Demeter, the eternal Mother, rejecting it as long as it has no connection with barley and is not proferred by a hand renouncing its sterility through the sublimation of its sexuality.

Mentha piperita – which we are beginning to glimpse beyond its origins and the plurality of its destiny – is found in various traits of heroes or legendary characters, and only becomes more human as a result. The crafty liar, Laomedon, for example, the first King of Troy – in spite of his undertakings – refused to pay their dues to the gods Apollo and Poseidon, who had built the walls of his city. In order to punish him, Poseidon ordered a sea monster to devour its inhabitants and to destroy the crops by spewing the water it had swallowed onto the land. In order to stop the calamity, Laomedon was ordered to abandon his daughter, Hesione, on the bank where she was to be tied to a rock before being swallowed up by the monster. Laomedon tried valiantly but in vain to give the daughters of his notables in exchange. It was Hercules who delivered the poor Hesione from her fate; he offered to kill the monster for the price of two white horses, light as the breeze, which were galloping towards the waters and wheatcrops (symbols for the feelings) which Zeus had offered to Laomedon. The latter accepted, but after Hercules, the victor, had come to seek his reward, again tried to deceive him with ordinary horses.

Equally, there is Ibsen's Peer Gynt, who steals the bride-to-be during a wedding, abandons her in the woods, forms an alliance with Aeolus, the king of the winds (the mind, connected with the element of air), then betrays him and commits one hideous crime after another, laughing at the trust of others without attaching the least importance to the fecklessness of his actions. After many ups and downs, however, he will return to his first love, Solveig, who symbolises purity, forgiveness and faith.

More socially, *Mentha piperita* is an exceptional person, whom – having once met – we find as difficult to forget as the smell and taste of the essence. The latter, in addition, has a particular characteristic – due to its ketones and reinforced in this case by *menthol* – which is the rapid reversal of its effects. Initially fresh and then burning, or the reverse, depending on the case, it leads us astray as it seems not to know any stability; like this volatile, tenacious fragrance – aggressive and engaging – the character attracts sympathy as much as he arouses concern.

Neither man nor woman – though he cannot be classed as androgynous – he goes from one extreme to the other depending on the fluctuations of his excessive nature, and plays with roles, titles and appearances as circumstances dictate, with his eye on an aim from which he alone will benefit. Unlike *Cinnamomum zeylanicum* who, in his childish lack of concern, disregards the laws of good and evil, *Mentha piperita* – who can, at worst, be devoid of any moral sense – uses them according to the opportunities he encounters for so doing. He thus laughs easily at the folly of the world by turning its own devices against it: trickery, ruses, greed and lies. An extreme vision, no doubt, but let us remember that this is the archetype, the strength of action of which sometimes need only touch a temperament for it then to manifest these character traits through certain tendencies sanitised in a number of slightly fraudulent people. In general, his lack of scruples gives him the gift of the gab and makes him liberal with his promises; these abilities consequently often predispose him for a career in politics, driven by a demogogic spirit little inclined to applying the precepts of a Plato who taught that "politics is the art of governing the city so that the citizens live happily". Happiness, for *Mentha piperita*, must – like charity – begin at home.

Mentha piperita is not, however, endowed only with faults – quite the contrary – and his lively nature may also, through his extremes, cause us to reflect on the dangers to which the lack of unity of the Ego may lead. His virile force, like *Satureja montana* with whom he gets on very well, upsets only the weak and deceives only the ignorant. His sympathy and his innate charm do not serve dire designs but, rather, personal interests, for want of being channelled into praiseworthy ideals.

His light-hearted nature, exceptional dynamism and insolent luck, gained under the auspices of a lucky star which was, it seems, created especially for him, refresh as much as they burn those around him, who may be jealous or deceived, admiring or concerned, charmed or full of hatred.

His life is, naturally, anything but monotonous; more often than not involved in risky situations – as rich as Croesus one day and living rough the next – he comes through it all with as much ingenuity as panache, and if he never does anything without a few feathers being ruffled, they always, in these cases, belong to other people.

His arrogant bearing appeals to those who are dissatisfied and who – from fear, respect for conventions or false morality – dare not, but dream of belonging to his emulators. Hence, the world is not innocent and whilst *Mentha piperita* does not have the sole rights to his dualist and dangerous, tempting and extremist nature, he at least has the honesty to confront the risks associated with his temperament.

In conclusion, *Mentha piperita* offers the best and the worst of himself and must, therefore – for the sake of what he is and may become – be channelled, controlled and, above all, kept under observation. In small doses, he works miracles but must take care about whom he associates with. Too actively involved in things, he could lead *Origanum majorana* or *Salvia sclarea* into dissolute ways, deflower *Helichrysum italicum* and unsettle *Chamaemelum nobile*, but what can he do against *Ravensara aromatica*, *Rosmarinus officinalis b.s. bornyl acetate*, *verbenone* or *Salvia officinalis*?

For the time being, *Mentha piperita* is a fire that burns, a volcano overflowing with energy and drawing his physical and mental strength from the bowels of the earth; but his spiritual source remains the ineffable, solar light of Tipheret, the high place visited by the glorified souls of Malkout, who were able to drink of the cup of Iesod, elevated by the purity of their intentions and the strength of their dedication.

Anethum Graveolens

In the morning, by my usual main roads
Crossing fields and orchards,
I set off bright and fresh,
My body wrapped round in wind and light.
I go, I know not where. I walk and am happy;
Celebration and joy are in my heart;
What care I for rights and doctrines,
Pebbles ring out and gleam beneath my dusty feet...
Emile Verhaeren

Origin and botanical portrait

Anethum graveolens or Dill belongs, like Fennel with which it is often confused, to the *Apiaceae* family. The leaves and flowers of both these plants
are, in fact, close cousins, but Fennel is a perennial and grows wild beside
the roads in France, a tall plant, sometimes more than 2 m, with a branchy
stem; whilst Dill, which has a slender stem, is smaller and an annual, only
found in France in the cultivated state or as a wild offshoot of a cultivated
plant. Originally from the East – possibly India or Asia Minor – Dill was
probably brought to the West by monks.

    Anethum comes from the Greek *anethon*, meaning Anise or Aniseed,
owing to Dill's connection with this plant, although the latter, however,
has a very different appearance. *Graveolens* comes from *grave*, which
means *strong*, and *olens*, meaning *smelling*; in other words, *strong-smelling*,
an epithet conferred on Dill due to the rather disagreeable aroma of its
fruit, hence its names of Bastard or Stinking Fennel in connection with
the aniseed-like smell of Fennel seeds. However, the scent of the plant is
absolutely exquisite, and this is, moreover, why we would recommend
using the essence from the whole plant, and not just the seeds, in aromatherapy.

A field of Dill in flower is a true joy to eye and heart – and nose, as well. The clarity of the colours with its blue-green stalks and leaves and bright yellow flowers, and the delicacy of its leaves, give the impression of lightness, movement and youth, enhanced by the play of the wind creating waves and a perpetual swaying motion.

Dill is an annual plant, small in size – from 50 cm to 1 m – with small, yellow flowers. It normally grows at low altitude in sunny spots sheltered from the wind and in fairly damp soil, which is why it is quite rare to find it in the Mediterranean region, and especially in the subspontaneous state near gardens.

It is preferable to pick the whole plant with its newly formed fruit for distillation, as the essential oil is fuller and its smell one of extraordinary delicacy, whereas the essence obtained from the ripe seeds is much more like that of Caraway (*Carum carvi*), which has a stronger, heavier smell.

Properties and indications
HEBBD *Anethum graveolens*
p.o. whole plant, *b.s. α-phellandrene, limonene*

Anethum graveolens p.o. whole plant is one of those very gentle essential oils devoid of toxicity and it can be used from early on in life (from three or four years of age) for all problems to do with the digestive, respiratory and renal systems. Where children are concerned, however, care must be taken not to use *Anethum graveolens* p.o. seeds, which has a stronger action and must be kept for adults only.

Anethum graveolens p.o. whole plant is an excellent stimulant and digestive antispasmodic for children with a delicate stomach and intestines – those who are given food which is too rich and whose troubles manifest through vomiting, colic, nausea, burning sensations and a feeling of bloatedness. It must be blended with *Citrus limonum* p.o. zest, *Rosmarinus officinalis b.s. 1.8 cineole* and *Ocimum basilicum.*

In cases of flatulence connected with hepatobiliary dysfunctioning in adults, it must be blended with *Rosmarinus officinalis b.s. bornyl acetate, verbenone* and *Mentha piperita b.s. menthol,* which are excellent tonics and decongestants, and *Juniperus communis* p.o. pure berries (an intestinal cleanser).

Anethum graveolens p.o. whole plant acts gently on the kidneys, without risk of irritation. It is a good diuretic and renal protector which must be blended with *Juniperus communis* p.o. berries, another essential oil with beneficial properties for the kidneys (much gentler than *Juniperus communis* p.o. twigs), as well as *Santalum album* p.o. wood, which has a good "terrain" anti-inflammatory action on the renal system. Nevertheless, it is only with difficulty that we advocate the use of Sandalwood, for these magnificent trees are tending to disappear, and the massive scale of distillation, combined with forestry, has a lot to do with it.

Still at the renal level, it should be blended with *Ocimum basilicum* where there is inflammation; add *Levisticum officinalis* in cases of retention and to balance more serious ailments – always in combination with conventional treatments. The toxicity of *Levisticum*, an essence which is nevertheless vital owing to its properties, is largely destroyed by *Anethum*, especially if it is blended with *Citrus limonum, Rosmarinus b.s. 1.8 cineole* and *Ocimum basilicum.*

We are stressing the regulating properties of *Anethum graveolens* as far as the renal area is concerned, since it is remarkably effective for children with breath that smells strongly of ammonia in the mornings, this being evidence of hepatobiliary and renal dysfunctioning. Not only does it regulate the function, but it also has a beneficial effect on the psyche of these children, who tend to get up in a bad mood, still tired, and even sad and depressive. *Rosmarinus b.s. 1.8 cineole* and *Anethum* blend very well together and to great advantage.

Anethum graveolens p.o. whole plant also exercises a mucolytic and decongestant action on the pulmonary area. It is a useful supplementary essence in cases of common bronchitis and acute inflammation, when blended with *Rosmarinus b.s. 1.8 cineole*, an essential oil specifically for ENT and lung complaints in children; *Citrus limonum* p.o. zest, a bronchial drainer; *Thymus vulgaris b.s. linalool*, an infection-fighting agent; and *Myrtus communis b.s. myrtenol.* In cases of flu, *Ravensara aromatica b.s. eugenol* – an essential oil specifically for viral infections – must be added.

Anethum therefore has the advantage of acting on the hepatobiliary, renal, gastro-intestinal and also the pulmonary areas, although it does not have a predilection for the latter. Nevertheless, one will find – due to the side of it that acts as a drainer and decongestant – clear improvement in skin conditions, mainly juvenile acne at puberty which is certainly caused by hormonal changes experienced psychically, to a greater or lesser extent, but also by a deficient diet. *Anethum* drains the emunctories and, blended with *Origanum majorana*, will regulate sexuality, tempering excesses or tendencies towards sexual repression with many complexes.

Antidepressant as a result of its tonic properties, due to its overall biochemical constituents which act on the nervous system, *Anethum* will be very effective – blended with *Helichrysum italicum b.s. neryl acetate, diones, Citrus limonum* p.o. zest and *Chamaemelum nobile* p.o. flowers – on young, sensitive people susceptible to emotional shocks which mentally unbalance and depress them. The characterology will be of great help in this regard.

Anethum graveolens p.o. whole plant is an essential oil which works gently but effectively, and is very useful for a number of problems which nowadays unsettle many people, particularly the young, and lead to unhappiness and dissatisfaction with life. It goes well with most essences, but can be obstructed by over-heavy woods (*Cupressus sempervirens*, for example), and tolerates better, if necessary, the phenols in *Satureja montana.* The young essences – of which it is one itself – suit it wonderfully: *Rosmarinus b.s. 1.8 cineole, Origanum majorana, Salvia sclarea, Thymus vulgaris b.s. linalool* and, of course, one which is not as young, but ageless in fact – *Ocimum basilicum*; their scents are, moreover, quite similar and their properties complement one another remarkably.

An unproblematic essential oil, easy to use and indispensable in the treatment of children – particularly for preventing serious ailments – *Anethum graveolens* p.o. whole plant must not be confused with the essence that comes from the seeds, firstly from a physical stance and secondly from a characterological point of view. The essence from the seeds will represent someone who is more uncompromising and sharper, less tolerant and joyous, and will consequently not have the same antidepressive, tonic properties. A young essence, enthusiastic and gay, its advantage is that it suits children, who are generally very fond of it. Long neglected and considered of less worth than Fennel or Aniseed, we believe it possesses intrinsic properties and the considerable advantage over the former of being easy to use. It is therefore a valuable asset in the aromatherapist's stock.

Characterology

"Do you choose, Lord, to participate in the bliss of this rhythm? To be hurled around, lost and broken in the whirlwind of this formidable joy?

"It all rushes around, unceasingly, without a backward glance, no power being able to hold back all the things moving faster and faster.

"Matching step with the rhythm of this tireless music, each season comes dancing up, then passes by – colours, hues and fragrances spill never-ending cascades into this overabundant joy which showers forth, gives up and dies at every moment."

This preamble, drawn from the vibrant poetry of Tagore, announces *Anethum graveolens* – a firework of life, evoking the invisible spirits which are said to populate and animate Nature. A charming character, its archetype lives in the land of the fairies and identifies with the gnomes and elves, reputed by the Nordic peoples to heal and protect humans, particularly from evil spirits. Whilst the Nature spirits – gnomes, sylphs, undines and salamanders – having no awareness of good and evil, obey whoever – whether black or white magicians – is able to command them, the spirit of *Anethum* seems to have a predilection for human company, especially that of the young, who celebrate life in all its beauty and bounty.

In earlier times, Dill was well known for its magical properties; thus, in his initiatory tale *The Golden Ass*, Apuleius describes the works of an apprentice magician who turns the hero into an ass: "See how unpretentious and ordinary they are, the plants through which miracles are performed. It's only a little Dill mixed with Bay Leaves in spring water, but it serves to prepare a bath and a potion." The plant used to chase away demons and witches: "A little Vervain blessed here and Dill there will enable you to overcome any spell!", we read in *The Muses' Elysium*. According to Rudolf Steiner, the reason is that essential oil of *Anethum graveolens* – brought forth from the sphere of fire – "strengthens the forces of awareness and snuffs out the crepuscular lights of atavistic clairvoyance... Burning it with St John's Wort kept away storms, which meant only that its candescent strength is in touch with the cosmic heat."[1] This warmth from the essence – both gentle and subtly pungent at one and the same time – bears witness to its fiery source and lays the foundations for the particular features of the character, more archetype than human being, of *Anethum graveolens.*

Anethum channels the life force of Nature and fashions from it the eternal cycles of death and rebirth. All pessimism being alien to it, it helps to dispense with the superfluous, reject the corrupt that poisons human existence and softly accompanies to its proper end that which must disappear in accordance with the life cycle, the laws of degeneration and evolution. An expression of imperishable youth, it carries in it the season of renewal, the ever-dawning promise of spring following the decline of winter – of life after death. Never feeling affected by events, *Anethum* operates according to the alternating of the natural cycles, without anxiety or rebellion, in the serene acceptance of the inescapability of Death, which is daughter to Life: "The same river of life running, night and day, through my veins runs through the world and dances in rhythmic beats.

"It is the same life which pushes its joy up through the dusty earth in countless blades of grass, and bursts into impetuous waves of leaves and flowers.

"It is the same life that balances ebbs and flows in the ocean-cradle of birth and death.

"I feel my limbs glorified at the touch of this universal life. And I take pride, for it is in my blood that the great heartbeat of the life of ages dances at this moment."[2]

Like Oberon, the King of the Elves in Scandinavian mythology whom Shakespeare made the hero in *A Midsummer Night's Dream,* *Anethum graveolens,* upright and loyal, matured by a certain intelligence, straightforward and true, serves life in all its forms – plant, animal and human: "Through this house give glimmering light, By the dead and drowsy fire: Every elf and fairy sprite Hop as light as bird from brier: And this ditty, after me, Sing and dance it trippingly...

---

[1] W. Pelikan.

[2] Tagore.

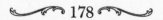

"Through this house each fairy stray, To the best bride-bed will we, Which by us shall blessed be; And the issue there created Ever shall be fortunate...

"And the blots of Nature's hand Shall not in their issue stand: Never mole, hare-lip, nor scar, Nor mark prodigious, such as are Despised in nativity, Shall upon their children be. With this field-dew consecrate, Every fairy take his gate; And each several chamber bless, Through this palace, with sweet peace."[3] Thus sang Oberon, leading his fairy train in a swirling farandole.

Joyous by nature, mischievous without the trickery or calculation of *Mentha piperita*, this young person – half-child, half-adolescent – seems not to know worries without being irresponsible, for all that. His purity seems to keep him safe from maudlin thoughts, immunise him against the below-the-belt punches of his rather unscrupulous fellow beings and enable him to retain an aura around him in which he lives – not in isolated self-sufficiency but in a sort of spiritual cocoon. "To exist and nothing more, is enough! It is enough to breathe! Joy, joy! Everywhere joy!",[4] he simply says.

One might doubtless fear that he will continue to exist in an unrealistic vision of life and his problems, but in our opinion, it's nothing of the sort. Illusion is dangerous when it leads us into disappointment; it is only what it is because of more or less well-founded expectations, but *Anethum* expects nothing and his soul is not waiting for anything. Is it therefore an illusion to base one's credentials not on the pride of human assurance but on the intuitive, sensitive perception of Nature and her cycles? It is enough to watch a field of Dill dancing in the wind and smell its freshness to understand that, although this rather magical little plant is well rooted in the earth, it willingly accepts being pulled up when the time is right. Cutting Dill in no way traumatises this beautiful annual plant which fully accomplishes its vegetative cycle – death, in its eyes, doesn't count for much, or at least is little more than night compared to day. *Anethum* is a living spring; and yet the name given to the stream is an illusion since, although its bed remains, the water flowing

---

3 Shakespeare.

[4] W. Whitman, *Leaves of Grass*.

over it means the stream is always changing.

There is nothing surprising in the fact that gladiators rubbed their bodies down with it before combat; as well as its pain-killing properties, Dill is not afraid of departing from Existence, for what life has produced will always go on living. We could say, in meditating on Dill, that we find ourselves before a symbol clearly attesting to reincarnation.

It is beneficial for young *Anethum* people to fully experience their sensitivity, to have special contact with Nature – to walk in the woods, bathe their limbs in streams, touch the grass and trees, speak to the birds and contemplate the stars. *Anethum* is a blessing for *Thymus vulgaris b.s. linalool*; it enables him to re-establish himself in relation to a point of focus other than himself, to look at the world and to feel concerned, even loved, by it.

Life is a game for *Anethum* – how can one talk to him about something which, in the eyes of the world, is serious, for this is a notion devoid of sense except for anyone who is not serious and, in order to allay suspicion, needs to take himself seriously? The Little Prince, *Thymus b.s. linalool*, in his inner sadness and vulnerability, is *Anethum graveolens* in relation to Saint-Exupéry; he reveals the basic values to him and his vision of the world is undoubtedly the least sensible of the two.

To play, to play at working, to play at living and dying, and at always coming back to life; to sing – not in order to exorcise what hurts or to try and establish harmony – to sing simply because life is singing, Nature is singing, the mountains, trees, dragonflies and wind are singing and it is absolutely natural to sing together, with them. Because unity is an obvious fact that does not need to be proven. *Anethum* doesn't prove anything – that is not his job, not his concern; *Anethum* is vibrant and acts without the slightest conception of the healing he brings. Yes, *Anethum* is a stream, a fresh spring, clear and limpid, sullied by no-one but from which everyone may quench his thirst.

The essence brings people simple, salutary joy; it reassures the anxious who, caught between the ups and downs of existence, forget how to ride them and how to contemplate the simple beauty of life around them, in spite of its blots of wretchedness and mediocrity. *Anethum* enables us to see the essential truth behind the impenetrable fog of our convictions and the obvious cruelties they cause us to perpetrate.

"I must go seek some dew-drops here, And hang a pearl in every cowslip's ear":[5] thus spoke Titania, Queen of the Fairies. In the turmoil of the important events and priorities in our lives, behind our notions and scales of values, the basic essentials seems stupid and vain; they are nevertheless essential, and express themselves with a kind word, a natural gesture or a confident look, not simply to do good but because *Anethum* carries confidence within himself; with a spontaneous rather than a dogmatic prayer, because it is normal and polite to say thank you and because lack of time is a false pretext. *Anethum* does not live or think like everyone else but, even so, is not a revolutionary. Pointless upheavals, strikes and subversion are alien to his nature – and to Nature. No doubt, we all need a little *Anethum*, a little of this spring that will wash the burning acidity from our kidneys.

Let us not, for all that, abandon our rational and concrete criteria, but let us also not be so sure that we are right when faced with *Anethum*; we must simply ask: am I still alive? The light air of a spring morning, the squirrel in the woods, the glacier on the mountain and the sparrowhawk soaring in the clear sky – do they know me? Did I ever once look at them, listen to them, talk to them? Perhaps I am not strictly a human being, a creature of this world which made me and that I want to remake, without quite knowing why?

Conciliatory and compatible, *Anethum graveolens* is a magical essence that works for life, in the name of the eternal laws and cycles of Nature.

"The sleep which flutters on the eyelids of a little child – who can say whence it comes? – I. I was told that he lives there, in the fairy village, where two shy and enchanted flowers bow down amongst the shadows of the forest tenderly lit by the fireflies. It is from there that he comes to lay a kiss on the eyelids of the little child."[6]

---

[5] *A Midsummer Night's Dream.*
[6] Tagore.

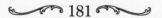

Daucus Carota

*The woman with the sweetest perfume
is the one who goes unperfumed.*
Plautus

Origin and botanical portrait

Daucus carota or Carrot is better known for its edible root than its essential oil. The wild plant with the slender, ill-smelling tap root produces – through farming selection – the familiar vegetable with the plump, orange-coloured tap root. The essence is contained mainly in the seeds.

Daucus comes from the Greek word *daukos*, commonly designating the various species of *Apiaceae* (or Umbellifers); this comes from the fact that there is nothing, as far as the layman is concerned, that looks more like an Umbellifer than another Umbellifer. *Daukos* probably comes from *daio*, meaning *I make hot*, a property common to many species of *Apiaceae*. The wild plant was known in antiquity; grown for 2,000 years in Europe, it only became widespread during the Renaissance. Until the nineteenth century it was a much spurned vegetable, eaten only by the most wretched of peasants in times of great scarcity, hence expressions like "to eat 'goviottes'" (or wild carrots) or "to live on carrots", which meant "to slim right down, to do with little".

Carrot is a very widespread plant in the wild and can be found on the roadside and in meadows, uncut fields, uncultivated ground or near crops. *Daucus carota* does not like heights, but grows as well in the south as the north of France.

It is a practically odourless aromatic plant growing more or less everywhere; it is not greatly concerned about sun but does, however, contain an essence that is only revealed when the fruits are distilled. This point should be noted with regard to the characterology.

The essential oil currently used in aromatherapy comes from distilling the seeds, but it is also worthwhile distilling the whole (wild) plant, as is often the case with the *Apiaceae*. In a wild field, the *Daucus carota* plants grow very much at a distance from one another, which makes it impossible to pick them all. Gathering is a difficult task, requiring the picker to move about a lot since the plants are dug up one by one.

Properties and indications
HEBBD *Daucus carota*
p.o. seeds, *b.s. carotol, α-pinene*

Daucus carota p.o. seeds is a very full essential oil and therefore a precious aid in therapy, and able to be assimilated just as well through the skin as orally. It acts mainly on the liver, kidneys, pancreas and skin.

Daucus carota is an excellent regenerator of liver cells; it is prescribed after the acute phase of hepatitis, a violent bilious attack or drug poisoning, but not at the critical moment of the pathology. During hepatitis, a complex compound based on *Rosmarinus officinalis b.s. bornyl acetate, verbenone, Citrus limonum* and *Mentha piperita* will be given. *Daucus carota* stimulates regeneration of the hepatocytes; it is therefore good in cases of cirrhosis, blended with *Anethum graveolens*, which will assist the action of conventional remedies.

The same complex compound, to which another *Apiaceae* plant – *Levisticum officinalis* – is added, forms an excellent depurative and renal diuretic, the anti-inflammatory action of which can be increased with *Ocimum basilicum var. basilicum.*

Daucus carota regularises bowel movements when blended with *Cinnamomum zeylanicum* p.o. bark; then supplement it with *Citrus limonum*, which will moderate the rather violent action of the Cinnamon.

Daucus carota reduces the cholesterol level, if need be, when blended with *Rosmarinus officinalis b.s. bornyl acetate, verbenone* and *Citrus limonum*, and is also a regulator of the pancreatic functions.

It is a remarkable essential oil for regenerating the skin cells, as it vitalises the hypodermis; it is in this context that it is often used in aesthetics. It is recommended for skin ailments such as scurf patches, acne, furunculosis and even – with caution – in cases of serious necrosis and tumours. It acts efficiently even in low doses and, like most essential oils, is best combined with other essences.

When blended with vegetable oil of wheatgerm, with which it has great affinity, *Daucus carota* forms a suntan lotion – which we do not advise blending, as often recommended, with *Citrus bergamia* (Bergamot), since the latter contains furocoumarins which are photosensitive and may cause skin depigmentation – and above all helps to nourish the skin and thus protect it from sunburn due to careless or unsafe exposure. It is blended with *Citrus aurantium var. amara* p.o. leaves and *Lavandula vera* in wheatgerm-sweet almond oil for dry and devitalised skin. One can use it with lipidic extract of *Hypericum perforatum*, wheatgerm oil and essential oil of wild *Lavandula vera* to regenerate skin which has suffered even serious burns.

Daucus carota is generally used after an attack of an illness and not during its paroxysm. It regenerates more effectively than it works at the critical threshold; a parallel is also to be drawn between this point and the characterology.

Daucus carota has good anti-anaemic properties which help to increase the level of haemoglobin and it is slightly neurotonic due to its alcohols. It is also an anti-inflammatory agent which helps to regulate the cardiovascular functions in cases of coronitis, particularly when blended with *Helichrysum italicum.*

Essential oil of *Daucus carota* is therefore – together with *Anethum graveolens* p.o. whole plant – one of the rare essential oils of the *Apiaceae* family which is gentle and non-toxic. Its properties will be wisely exploited if one bears in mind that this is an essential oil whose sphere of activity is greatest not during, but after the acute phase of a pathology.

Daucus carota can prove quickly nauseating and must always be blended with other essences. Naturally, it has an affinity with the other *Apiaceae*, and also the *Asteraceae*, whether internally or externally, and generally with the *Lamiaceae*. The *Lauraceae*, such as *Cinnamomum zeylanicum*, will go very well with it, but a reservation must be made about *Ravensara aromatica*. In general, the warm, sweet odours go with it perfectly (*Cananga odorata, Pelargonium graveolens*, etc.).

Daucus carota must not be used indiscriminately, but selectively – almost superficially on occasions, bearing in mind its characterology –

except in specific cases, such as some cancers (of the breast, for example), where it can, astonishingly, prove exceptionally effective.

Daucus carota is an essential oil somewhat in its own class, more often than not misunderstood, but possessing significant properties.

Characterology

Niobe, the Queen of Thebes and mother of seven sons and seven daughters of whom she was inordinately proud – as of everything that concerned her – was the archetype of *Daucus carota*, having reached the peak of her achievements: of noble lineage, a royal marriage, beauty and presence. She was so proud and pretentious that, one day, she dared to compare herself with the goddess Leto and to denigrate her for only having had two children. In spite of advice to be cautious and the sacrifice made by the priestess, Manto, to appease Leto, Niobe did not mend her ways and even interrupted the ceremony. She had cause to regret it – the two children were Apollo and Artemis, and their father was Zeus. In order to avenge the insult to their mother, the two divine archers rained down arrows and killed Niobe's children. So devastated was she that the gods, taken with pity, changed her into a block of marble from which gushed a spring like the floods of her tears.

Fortunately, not all *Daucus carota* types bring such a tragic fate upon themselves, and there are even rarely those who attain the highest honours. Nevertheless, even in a group, a *Daucus* does not blend in and likes to keep a privileged position for herself which is recognised by all as her own.

If we wish to get to the heart of the private life of *Daucus carota*, we must patiently observe the way the plant grows; what characterises it in the wild is the isolation of each standing crop in relation to the others of its kind. One can stand before a field of Lavender and say "That's Lavender" as much as one can stand before a meadow of wild Carrots and clearly state "Those are *Daucus.*"

This individualism within the collective is also demonstrated by the appearance of its corolla: an umbel of white flowers with a single flower – red or black, as the case may be – in the centre. Red or black, that is certainly *Daucus carota*, the symbol of life or death, the gift of self or egoism in the middle of the crowd, who seems to use both these tendencies according to the opportunity of the moment and the advantage she hopes to get out of it.

Daucus carota is a special plant which holds its essence in its fruits but which, curiously – once the seeds have come to maturity – closes its umbel back on itself, as if to profit selfishly from its gains instead of disseminating them and spreading its richness around itself. In fact, the *Daucus* person flourishes with others so long as she has not attained the fullness of her aims; once she has reach her ends, she teaches by example that charity begins at home.

A full and relatively balanced essential oil, *Daucus carota* is thus a character sufficient unto herself and, most of the time, sufficient only unto herself.

This is a handicap to the extent that, having reached a degree of evolution which she deems satisfying and comfortable, *Daucus* contents herself with her psychomoral gains and her material assets, only to stagnate in the intellectual security of those who need prove only to themselves that they are the best.

Relatively intelligent and versatile, *Daucus* is a feminine soul whose ingenuity and vanity attempt to convince the world of the validity of the esteem she brings to her irreplaceable presence and indispensable functions.

Unstable of mind, although convinced to the contrary, she would have been one of those courtesans who used their undeniable faculties of adaptation to position themselves as the King's favourites – not necessarily the most beautiful, but undoubtedly one of the craftiest, for she cleverly knew how to get herself noticed, if not for her qualities, then at least for her faults presented as the whims of a superior soul.

Curious about anything new which she might be able to echo in order to shine in society, she can be compared to Cathos, one of the *Précieuses ridicules* depicted by Molière: "In fact, I find that it's more than ridiculous that a person should pride himself on his mind, and not be aware of the slightest thing that goes on each day; for my part, I would be mortified if someone were to come to me and ask if I had seen something new that I had not in fact seen."

These days, one often encounters her in the "New Age" environment – much too superficial to be really interested in spirituality, but swimming with ease in the muddy waters of cheap religiosity and facile occultism, where shamans and false gurus, mediums and clairvoyants, healers and witches act as initiates whom it is pleasing to associate with and flatter skilfully – along with one's own ego – in order to appear important in a world where the easy, the ephemeral and shallow veneer shamelessly take the place of the qualities and virtues of the spirit. As Madelon, another *Précieuse*, says: "That's where you'll get yourself noticed in company."

Discretion is, by nature, of little interest to our character; straight-forward, sincere men scarcely appeal to her, unless for the purpose of being in her service, whereas the beautifully eloquent – who, by the gloss of their scientism shine in the eyes of the ignorant – attract favours from *Daucus*, without her often indulgent virtue being able to hold them for long; "for, in the end", declares Madelon, "one must know all those gen-tlemen if one wishes to be part of high society. It is they who set Paris in motion; and, you know, there are some of them you only need to associ-ate with once for it to be rumoured that you are an expert, when there is no more to it than that."

With an obvious smile, a perfume if not vulgar at least very notice-able, a dress showing what needs to be shown to be noticed without for all that attracting discourteous remarks, *Daucus* sails comfortably in the wake of celebrities, stars and media people, wandering about with absolute perseverance and the assurance of those who question the world more easily than they do themselves. "I like", wrote Katherine Mansfield in her journal, "to appear in any company, absolutely at my ease, aware of my own importance which – in my own eyes – is bound-less; amiable, with a quick wit and understanding. I like to have a slightly condescending air – very 'high society' – and be the focus of everyone's interest. Yes, but sometimes, to my greatest displeasure, I am overcome by an undeniable, grotesque shyness. I think only of running and hid-ing, and I blush over nothing."

Lacking the patience and virtues enough to earn and be worthy of it, *Daucus* appropriates to herself the glory or prestige of those over her, be it good or bad.

Daucus carota has the failings of her qualities, and no doubt the qualities of her failings as well. A woman of solid appearance, she may involve herself in the life of others, deigning to give the benefit of her relative stability to those who call upon her services, without necessarily being sure of enjoying the, if not material – although money interests her – at least moral gratitude of those souls under her wing.

Too intelligent to be modest and not intelligent enough to be humble, *Daucus carota* hides her touchiness behind the disdain she readily shows when one points out her faults. She will not tolerate a *Ravensara*, who is too much of a psychologist to be taken in by her stratagems and will cruelly make her aware of how ordinary she is when she cared to think of herself as exceptional, nor a *Laurus*, who despises her. *Daucus carota* cannot admit that she is *Daucus*, considering herself to be at worst a *Chamaemelum nobile* and, ideally, a *Rosa damascena*.

Lavandula vera will be able to help and influence her by trying to show her the inestimable value of discretion, and will attempt, with love and patience, to awaken in her the need to give of herself without expecting anything in return; but this is undoubtedly something of a challenge in the face of a *Daucus* little inclined to change, so high an idea does she have of her level of evolution.

In conclusion, one must accept *Daucus carota* for what she is and appreciate her for what she can do. As time passes, and the plant and human kingdoms evolve, her opportunism and vanity will no longer suffice to make her one of the gentry, and she will only be permitted the access to royalty of which she dreams as a result of the higher virtues of the soul which she will perhaps be able to develop.

Until then, may she learn that the charm of the flower whose scent come from device rather than suffering and effort is short-lived.

Laurus Nobilis

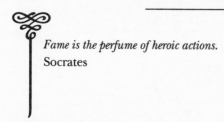

Fame is the perfume of heroic actions.
Socrates

Origin and botanical portrait

A native of Asia Minor, *Laurus nobilis* – Noble Laurel or Grecian Laurel – is a tree that has been venerated since furthest antiquity. These days, with very pale remnants of its ancient reputation (see characterology), Laurel is confined to the kitchen, hence its common name of Bay Laurel.

Reputed to shrink from the cold, *Laurus nobilis* would have coped successfully, however, with the Quaternary glaciations in the area of the southern coasts of Europe, to judge by the impressions of leaves left in the geological layers.

Laurus nobilis is the only European representative of the *Lauraceae* family, various species of which were widespread in our regions during the Tertiary era, including Cinnamon trees, Camphor trees and Sassafras.

A shrub 2 to 10 m high, it is a dioecious species (male shrub and female shrub). Frequently grown in gardens as an ornamental tree, it has become very acclimatised to the shores of the Atlantic stretching from the Lower Pyrenees to Finistère, where it finds the climatic conditions favourable. Despite its fairly extensive area, *Laurus nobilis* is still quite rare and it is difficult to find wild sites of it. It grows here and there in the south of France – these are often the remains of cultivated trees which have been abandoned and returned to the wild. It can be found on rocks, in valleys where the soil is rich, beside little courses of water or in the woods. It is found all over the Mediterranean region – in North Africa, Spain, Italy and former Yugoslavia.

Laurus nobilis or True Bay must not be confused with the "fake Laurels": Cherry Laurel (*Prunus laurocerasus L.*) forming hedges around houses, Common Oleander or Rose Laurel (*Nerium oleander L.*) jutting out on southern roads and Laurustinus (*Viburnum tinus L.*) preferring the rather fresh positions of the green oak scrub, all the more so since Cherry Laurel and Rose Laurel are poisonous.

Essential oil of *Laurus nobilis* is distilled from the leafy branches, thoroughly cut up into little pieces in order to increase the contact area with the steam and, consequently, the yield. The plant material is distilled half-dry for a minumum of three hours. This distillation is very enriching, less intoxicating than some, but extraordinarily fragrant and reviving. Right from the start, the smell is strong, full and characteristic, without allowing itself to fade too much due to the heat from the operation. For use in aromatherapy, on the other hand, we would recommend keeping essential oil of *Laurus nobilis* for a year before using it, its fragrance becoming stronger over time and its very complex composition thus having time to readjust.

Properties and indications
HEBBD *Laurus nobilis*
p.o. leaves, *b.s. 1.8 cineole, α-terpineol acetate*

Laurus nobilis has been recognised since antiquity for its regenerating and antiseptic properties. Its essential oil is to be used first and foremost when the therapist is faced with an illness involving degeneration, sepsis or various forms of necrosis; it is, moreover, interesting to note that the roots of the cut tree are rotproof. Laurus nobilis forestalls physical ageing and the weakening of the mental processes, and is perfectly suited to sclerotic tendencies.

It is also a good infection-fighting agent, bactericide, viricide and fungicide, particularly for recurrent or chronic pathologies and as part of a blend since these are, when all is said and done, not its main properties. Nevertheless, due to its decisive action at "terrain" level, it is wise to use it as a supplement to essential oils rich in phenols or monoterpenols, in particular for broncho-pulmonary and intestinal ailments.

It is a good expectorant with mucolytic properties, and helpful in cases of pneumonopathies and lung abscesses (which sometimes indicate a cancerous pathology), in cases of chronic bronchitis and emphysema. For these pathologies, it will be necessary to blend it with other pulmonary regenerators: *Eucalyptus globulus*, which is expectorant and mucolytic; *Myrtus communis b.s. pinene, 1.8 cineole, Hyssopus officinalis b.s. pinocamphone* (with caution!), anticatarrhal and pulmonary anti-inflammatory; *Rosmarinus officinalis b.s. bornyl acetate, verbenone*, mucolytic and antispasmodic; and *Cupressus sempervirens*, a lung decongestant and cough remedy in cases of spasmodic coughing.

An excellent anti-flu agent when blended with *Ravensara aromatica* and *Lavandula spica* (viricides and expectorants), *Mentha piperita b.s. menthol* (a viricide and tonic) and *Rosmarinus officinalis b.s. 1.8 cineole* (an expectorant and mucolytic), *Laurus nobilis* is a remarkable immunostimulant which enables the speedy regeneration of all physiological functions following any infectious process.

Its esters make it moderately antispasmodic, a property which is more complementary than primordial, but which tempers the strength of its action. It treats certain asthmas (the asthma of the "suffocating mind" which shows through in the characterology) when blended with *Ravensara aromatica*, and if necessary with a little *Ammi visnaga*, a powerful antispasmodic during attacks – but which quickly becomes toxic to the liver, like many *Apiaceae*; *Hyssopus decumbens*, an anti-asthmatic; and *Rosmarinus officinalis b.s. bornyl acetate, verbenone*. It is a cardiovascular tonic when blended with *Lavandula spica*, if necessary with *Lavandula vera* and *Helichrysum italicum* if it is important to resort to powerful antispasmodic and anti-inflammatory essential oils, and *Rosmarinus officinalis b.s. borneone*, which is cardiotonic in small doses (externally). Vasocoronarodilatory, it is a valuable aid where there is deterioration of the cardiac functions – spasms, arteriosclerosis and pre-infarctus.

Laurus nobilis is an excellent agent against intestinal sepsis blended with *Juniperus communis* p.o. berries and *Cinnamomum zeylanicum* p.o. bark, these essences being cleansers and intestinal antiputrefactives; it fights cases of zymosis and sepsis which are infectious or degenerative in origin – enterocolitis, tropical illnesses, necrosis, etc. It is very helpful in cases of intestinal tuberculosis and cancers.

In cases of skin complaints, ulcers, boils, acne, abscesses and mycosis, *Laurus nobilis* will act at the level of their chronicity and accelerate the process of regeneration of the epidermis, blended with *Lavandula hybrida var. super*, which is anti-inflammatory and cicatrising; *Cymbopogon martinii var. Motia*, antifungal, antiviral and a skin toner; *Melaleuca alternifolia*, a skin antiseptic; *Salvia officinalis*, infection-fighting, lipolytic and cicatrising; *Cymbopogon winterianus*, anti-inflammatory and infection-fighting; *Melaleuca quinquenervia b.s. viridiflorol*, infection-fighting and an agent to prevent the skin from degenerating; and *Citrus aurantium var. amara* p.o. leaves, anti-inflammatory and a skin regenerator.

It also treats genito-urinary infections in women, blended with *Salvia officinalis*, a genital balancer, particularly when acting at the level of mental and emotional stability. For men, blend it with *Rosmarinus officinalis b.s. bornyl acetate, verbenone* or *Cupressus sempervirens.*

Its powerful, warm odour is an excellent cerebral stimulator and a nerve tonic for those who doubt themselves (before an exam or an interview with an employer, for example). With *Ravensara aromatica*, a powerful nerve tonic, it combats anxiety, fear, morbid states and psychoses. *Laurus nobilis* is an antidepressant for people unable to verbalise and give concrete expression to their abilities, and who are afraid of themselves as much as others. It then brings a powerful, exorcising fire, affording the person the opportunity of a certain degree of self-domination. It may be used in conjunction with *Lycopodium* and *Natrum muriaticum* within the context of the homoeopathic characterology.

Laurus nobilis is antisclerosant and analgesic. Blended with *Citrus aurantium var. amara* p.o. leaves, a nervous rebalancer and anti-inflammatory agent (also during the perimenopause), as well as *Gaultheria fragrantissima*, antispasmodic and anti-inflammatory; *Sassafras albidum*, analgesic and antirheumatic; *Eucalyptus citriodora*, anti-inflammatory and analgesic; *Juniperus communis var. nana*, anti-inflammatory and analgesic; and *Mentha piperita b.s. menthol*, analgesic and anaesthetic, it acts in cases of rheumatism by fighting premature ageing, osteoarthritis and sclerosis. When blended with *Lavandula stoechas, Rosmarinus officinalis b.s. 1.8* and *Commiphora myrrha* p.o. resin, which are anti-inflammatory, it curbs the development of osteoarthritis (in a base of lipidic extract of *Hypericum perforatum*).

It is good for bedsores, blended with *Salvia officinalis, Lavandula officinalis, Cistus ladaniferus* (very little) and *Melaleuca quinquenervia b.s. viridiflorol*, which are cicatrising and infection-fighting, as well as cases of necrosis and gangrene – in short, all pathologies involving degeneration, both physical and mental, which the characterology will confirm.

Laurus nobilis is therefore a very versatile essential oil with the advantage of being effective even in low doses – 10% in a complex compound is already quite sufficient and one seldom needs to use more than 20%. Its antidegenerative and antisclerosant action is unequalled in its impact on people suffering from psychic ailments – whether slight or more crippling – particularly fears, anxieties, obsessional states and various psychoses. Its use is not without consequences and its effects are lasting. Blending it is relatively easy, as its scent does not allow itself to be toned down by any fragrance; it obviously combines extremely well with *Rosmarinus officinalis b.s. bornyl acetate, verbenone, Ravensara aromatica, Cupressus sempervirens, Salvia officinalis* and *Myrtus communalis*, but equally with essential oils that are more difficult to blend, such as *Cinnamomum zeylanicum.* The spices generally go with it very well; the fragile, delicate, feminine essences such as *Helichrysum italicum, Salvia sclarea, Lavandula vera* and *Chamaemelum nobile* can tolerate the impact of *Laurus nobilis* if it is not used in too great a proportion. It is, in any case, a powerful essential oil, with properties able to be understood very clearly when one looks at its quite remarkable – although sometimes excessively uncompromising – characterology.

Characterology

The respect given to *Laurus nobilis* and its use in religious worship is that reserved for the major sacred plants, such as Olive, Rosemary, Hyssop, Sandalwood, Myrrh and other "plant deities", to the extent that in Greece and Rome it was not allowed to be put to any profane use. In Egypt, it was offered to the gods with Myrtle, Jasmine and Marjoram. In the geographical area where Laurel grows, this shrub has always been an object of veneration due to its capacity to burn even when green, with an impressive crackling and exceptional fragrance which likened it to the fiery, solar forces: "Thus, in the Laurel-crowned mountains, the fire spreads and shoots up with the whirling winds and carries the blaze everywhere; and what is there that can only be consumed in an inferno more terrible than the Delphic Laurel of Phoebus when it is enveloped in the crackling flames?" narrates Lucan, a first-century Latin poet. It was no doubt for this reason that the Roman soldiers, according to Pliny, used Laurel wood instead of flint, which they rubbed against ivy wood to start a fire.

In Greece, the alliance between Laurel and the star of light – the sun – led to its being dedicated to Apollo, the mythological archetype of power, wisdom and manly beauty. Apollo, crowned with Laurels, is a god who purifies, illuminates and emerges victorious, and whose emblem is – in his image – reputed to bring light and bequeath glory. Just as the sun is the eye of God, who sees all and also enables us to see, Laurel reveals to us that which is hidden.

According to mythology, it is Gaia, the Earth Mother, who established the first oracle – *Daphnis* – at Delphi. After having killed Python, the oracular dragon, who was threatening his mother and guarding the sacred crevice at Delphi, Apollo seized the Delphic oracle, built himself an altar made from Laurel branches and set Pythia, his priestess, up in her sanctuary on a tripod placed over the crevasse out of which the divinatory vapours rose. The prophetess used to chew Laurel leaves before revealing the oracles received as the sacred word of the gods; a priest assisted by burning barley, hemp and Laurel to induce her trances.

Laurel was also dedicated to atonement for Apollo first had to cleanse himself of the blood of Python.

The Romans called Laurel *Laurus*; this incorporates the word *aur* – gold – an etymology which we also encounter in the Jewish word *aur* – light – which indicates Laurel's link with the Sun God ("Apollo, all shining with gold", says Callimachus); gold, according to esoteric tradition, is condensed solar light. The Greeks called it *Daphnê*, after the name of the nymph pursued by Apollo who was smitten with love for her, and who was turned into a Laurel tree by the gods – an allegory of the dawn pursued by the sun and which disappears into her eternal light, symbolised by the Laurel tree. From then on, the god wore a Laurel wreath and decorated his lyre and quiver with Laurel leaves.

Thus it is that Laurel – with its evergreen foliage and powerful fragrance, the holder of eternal vitality and the power of survival and preservation which reassures the living, concerned for their souls – became a symbol of immortality. It was also an emblem of glory won by the spirit (Apollo is companion to the nine Muses) as much as by arms. A crown of Laurel was also worn by Asclepius, the god of medicine and son of Apollo, by which the Ancients rendered homage to its many medicinal properties.

Laurus nobilis symbolises greatness and victory. Roman conquerors were honoured by a crown of its branches during a triumph held in celebration of their victory.

Over the centuries, the Laurel has retained a vestige of the glory of its Apollonian apogee – it controls and protects from forces of darkness and unlucky fates: "Rats are killed simply by the touch of Laurel", says Liébault in the sixteenth century; perhaps this echoes the murder of Python by Apollo, the rat being considered an infernal creature. Is this the memory of the Delphic oracles? Laurel was long associated with prophecy, and its revitalising properties at the mental and psychic levels would indeed lead one to suggest that it has an occult-mediumistic use, based to a greater or lesser extent, it is true, on whoever claims to use it for this property. At all events, the crackling of Laurel leaves in the flames was, until recently, deemed a happy omen, sometimes even the sign of a good harvest; it was recommended to sleep with Laurel leaves under one's pillow in order to divine the future through dreams.

Laurel is blessed on Palm Sunday, which is sometimes known as "Laurel Sunday" – "When you hear thunder, throw a branch of Laurel blessed on Palm Sunday or Good Friday into the fire", recommends a saying in the south of France. In *La Mare au Diable*, Georges Sand tells of a marriage ritual in the Berry region of France where Laurel tied to the mantelpiece and decorated with ribbons constitutes the "exploit" or notice, in other words the couple's wedding invitation card. Today, a vestige remains of the ancient traditions connected with Laurel in the name of the examination taken by would-be holders of the French equivalent of English A-levels: the *baccalauréat* (from the Latin *bacca laurea* or Laurel berry).

In India, the glory, power and sacrifice of *Laurus* are symbolised in the cult of Shiva; we find this both virile and celestial power, the mark of justice and a higher Love, in the victories of Rama and Krishna.

There naturally emerges from this collection of myths and values associated with *Laurus*, to which few plants can lay claim, the symbol of victory; but victory above all means battle. War, which is an intrinsic part of the life of man, is not won without the inspiration of a leader or without the exemplary authority that renders armies dynamic. Nevertheless, war wears many faces, non-violence being one of them – and undoubtedly the most sublime – for it represents an inner war directed against our instincts, our atavistic passions and our secular vices. That is where the real battle and the real victory lie, and towards which deserve the palms of Apollo, the Sun God, symbol of spirit over matter.

But the story of Laurus is not one of glory alone, for its power and light kindle within it arrogance – a characteristic trait of those who, in their human weakness, embody the solar archetype of Noble Laurel.

The very first pride of a true *Laurus* – an example of pride that brought so many others in its wake – was probably that of Lucifer, the light-bearer, who, through his power and good looks, meant to oppose God by comparing himself with Him. His fall was fatal not only for himself, but for the angelic cohorts that were the subjects of his kingdom, for another *Laurus*, distinguished by nobility and loyalty, stood before him and uttered these fateful words: *Mi-Ka-el?* in Hebrew (Who is like as to God?). God then gave this archangel the name of Mikhaël or Michael; having become leader of the heavenly armies, the archangel Michael ever strikes down the dragon, and it is perhaps he whom St John describes in the Apocalypse when he sees him holding the seven candelabra, whilst a double-edged sword springs from his mouth, the sword of the omnipotent Word which cuts and separates the wheat from the chaff.

Symbolically, the duality of degrading pride and rewarded humility is extremely interesting from the perspective of understanding the characterology of *Laurus nobilis*. *Laurus* has been humanised since mythic times, and whilst we do sometimes find traces of the glorious spirit of the person guided by duty, the life of *Laurus* is, for the most part, nothing but the expression of his dreams of power. The first character is inspired by his archetype and noble virtues show through in his life; the second, guided by all too prosaic and human ideals, turns his natural authority into tyranny, strength into violence and a brilliant future into obscure designs. On earth, in fact, *Laurus* does not possess the glory of the gods – his glory is too human and transient, for pride is his pitfall.

We encounter the warrior temperament of *Laurus nobilis* throughout human history, sometimes in the expression of his higher soul:

"There is above all no feature in the face of Don Rodrigo
Which is not the highest image of a man of brave heart,
And he comes from a family so rich in warriors
That they are born surrounded by Laurel trees",[7]
often in the violence of a pride that knows no bounds and drives him to the worst follies. All the famous conquerors were inherently *Laurus*, from Alexander the Great to Napoleon, whose Laurels were less noble, and including Julius Caesar and Ghengis Khan: "We have so much pride that our gold becomes ash."[8]

Within the social context, *Laurus* always retains his temperament of boss and leader, and is employed in many key posts in our society. His strength of character and his assurance entitle him, in his eyes, to impose his will on others, at the risk of stifling them. *Laurus* is essentially a mind that is not content with tepid, dead-end emotion, which is all to his credit; but his coldness very often cuts him off from genuine, uncomplicated and invigorating love. More inclined to passions in which he is able to prove his strength and virility, he conducts his love life like a battle in which he sometimes exhausts a fair number of companions, weary of or rebellious against the one they admired but who often made them cry too much.

On this score, *Laurus* can readily temper the feelings of some people and help them to overcome their fears and inhibitions; he develops ambition and assurance and makes the person aware of his value and gives him the will to act.

The use of this essence has a great psychological impact. Characterologically, one must therefore be cautious of allowing the *Laurus* type to associate with *Origanum majorana*, for he could divert part of the latter's delicacy and sensitivity and lead this pure-hearted rebel along the paths of premature conquest. On the other hand, he helps *Citrus aurantium* p.o. leaves to emerge from her emotional deadlock – that is, if she can accept to put up with the stable, but not very affectionate, strength of this character. When with *Salvia officinalis*, equally cold and mental in outlook, they both act very powerfully although over-strictly.

---

[7] Corneille, *El Cid.*

[8] Victor Hugo.

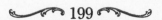

Conversely, *Cupressus sempervirens* relaxes *Laurus* and is beneficial to him, as is *Rosmarinus officinalis b.s. bornyl acetate, verbenone*, which tempers his pride. *Ravensara aromatica*, who symbolises the sage within every great man, controls the excesses of *Laurus*.

Laurus nobilis, an essence commensurate with an exceptional character, can encourage each person to discover his power, to take responsibility for himself both mentally and physically, and objectively helps the individual to shake off emotional turmoil and mental torpor. A life-enhancing essence, it fights anything putrid, septic and degenerating.

Imbued with mysticism and prophetic glory, *Laurus* and its legends remain eternal; an ineffable presence which lights up human existence, *Laurus* transcends the ordinary and raises our awareness by its powerful aura, strengthens the weak and heals the old. An invitation to the Mysteries and the finding of one's Grail, *Laurus* acts and does not leave one indifferent, even if its depth and hermetic symbolism – wherein lies the duty – oblige the layman to remain outside the temple until his soul, cleansed of the past, can without shame, and as at the beginning, "eat fire and drink light".

"Do you know it, Daphne, that ancient love song,
At the foot of the sycamore, or under the white laurel trees,
Under the olive tree, myrtle or trembling willows,
That song of love that ever begins again?...
Do you recognise the Temple with its huge peristyle,
And the bitter lemons marked with your teeth,
And the grotto, deadly to foolhardy guests,
Where sleeps the ancient seed of the vanquished dragon?...
They will return, these Gods for whom you still weep!
Time will restore the order of former days;
The earth has quivered under a prophetic breath...
Yet the Sibyl with the Latin face
Is still asleep under the Constantine arch
And nothing has disturbed the stern portico."
Gérard de Nerval, Delphica

Ocimum Basilicum

Mother Tulsi,
You who bring joy to the heart of Govinda*,
I gather You for the cult of Narayana*.
Without You, Blessed One, all works are fruitless;
And that is why I gather You.
Hindu prayer

Origin and botanical portrait

Native to India, the various species of Basil (there are more than about one hundred of them) have been widely cultivated in several hot areas. The *Ocimum* genus (of the *Lamiaceae* family) is difficult to classify since the species are very polymorphous and there are many hybrids and different varieties.

Only a few species are used for their essence and aromatic properties:

Ocimum basilicum L.: Garden Basil

Ocimum canum Sims.

Ocimum gratissimum L.

Ocimum sanctum L.

Ocimum viride Wild.

Each of these species produces a different essence. The Basil most often used in therapy is the species called *Ocimum basilicum L.* However, as this Basil is grown more or less everywhere in the world (France, North Africa, Reunion, the Comoro Islands, Madagascar, Vietnam, India, Egypt, former Yugoslavia), the biochemical specificity of the essential oil must always be clearly stated.

---

* Other names of the god Vishna

Ocimum comes from the Greek word meaning "I feel" and *basilicum* from *basilikos* – "royal", hence its name of Royal Herb.

In France, there are several varieties of *Ocimum basilicum* or Greater Basil, known as *pistou* by the people of Provence, such as the "great green" variety (the commonest) or the "lettuce leaf" variety. Bush or Lesser Basil belongs to another species – *Ocimum minimum L.*

The most frequently used essential oil of *Ocimum basilicum* comes from the tropical regions of the southern hemisphere – Reunion, the Comoro Islands and Madagascar; it is also found in Vietnam and India. Its botanical name is *Ocimum basilicum L. var. basilicum.*

The scent of Greater Basil is strong, but loses its aroma as it dries and is therefore difficult to keep.

Properties and indications
HEBBD *Ocimum basilicum var. basilicum*
p.o. flowering plant, *b.s. methyl chavicol*

Essential oil of *Ocimum basilicum* is remarkably relaxing, due to its high methyl ether content. We recommend it for people with schizoid tendencies as it soothes, calms and relaxes; it is the antistress essence *par excellence.* Very powerfully antispasmodic – even more effective than the ester essences – it has a definite effect on tense people who eat too fast without properly chewing their food. It calms gastro-intestinal spasms, aids digestion (with *Carum carvi, Rosmarinus officinalis b.s. bornyl acetate, verbenone, Mentha piperita, Anethum graveolens* and *Thymus vulgaris b.s. linalool*) and soothes pains due to irritation, acidity and stomach ulcers (*Rosmarinus officinalis b.s. bornyl acetate, verbenone, Mentha piperita and Laurus nobilis*).

Ocimum basilicum acts well on spasmophylic syndromes caused by anxiety, for which a "terrain" treatment is essential – *Chamaemelum nobile, Lavandula vera* and *Citrus aurantium var. amara* p.o. leaves, in particular, will also assist (refer to the characterology).

It is a venous decongestant for people whose food is too rich and for men suffering from prostatitis (with *Rosmarinus officinalis b.s. bornyl acetate, verbenone* and *Cupressus sempervirens*).

It will be blended with *Anethum graveolens, Levisticum officinalis* and *Mentha piperita* to stimulate the adrenals of patients having had to undergo long courses of allopathic treatments, particularly prolonged antibiotic treatment.

Its antiviral properties are weak, but it is effective internally at "terrain" level in cases of neuritis, shingles and certain forms of herpes manifesting through predispositions that are deficient, overworked, etc. with *Ravensara aromatica* and *Thymus vulgaris b.s. thymol* blended with specific essential oils – *Origanum majorana, Salvia officinalis and Laurus nobilis.*

It is a liver decongestant and cholagogue, which is very helpful in cases of bile shortage or food poisoning, and also for indigestion and travel sickness (with *Rosmarinus officinalis b.s. bornyl acetate, verbenone* or *1.8 cineole,* as necessary, and *Citrus limonum*).

Ocimum basilicum is an excellent calmative and sedative for prescribing for digestive insomnia in people who "digest" their worries during the night. It rebalances those who use their intellect a lot and are mentally exhausted and people suffering from high blood pressure who end up mentally depressed. In this, it works in a similar way to the homoeopathic remedy, Nux vomica.

It is anti-inflammatory when used internally in cases, for example, of rheumatoid polyarthritis with *Citrus aurantium var. amara* p.o. leaves, and *Helichrysum italicum* in cases of arthritis.

It is easy to use and suits all ages. *Ocimum basilicum* is slightly hypnotic in high doses. It is not used externally, but always internally and mainly administered orally.

It blends well with the *Lamiaceae, Asteraceae* and *Apiaceae,* and with the *Lauraceae,* if necessary, though combining it with the *Myrtaceae, Cupressaceae* and the woods in general – with the exception of *Santalum album* is cases or urological complaints – is trickier.

Characterology

Owing to the origins of the plant, the characterology of essence of *Ocimum basilicum* reveals a spiritual character which its organoleptic properties and the inner well-being it affords would not be able to deny.

An Indian plant, Basil is dedicated to Vishnu and regarded as the incarnation of his wife, Lakshmi, goddess of fortune and beauty; we are talking here about *Ocimum sanctum L.,* a sacred Basil which is called *Tulsi,* a sacred plant *par excellence* and considered as a veritable panacea.

Every traditional Vishnuite house has a pot of *Tulsi* which is greeted every day and "married" every year to Vishnu during a family ceremony; the plant is then called *Tulsi Devi* (goddess) to show that it is a manifestation of the divine Lakshmi: "*Tulsi* is the goddess Shri! O Beloved, O Beauteous One, O Destroyer of the evil, O Purifier, honour to you, O Goddess praised by Nârada**, O Dear Heart of Vishnu!" sings the ritual, and then the goddess is invoked to protect each part of the body.

Yet another origin, just as sacred, is attributed to *Tulsi* – she is said to be born, like Lakshmi, from *amrita*, the ambrosia pulled from the churning sea of milk by the *devas* and *asuras* (gods and demons) under Vishnu's authority.

Krishna, an incarnation of Vishnu, also adopted *Tulsi* for his cult, hence the name *Krishnatulsi* which is sometimes given to it.

Tulsi is called upon for life and death, for various acts of life and above all for giving children to those who want them, and it is believed that Vishnu punishes the impious who mistreat this plant with infertility and great misfortunes. The heart of God is full of worry and anger, it is said, when people break off a sprig of *Tulsi*, his wife. The *Kriyayogasara* (*Substance of the Yoya of Actions*, a Vishnuite ritual manual and supplement to the *Padmapurana*) advises that, in religiously cultivating *Tulsi*, people earn the privilege of ascending to the palace of Vishnu, surrounded by ten million ancestors.

The sage Narada sang the praises of this immortal plant, the bearer of all perfections, which keeps away torments and demons, and purifies and guides the pious towards Heaven. That is why a *Tulsi* leaf is placed on the chests of the dead and their heads washed with water in which the plant has soaked.

In Bengal, where Shivaism predominates, *Tulsi* is linked to the worship of many goddesses, personifications of the generating energies of Shiva, the *Shakti*; each standing plant of Basil is associated with only one goddess, and Hindu families therefore grow as many plants as they wish to have protective goddesses.

**The great Rishi Nârada, a musician who invented *vînâ* and was messenger of the gods, considered as one of Visha's minor incarnations.

According to many traditions, Basil is supposed to protect from unfortunate destinies and evil spirits. The devil, it is said, loathes its smell; the *Soussou* (African) name of *Ocimum viride* is *barikiri*, which means *devil-chaser*. To the Bambaras (another African people), Basil is known as *su-kola*, in other words *dead-wash*, which correlates with the significance it had for the Greeks and the Romans, who also attributed a funeral meaning to it, as well as an erotic one since they made it a herb dear to women. Pliny consequently considered the plant an aphrodisiac, and it was given to horses and donkeys when they were being covered. This reputation lasted until our times, for not long ago, in the south of France and in Italy, lovers used to slip a sprig of Basil behind their ears before visiting their beloved, whilst virgins in southern Italy used to put a little bunch of it between their breasts, and married women wore it on their heads.

A tale by Boccaccio, a Byzantine by origin, taken up by the poet, Keats, recounts the story of *Isabella or the Pot of Basil*, in which the lover, Lorenzo, was killed by his brothers, who considered him a weakling. His beloved was dying of grief when Lorenzo appeared to her in a dream and told her where his grave could be found. After finding the body, Isabella hid Lorenzo's head in a vessel:

"... a bowl where she placed it

Then covered it with compost in which she planted

The noble basil, and watered it with her tears."*

Is this sentiment specific to English poetry? The fact remains that it is Shelley who also associates Basil with heartache:

"Madonna, Madonna, why then this offering,

This basil, this reseda?

Signs of love and health that never

Are found in the same garland?

Alas, these drenched flowers!

Could it be by kisses? Or is it by tears?

For neither rain nor dew

Could have drawn from them so sweet a smell."

Ocimum basilicum, a spiritual principle of love, is naturally connected

---

*John Keats

with a heartful character, in whom emotional excesses and impulses are stronger than wisdom and reason. We see it as a woman with her head in the clouds and both feet slightly off the ground. *Ocimum* seems, in fact, to hover over events, unaware of the concrete reality of existence. Of no particular age, she appears to navigate unhindered between youth and old age, having no great pretensions or tenacious desires; shifting rhythmically with the seasons, she swings between spiritual love and personal affectivity. By nature devoid of pride or ambition, she is content with an innate intuition, which serves her as wisdom, and an existential lack of concern which can sometimes pass for foolishness.

Like everyone, *Ocimum* sometimes suffers from heartache, but without violence, rage or rancour. Her kind heart, a manifestation of her beautiful soul – which by nature makes her little inclined to criticism or even bad thoughts – tends to see in others only her own qualities, even if she has to search hard to find them and, if necessary, invent them; thus to hear her, liars are but sincere people needing to express themselves. Her optimism serves her as good humour, her faith gives a meaning to her life and her trust in humanity justifies and nurtures her hopes.

Somewhat "out-of-the-body" and rather clumsy, she goes about the world like a lamb whose dark fleece would pass almost unnoticed amongst the wolves, making the task of her guardian angel difficult. Her irrationality can make her asocial, but she manages to fit in, despite everything, the gift she makes of herself being the pledge of her goodwill.

Her mystical nature makes her a perfect nun, who finds her place and joy in a spiritual community, as well as encouragement of her childlike proselytising, reflected in words as flowery as they are disordered, but no doubt aimed at the soul rather than the intellect.

Whilst *Ocimum* can sometimes be irritating, one generally capitulates before her open smile, her aura of authenticity, her unflappable character and her devotion. Her absent-mindedness, however, together with her lack of practical sense, cancels out a good part of her services. Often without any sense of proportion, she acts and reacts alternately, always with the best aims but sometimes the worst results. Full of good intentions, *Ocimum* slips a hot-water bottle into the bed but forgets to put on the stopper, inadvertently adds salt to the chocolate cake, puts the delicates into a boiling wash and obliges those around her to work on cultivating patience and detachment from events.

The beautiful nymph, Syrinx, of whom *Ocimum basilicum* may be reminiscent, was one of the followers of Artemis, who used to charm her companions with her songs and mischievous gaiety. Extremely devoted to the goddess, she did her washing and looked after her dogs, which she fed on lotuses and reeds, for she detested shedding the blood of animals.

One day when she had been drying Artemis's tunic on the grass and, in her absent-mindedness, had completely forgotten it, a violent wind blew it away. Syrinx started to go after the tunic and, led ever further away, was surpised by the god, Pan, who was besotted with love for her. In order to escape from him, Syrinx – driven to the edge of a river – called on the water nymphs for help and they turned her into a field of reeds. Pan made from the reeds a flute to which he gave the name "syrinx".

Ocimum's life is thus punctuated with constant distractions and existential ups and downs which do not seem in the least to alter her goodwill or her humour, her convictions or her fate.

Like her essence, *Ocimum* is self-contained, ethereal, often a poet or artist – in any case, nebulous and disembodied. Her life reminds one of the unreal world of *Alice in Wonderland,* where pears smell like a rose, pepper like lavender, and where mad hatters and Cheshire cats get on together. With *Ocimum,* nothing is really what it seems, or for what it was created, because she re-creates everything – not out of pretension or to be difficult, but because she has probably never been able to see the world as it is and rediscovers it each day through rose-tinted glasses.

In no way troubled by the dualism of life, good and evil, hot and cold seem not to affect her, and in high summer she will abandon her winter dressing habits for shorts and sandals, which she will continue wearing until the end of December, when people concerned for her well-being will point out the chilblains on her feet.

Ocimum is a phenomenon; almost adorable, often overflowing with kindness, the fact remains that she is socially handicapped, a stranger to the present moment and seldom in the place or state where logic would wish her to be.

Ocimum is a pleasant essence which relieves stress and soothes and embellishes our life without ever drugging us. Helpful to stressed businessmen, those who are depressively tormented and psychotic worriers, it also obliges ketonic temperaments such as *Salvia officinalis* types to work on tolerance, and refines hot, phenolic natures such as *Satureja montana* and *Thymus vulgaris b.s. thymol* types.

Blended with *Mentha piperita*, it becomes incredibly impish and mischievous, it spreads gaiety with *Rosmarinus officinalis b.s. 1.8 cineole*, lifts *Helichrysum italicum*, and alongside *Lavandula vera* would almost make the misogynist *Rosmarinus officinalis b.s. camphor* smile.

Certainly, the deep nature of *Ocimum* is very seldom revealed in her integrity, but this simple soul – simple, that is, by way of her spiritual archetype – is far from being simplistic. When she shows her mystical side, *Ocimum* invites us to meditate in the exorcising silence of Basil, wherein eternally burns the sacred flame of renunciation. "I will always try to dismiss all malice from my breast and to keep my love in flower, knowing that you reside in the secret altar of my heart," she might say in the words of Tagore.

Posing vital questions, she leads us to discover the right answers that will liberate our hearts and minds from the chains of a rationalism that is not always as objective as we would like to believe. Perhaps then we will be able to say, like India: "I adore *Tulsi*, whose roots are the journey's end of any pilgrimage, whose stem is the abode of the gods and on the branches of which are written all the Vedas."

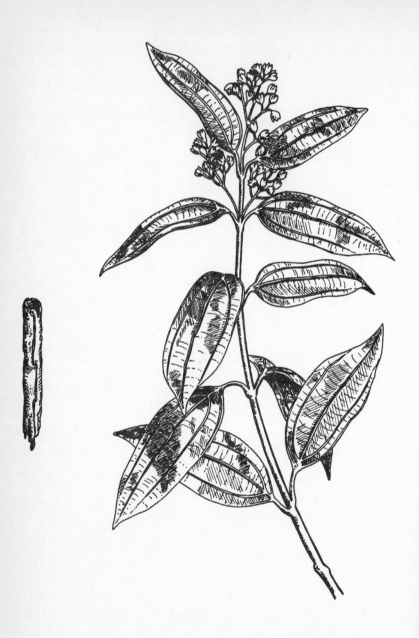

Cinnamomum Zeylanicum

*I have perfumed my bed
with myrrh, aloes and cinnamon.
Come, let us take our fill of love till morning...
Let us delight ourselves with love,
for my husband is not at home.*
Proverbs, 7:17-18

Origin and botanical portrait

The Cinnamon is a tree growing in tropical regions and belonging to the
Lauraceae family. Several species of *Cinnamomum* provide commercial
Cinnamon, but the best kind comes from the Ceylon Cinnamon tree:
Cinnamomum zeylanicum Nees. A native of China, western India and Sri
Lanka, the Cinnamon tree was introduced into several tropical countries,
including Madagascar, the West Indies, Malaysia, etc. but the Sri Lankan
plantations provide the most sought-after bark.

Cinnamomum means Chinese *amomum*, or Chinese Laurel; cinnamon
("cannelle" in French) is the diminutive of the Latin *canna*, meaning
reed. We might note whilst discussing Cinnamon that the Ancients used
to use the terms *cinnamomum* (Cinnamon) and *cassia* without making any
clear distinction between the shrubs to which they referred. According to
Dioscorides and Galen, *cinnamomum* and *cassia* come from the same plant,
cinnamomum being the tender, whole rejected parts of the tree. We should
point out that in the past, Cinnamon went under the name of "aromatic
cassia" or "'clove-like' cassia". Another possibility is that *cinnamomum*
could be *Cinnamomum zeylanicum*, whilst *cassia* could be *Cinnamomum cassia* (Chinese Cinnamon) – keeping in mind, however, that the term *cinnamomum* itself already inherently signifies Chinese Laurel.

In the wild, Ceylon Cinnamon is an evergreen tree 10 to 15 m high.
It is made up of many branches and has a thick, scabrous bark. In the

cultivated state, Ceylon Cinnamon is a bushy, robust sub-shrub 2 to 3 m high. It grows especially in the south-eastern part of the island of Sri Lanka, in the white sands of the Negombo and Colombo districts.

Cultivation demands a great deal of rain, light, rich soil and a high temperature (25°C on average). Gathering takes place in winter in the Colombo region, during the rainy season, because at that time the sap is more plentiful and decortication easier. The amount of bark normally increases with age, but as the trees are overexploited, it remains thin.

It is the cuttings, chips or broken twigs/inner bark which are particularly used for distillation; their yield is low: 0.6%. The leaves can also be distilled, and the yield then exceeds 1.8%, but they provide a very different essential oil from the bark, notably due to an increase in the level of *eugenol* and a reduction in the *cinnamic aldehyde*.

The essential oil is almost systematically diluted by adding leaves to the bark during distillation or by adding essential oil of leaves after distillation; the *eugenol* level may then reach 20%. With a few rare exceptions, the quality from Madagascar is harsher and less sweet-smelling than that from Sri Lanka, but it has the advantage, however, of being little adulterated.

The root of *Cinnamomum zeylanicum* contains an essence with a predominance of *camphor*, but is not used.

In conclusion, we would note that – a rare occurrence in essential oils – essential oil of *Cinnamomum zeylanicum* p.o. bark has a higher density than water (>1.01); the essential oil from the leaves is, due to its amount of *eugenol*, even denser still (>1.03).

Properties and indications
HEBBD *Cinnamomum zeylanicum*
p.o. bark, *b.s. cinnamaldehyde*

Essential oil of *Cinnamomum zeylanicum* p.o. bark is a good infection-fighting agent (although not as powerful as *Satureja montana*). It acts particularly on the intestinal and urinary areas, but there is a risk of irritation in too high a dose.

It is an excellent gastro-intestinal stimulant, which resorbs flatulence and regularises bowel movements. It increases peristalsis in cases of constipation – blended with *Daucus carota* – and reduces it if there is diarrhoea or dysentery, whilst playing an antiseptic role.

As a general rule, we recommend blending it with *Eugenia caryophyllata*, with which it has great affinity and which is also an excellent antiseptic; and *Citrus limonum* which, on the one hand, sweetens the very strong, burning taste of the Cinnamon-Clove blend and, on the other, will play the role of regulator and liver stimulant, essence of *Cinnamomum zeylanicum* being hepatotoxic in high doses and even difficult to tolerate in low doses by people with a delicate liver.

Cinnamomum zeylanicum is a very good antiseptic, a vermifuge which fights amoebae and intestinal worms, with *Santolina chamaecyparissus*, and tropical diseases, blended with *Eugenia caryophyllata* p.o. cloves, *Ravensara aromatica, Laurus nobilis, Citrus limonum* and *Rosmarinus officinalis b.s. 1.8 cineole*. It is hyperthermisant in cases of a fall in temperature, which is useful in winter.

Cinnamomum zeylanicum p.o. bark is a general stimulant, but an excitant in high doses. It is effective in cases of nervous depression which are physical in origin and suitable for people who are devitalised, emaciated or even anaemic (blended with *Daucus carota*), and whose debility affects the psyche. It is a mood elevator which can be given to people who are completely introverted as a result of relational blockages, although care must nevertheless be taken not to administer it to excess; in this sense, the characterology is telling.

It is a good muscular tonic for use before a period of exertion, although one must be vigilant about over-use, for it provides such a feeling of well-being that one may tax the body excessively. It is an excitant in high doses, which then leads to physical depression with a rapid hypotensive tendency.

Essential oil of *Cinnamomum zeylanicum* p.o. leaves is, in fact, excessive in all spheres and must therefore be used sparingly. A very physical essence, extremely vibrant and emotional, as its characterology will show, it is too powerful for *Chamaemelum nobile* and *Helichrysum italicum* people, or others of the same type, unless a "strong medicine" is necessary and one deliberately wants to cause a reaction. Toxic to the liver in high doses, hypertensive and a nerve excitant, its beneficial effects can quickly turn into drawbacks. It will often be blended with *Eugenia caryophyllata* and *Citrus limonum,* which balance and relate to it, without diminishing its advantageous properties – quite the contrary, in fact.

As *Cinnamomum zeylanicum* is too harsh on the skin, it is preferable to administer it via the oral and rectal routes.

Characterology

Many legends were rife amongst the Ancients concerning Cinnamon, interest in which lies in the fact that although it is very difficult, botanically, to distinguish *cinnamomum* from *cassia* – both, most likely, representing sometimes Ceylon Cinnamon and sometimes Chinese Cinnamon – from the mythological point of view, there is a very clear line between the two species, which then depict Cinnamon's two tendencies: the first associated with the archetypes of the finest *Lauraceae* (*Laurus nobilis* and *Ravensara aromatica*), and the second being the expression of a prosaic and, at times, crepuscular nature.[1]

All the accounts concerning Cassia go back to chthonic concepts – it grows near marshes or lakes and is associated with infernal creatures such as worms, bats or winged serpents. At the opposite end of this description evoking the quagmires of the astral plane, things to do with *cinnamomum,* on the other hand, come under solar notions – a plant consecrated to the Sun and Jupiter, reposing on inaccessible heights, it blazes spontaneously and forms the abode of solar birds, even the Phoenix, when it is not the product of miracles through them.

Cinnamomum therefore appears to have been for the Ancients, like many other aromatic plants, a solar symbol, the seat of the spirit – which is understandable since its name signifies "Chinese Laurel" – and *cassia,* a symbol of the earthly, mortal body animated by the life force of procreation, a simple lunar reflection of the Ego.

These days, Cinnamon is in a way the "personality" (from *persona,* meaning mask in Latin, reflecting the life and theatrical game of Existence) of the great mythic *Lauraceae,* and is far removed from the Apollonian archetypes they represent.

The *Cinnamomum zeylanicum* character, as he appears, embodies

---

[1] This distinction was very clearly shown by Marcelle Détienne in *Les Jardins d'Adonis* [The Gardens of Adonis].

cassia more than *cinnamomum*. Although a few remnants of the original, spiritual *Lauraceae* from the land of Dionysus are crudely reflected in his ego through his naive fascination for the brilliant, the flamboyant and the magnificent, his daily existence is familiar with the earthly limitations and pleasures associated with the legendary *cassia*, his lunar shadow – connected with the Bacchic, incarnated side of the god.

Midas was a *Cinnamomum zeylanicum* – that king so fond of wine, riches and Venusian pleasures who, unfortunately for him, was also a bit simple-minded. His good-natured disposition had led him to gather up Silenus (*Silenus* and *Selene*, the moon, have the same etymology), the companion of Dionysus, when the fellow was blind drunk, and this won him a reward from the god, who asked what wish he wanted to have granted. "That everything I touch should be turned into gold!", replied Midas. Immediately all objects, including food and drink, turned to gold as soon as Midas touched them, to the extent that he soon found himself almost dying of hunger and thirst and had to beg Dionysus to deliver him from his wish; once again, the god conceded.

Midas, alas – though he was perhaps put off by gold – did not sharpen up his wits or refine his tastes, even so. One day, there was a musical competition between Pan's flute and Apollo's lyre and when the latter was declared the winner, Midas – more taken by rural rhythms than celestial melodies – contested the decision and thus incurred the wrath of the Sun God. In order to punish him, Apollo made poor Midas grow donkey's ears, which he had to hide under a Phrygian cap.

The biochemical composition of *Cinnamomum zeylanicum* p.o. bark, through its phenols and aldehydes, reveals a person who is more inclined towards the physical and emotional than the mental. The characteristic of *Cinnamomum zeylanicum* p.o. bark is precisely the lack, not of intelligence – for he can be practical – but rather of intellect and, above all, subtlety.

In his oafishness, his love for exuberant passions and exaggerated displays, Cinnamon does not pass unnoticed; where some people simply make their presence felt, he blatantly parades his. Conceited and a bully, sometimes pleasant, sometimes vulgar, *Cinnamomum zeylanicum* p.o. bark tries to please but, most of the time, pleases only himself – which, in the end at least, isn't so bad. He makes a cult out of the physical body and the efforts he deploys in body-building sessions and weightlifting competitions are only equalled by the pride he takes in unrestrainedly showing off his measurements at the least excuse.

'When I want, I horrify, and when I want, I charm;
And, as the notion takes me, in turn I fill
Men with terror and women with love',
exclaims our braggart.[1]

More poetically, he is a worthy emulator of Papageno, a jolly fellow, chatterbox and fibber, whose ideal is to have a pretty little woman, merry and round, who will provide him with tasty meals, a cool jug of wine and a warm bed.

Cinnamon is an instinctive being who likes to touch and feel what he desires to own. His good-natured greed impels him to enjoy life and live as his moods dictate; unstable, sometimes unfaithful and a little untruthful – not like *Mentha piperita*, who lies through trickery and calculation, but through naive unawareness – he sees only the commonplace in life and this mirrors him.

An adolescent, one sees him playing with young children, sure at least of being the big, strong hero – the playground Rambo. Later, his desire to shine and his confidence of being the best drive him to excesses which most often make one smile – as when Mohammed Ali proclaimed from the ring as he left it, victorious: "I'm the strongest man in the world and faster than light!" – but which, sometimes, may create an Idi Amin Dada, if his destiny lies that way. By the same token, in this case, he loses his juvenile qualities and magnifies the grotesque, which then affords no respite for smiling.

All in all, he is a likeable character – even if his idea of a perfect life is often limited to money and women (or men) – who at least has the advantage of practically never being ill and does not know the meaning of nervous depression. His essence can be useful for unsticking those who are mentally constipated by affording a warm environment and the lifestyle of islands and cheap cocktails. Cinnamon, for his part, is controlled by the strength of character of *Eugenia caryophyllata*, his protector, and *Citrus limonum*, the children's essence, naturally appeals to him.

---

[1] Pierre Corneille

Conversely, associating with a luscious *Cananga odorata* risks giving the neighbours sleepless nights.

Cinnamomum zeylanicum p.o. bark is a physical essence – they are needed – which, even if it is a little explosive, restores a taste and vigour for life to the depressed, and the fire of courage to the belly of those who may have lost it in the maze of melancholia. The life force in its raw state, it will one day rise right up the trunk and the primal sap that it currently represents for the time being will rejoin its lauric archetypes to grow upon the roots of instinct the fruits of awareness and mastery of self.

Eugenia Caryophyllata

I prostate myself forever before God
who is in fire and water,
who impregnates the whole world,
who is in the yearly harvests
and in the tall trees.
Shvetashvatara Upanishad

Origin and botanical portrait

Eugenia caryophyllata, from the Greek *karuophullon*, "clove-like", also known as *Syzygium aromaticum* or Clove tree in English, is a little tree belonging to the *Myrtaceae*, a family mainly consisting of tropical species, including several aromatic trees. Natives of the Molucca Islands (Indonesia) and known to the Chinese well before our times, Cloves were carried across the world from the sixth century and made up a large part of the spice trade.

It was only in the sixteenth century that their country of origin was discovered. After the Arabs, the Portuguese held a monopoly over the Clove trade for nigh on a century. Then, in the seventeeth century, in order to preserve this monopoly that they now held, the Dutch destroyed the cultivated trees sited in countless little islands belonging to the Molucca archipelago. Despite these precautions, plants were introduced into Ile-de-France (Mauritius) around 1768 and established in various tropical regions from the end of the eighteenth century, particularly in Zanzibar and Pemba (nowadays part of Tanzania). These two islands became the biggest Clove producers (3,600 tons in 1971-72), followed by Madagascar and Indonesia. Today, the latter two have taken over first place ahead of Tanzania.

The Clove tree today grows in all tropical areas and produces a spice which is much appreciated for its antiseptic qualities as a food and as a medicine, particularly dental.

The Clove is a little tree 10 to 15 m high, very leafy, with a pyramid-like bearing and tough, evergreen foliage. It likes warm, humid climates, low altitude (200 to 300 m) and wet, but not flooded, clayey-sandy soil.

The different parts – roots, twigs, leaves, flowers and fruit – all contain an essence. The parts used for extracting the essence are the flower buds and flowery pedicels; the buds are called "cloves" and the pedicels are called "claws", because the top of the pedicels is crowned by a series of bracts in the shape of claws.

It is from the flower, in the shape of a clove, picked just before the flowering of the corolla and then dried, that essential oil of "Cloves" is extracted; essential oil of "Clove claws" (Clove stem oil) is extracted from the combined floral pedicels forming the inflorescence. An essential oil is also extracted from Clove leaves.

The essential oils from the leaves and stems are often sold as essential oil of Cloves, which is more precious; once again, adulteration and falsification are easy and the lack of rigour in aromatherapy encourages this kind of misrepresentation.

With a strong, warm odour reminiscent of the aroma of old island rum, essential oil of Cloves has a bitter, burning taste. Depending on the quality of distillation, the colour of the essential oil varies from light to dark brown-yellow, a colour which indicates a burned or old essential oil.

Properties and indications
HEBBD *Eugenia caryophyllata*
p.o. "clove" buds, *b.s. eugenol*

This essential oil, so warm to the sense of smell, reveals a powerful action, like a fire that sets the earth ablaze and cleanses it of its impurities.

Apart from its antiseptic properties, to which we will return, one of the main therapeutic virtues of *Eugenia caryophyllata* p.o. buds is that of being a remarkable uterine tonic; it helps dilate the uterine muscles and thus prepares the mother for an easy birth physically, but also psychically, since it lessens anxiety about the delivery.

One can blend it with *Cinnamomum zeylanicum* p.o. leaves and *Citrus limonum* p.o. zest – the latter, on the one hand, because it aids the hepatobiliary assimilation of the other two phenolic essences and, on the other, because it is the essence for children and infants. It is also possible to add a little essential oil of *Salvia officinalis*, which is remarkably effective on the gynaecological area as a whole, but we would advise extreme caution and recommend only including this essence if one is very proficient in aromatherapy, for the ketones in *Salvia officinalis* are abortifacient in the wrong dose (see monograph on this matter). Such a preparation greatly assists uterine dilation, and also palliates post-natal depression when the mother, two or three days after the birth, feels that the "child's soul" has left her.

For premature contractions, *Eugenia caryophyllata* should be blended with *Pistacia lentiscus* and *Cupressus sempervirens*, and in cases of infection or bleeding, with *Salvia officinalis*, *Cistus ladaniferus* and *Satureja montana* – the same recommendations apply as before with regard to *Salvia officinalis*.[2] Obviously, these instructions do not obviate the need for special gynaecological supervision.

Eugenia caryophyllata is, as we said earlier, an excellent antiseptic, bactericide and viricide. A mother prepared for delivery with *Eugenia* has a very good chance of giving birth to a healthy infant, one better protected against post-partum infections.

An indispensable essence for tropical diseases, it is recommended that it be supplemented with *Cinnamomum zeylanicum* p.o. bark, *Ravensara aromatica*, *Citrus limonum*, *Rosmarinus officinalis* b.s. bornyl acetate, verbenone and, if necessary, a little *Mentha piperita*.

For pathologies as grave as plague, cholera and leprosy, Eugenia, as well as other essential oils, can render excellent service but the process of making up the treatments is, as we have already had occasion to test out, rather complex.

Eugenia excels in treating infectious gastro-intestinal illnesses and immune system deficiencies, alternating with complex compounds of essential oils based on *Satureja montana*. This essential oil, especially when blended with *Cinnamomum zeylanicum* p.o. bark – we are stressing the point at the risk of repeating ourselves, but the synergy between

---

[2] Dosages are deliberately not given in order to prevent ill-advised use. A forthcoming volume will be entirely devoted to formulae and prescriptions.

these two essences is nothing short of amazing – has disinfectant and cleansing properties which enable zymosis, sepsis and flatulence to be cleared away. It stimulates and cleanses the intestinal functions, and proves vital to people who eat red meat, cooked pork meats and a lot of cheese. It is, moreover, antiparasitic and antifungal, blended with complementary essential oils, and antiputrefactive with *Cinnamomum zeylanicum*, *Laurus nobilis* and *Ravensara aromatica*.

It is, of course, an excellent dental antiseptic, and also analgesic, *Eugenia* always having been known for these properties. Very powerful in cases of neuralgia and dental infections, it is regrettable that dentists only use eugenol, thereby relinquishing the essential oil's molecular synergy, which is much more therapeutically effective than the isolated active principle.

All the same, we would make it clear that although an adult may find momentary relief (aromatherapy can fight an infection and have analgesic power, but obviously cannot fill in a cavity or regenerate a bad tooth) through the local use of essential oil of *Eugenia caryophyllata*, it is categorically not recommended for use with teething infants, at the risk of burning them. Eugenol is very hot and can only be tolerated by adults. For children, we should use *Lavandula spica* and *Rosmarinus officinalis b.s. 1.8 cineole* externally, as indicated in the respective monographs for these essences.

A fine tonic, both physical and mental, *Eugenia caryophyllata* quickly fights off drowsiness, in a car for example, blended in this case with *Mentha piperita b.s. menthol*.

Finally, it is a good mental revitaliser, in particular for strongly emotional people; if necessary, blend it with *Laurus nobilis* and *Ravensara aromatica* in cases of primary psychosis and fears resulting from an unresolved poor maternal relationship or from anxiety in "giving birth to oneself", in other words, taking responsibility for one's life and cutting the umbilical cord. The characterology will, in this instance, provide helpful answers.

Eugenia caryophyllata is consequently a remarkable essence and one used systematically in aromatherapy during pregnancy. Nevertheless, one must not overlook the fact that it is a phenolic essence and, whilst it is more accommodating than *Satureja montana*, it must not be employed thoughtlessly. The characterology shows the link that it has with the crucial period represented by the preparation for birth.

Unless an impossibility, one must always use the essential oil extracted from the flower buds, in other words the "cloves"; the essential oils from Clove stems and leaves are of lesser quality, even though the composition of these essences is fairly akin. It is easy to blend with the spices, the other phenolic essences and the strong essential oils, particularly the woods (*Laurus nobilis, Ravensara aromatica, Rosmarinus officinalis b.s. bornyl acetate, verbenone, Cupressus sempervirens, Pistacia lentiscus*, etc.), but should not be combined with fragile essences such as *Helichrysum italicum, Chamaemelum nobile, Origanum majorana*, etc. since – due to its somewhat imposing strength – *Eugenia* does not act in total synergy with them. One only need smell Clove essence to judge which blends would work best.

Characterology

This remarkable plant, long exploited for its many properties, has a very beautiful name which is revealing of its virtues: *Eugenia*, with the prefix *eu*, meaning well, good; and *genia, genesis*, meaning birth, genesis, generation. Its name signifies, in effect, "good birth". St Eugenia is still today the patron saint of midwives, to whom mothers-to-be used to pray in times gone by for a successful delivery, and the origin of whose worship perhaps dates back to that of the Greek goddess, Ilythye, whose name means "she who comes to the assistance of women in childbirth". This daughter of Zeus and Hera, goddess of births and midwives, corresponds to the very archetype of *Eugenia carophyllata*.

A great and mighty goddess with potent magical powers, Ilythye, "who assists women at the dreaded time of childbirth", as Ovid clearly tells us, could precipitate or delay the delivery at will. When the jealous Hera wanted to prevent her rival, Alcmene – pregnant through Zeus's efforts – from giving birth to Heracles, she forbade Ilythye to help her. The goddess had to sit on the doorstep of Alcmene's house, legs, arms and fingers crossed, and it was only when she uncrossed them that Heracles could be born.

In Rome, Ilythye's counterpart was Juno, wife of Jupiter, in this case called Juno Lucina, from *luce*, meaning light, the first element perceived by the new-born child who "sees the light of day". Goddess of beginnings, women and marriage, Juno (from *juvenis*, meaning young, newly married) had a close relationship with the moon, traditionally and physically associated with women and their cycles. She presided over the calends, the days of the new moon which opened the month, whilst her husband presided over the ides, the days of the full moon, when it received the full light of the sun, a period which corresponds (or, to be more precise, used to correspond) in women with the favoured time that was most opportune to fertility.

Eugenia thus carries in her the mark of divine ancestors creating and influencing her spiritual archetype, which she manifests very concretely in matter and in her work on behalf of birth.

With respect to the plant itself, and more specifically the floral bud, *Eugenia caryophyllata* – like many other plants – confirms the theory of "signatures" developed by Paracelsus, by revealing through its shape a marvellous aspect of the symbolism of birth.

Formed initially by four sepals, then four petals – the former red, the latter white – it carries in it the colours of the two aspects of life that will nourish the infant during its intra- and extra-uterine life. Four, the number of matter and incarnation in the physical world, sustains as much as it encloses the being who is incarnating on earth and must draw nourishment from red and white, blood and milk – symbols of a communion with the earth that precedes communion in spirit, by the white and red, bread and wine. "Unless one is born of water and spirit, he cannot enter the kingdom of God" *(John, 3:3)*. This allegory, the profound symbolic significance of which it is not possible to expand upon in this work and which may be compared to the separating of the "waters above" and the "waters below" in Genesis, also invites us to think about the importance of the intra-uterine water, this original matrix in which the infant is bathed and nourished as much by the mother's physical elements as by her love and attention. It is often said that a child has two mothers – his biological mother and the one who, by her deft hands with their sure movements, helps out and welcomes the new-born into the world. *Eugenia* clearly represents the second mother: from the semblance of the plant in which the clove seems to appear like a child's head emerging from the maternal womb, in the sublime effort and sacrifice that its incarnation constitutes for the mother; in its properties and, of course, its characterology, everything seems to relate to probably the most beautiful and profound event of creation – birth.

Socially, the *Eugenia* person therefore appears as a wise-woman, a midwife on several levels, and if she does not work in this area, her occupations are generally not far removed from it. Nurse, kinesitherapist, social worker or secular nun, her character induces her to devote herself, to give of herself with amazing strength and courage, participating in births and rebirths, just as likely to be physical as moral and spiritual.

A missionary soul, quite akin in this sense to *Lavandula vera* and *Ocimum basilicum*, but less delicate and subtle in practice, she renders kind deeds and support, and produces, if not children, at least hope and faith in the hearts of children of all ages. She could be that angel of whom St Teresa sang, a symbol of comfort and understanding:

"That beautiful angel, O profound mystery!
called me her little sister;
she had the features of a Mother
and I rested on her breast.
In the shade of her white wings
I grew rapidly,
already the eternal shores
had delighted my child's eyes."

Uncomplicated, genuine, sometimes a little rustic, although her lack of intellectualism is an asset in smoothing human relationships, with an enterprising, determined character, she seems and believes she can – thanks to her unflappable spirit and youthful optimism – resolve any problem she comes across, mainly in the lives of others. Inevitably possessing the failings of her qualities, her heavy stoutness and large hands are as disturbing in their exuberance as they are reassuring by their efficient presence. Sure of herself – out of faith, not vanity – she employs her wholly unpretentious and jovial temperament to bring good humour and confidence to the places where worry and isolation prevail.

Always warm and pleasant, *Eugenia*, as a living example, makes one want to act and smile. She is a character of great moral value with whom it is agreeable to associate for she lives and embodies her faith in acts, and makes of her work her daily prayer.

"Before reaching the fountain, he was seized with the beauty of a young mother draped in a red sari, sitting in the street, her back perfectly straight, a baby placed on her outstretched legs. The infant was naked, a chubby child... A strange flame moved between their glances. One would have said they were talking with their eyes... The woman had just dropped a few drops of mustard oil on her palms and began massaging the little body. Skilful, intelligent, attentive, her hands rose and fell, animated by a rhythm as subtle as it was steadfast. Working in turn, like waves, they left the baby's flanks, crossed his chest and moved up to the opposite shoulder... She stretched his arms and massaged them gently, one after the other, singing old counting rhymes to him, telling of the loves of the god, Krishna, or some legend from the dawn of the epic ages... The child babbled with bliss. It's a veritable ritual, he thought, dazzled by so much love, beauty, intelligence. For he was imagining all the extra-corporal nourishment this massage was bringing to the little body threatened by so many deficiencies in the external world."[3]

---

[3] Vous êtes la lumière du monde, La Cité de la Joie, *[You are the light of the World, The City of Joy]*, Dominique Lapierre.

Eucalyptus Globulus

*The wise man fans the perfume of his virtue
In all directions.*
Gautama Buddha

Origin and botanical portrait

General points on Eucalyptuses

The *Eucalyptus* genus belongs to the *Myrtaceae* family, which includes more than six hundred species and varieties.

The Eucalyptuses (the name given to them by L'Héritier in 1778) are woody plants of all sizes. Whilst some are small trees, others are part of the giants of the plant kingdom, able to reach 100 m in their country of origin, the subtropical lands of the southern hemisphere – Australia, Tasmania and Malaysia.

Towards the middle of the nineteenth century, about fifty species were introduced to South America, particularly Brazil, other tropical regions and southern Europe.

One of the most valuable services the Eucalyptuses provide for us is the draining of the marshy regions. Thanks to their huge, strong roots – capable of absorbing enormous amounts of water – and by the intense evaporation at leaf level, they symbolise an important factor in the disappearance of the marshes and, because of this, of paludism in Europe.

A sometimes unrecognised point of significance is that not all Eucalyptuses are aromatic; the aromatic species contain essence mainly in the leaves, where the numerous secretory sacs are then transparently visible at the limb.

The main species of the *Eucalyptus* genus used in aromatherapy and classified according to the principal constituent are:

- With a 1.8 cineole base:

- *Eucalyptus globulus* Labillardière
- *Eucalyptus camaldulensis* Dehn. (Eucalyptus rostrata Schlecht)
- *Eucalyptus radiata Sieber* (Eucalyptus australiana Baker & Smith)
- *Eucalyptus polybractea* R.T. Baker (Eucalyptus fruticetorum F. Moell.)
• With a piperitone and phellandrene base:
- Eucalyptus dives Schauer
• With a citronnellal base:
- *Eucalyptus citriodora* Hooker.

There are nevertheless numerous varieties able to yield different essential oils, which makes the *Eucalyptus* genus difficult to classify. The best known, from the point of view of its name, is *Eucalyptus globulus*, but other essential oils of Eucalyptus are sometimes sold under this term, often derived from "communelles"[4] and taking no account of the authenticity of the raw material used. *Eucalyptus globulus*, with its strong, very characteristic odour, is far from being an ordinary essence, as its properties, directions and characterology will show.

Eucalyptus globulus is frequently rectified in order to remove its natural odour – considered by some to be disagreeable and strong – which it gives off after being extracted by steam distillation. Rectification consists of redistilling the crude essential oil and separating the fractions from it at various boiling points. The aim of this process is to remove molecules such as *isovalerianic aldehyde* and to enrich the rectified product with *eucalyptol* (or *1.8 cineole*). In this way, many companies produce various grades of *Eucalyptus globulus* according to how rich they are in *eucalyptol*: 90-95%; 80-85%; 70-75% or 60-65%. This process results in the disappearance of many constituents. Just as rectification can be reasoned if one reserves the essences processed in this way for the perfumery industry, so – from a therapeutic point of view – is it vital to use the complete essence of *Eucalyptus globulus*, that is to say, with the assurance that it has not been rectified. The intrinsic properties of this essence do not depend solely on the *1.8 cineole*, all in all a very common constituent, but the synergic set of its constituents.

---

[4] *A mixture of several batches of the same essential oil.*

Eucalyptus globulus

This is Blue Gum Eucalyptus, officinal or globulous Eucalyptus, a native of Australia and Tasmania – called *Ballook* by the Aborigines – and the species of Eucalyptus most widely planted around the Mediterranean. It was introduced into the south of France in 1860 with a view to draining the marshes, and today its decorative branches brighten up florists' bouquets.

It is a tall tree reaching 40 m, the oldest bark of which scales off in long reddish patches, leaving a smooth, pale grey bark. *Eucalyptus globulus* wood is hard, heavy and cracked; it is the best Eucalyptus in Europe for cellulose pulp. Its strength and longevity are exceptional, even in water, but it does not, however, like temperatures below −5°C.

The Eucalyptus leaves used in herbal medicine most often come from trees acclimatised to the Mediterranean region, Provence and, above all, Spain. Only the old leaves about to fall, being very aromatic, are used. Essential oil of *Eucalyptus globulus* has a penetrating odour which makes itself felt through its fullness.

Properties and indications
HEBBD *Eucalyptus globulus*
p.o. leaves, b.s. 1.8 cineole, globulol

Due to its heavy concentration of *1.8 cineole*, *Eucalyptus globulus* has a pronounced action on the respiratory tract, a property known throughout the ages. To be more specific, the area of activity favoured by *Eucalyptus globulus* is the bottom of the respiratory function – the bronchi and lungs, the top being more effectively treated with *Eucalyptus radiata*. On breathing in *Eucalyptus globulus*, one feels its strong odour penetrate the lungs, stimulate the respiration and bring an immediate sense of release and wellbeing. However, the smell is also very heady, fragrant and "transparent" and does not suit everyone, particularly people who are withdrawn or over-sure of their criteria (see characterology).

Eucalyptus globulus is therefore very effective in treating bronchopulmonary complaints, from the most benign to the most serious. An excellent expectorant, mucolytic and antiseptic, it is successful in cases of bronchitis and some cases of broncho-pneumonia. It is also anti-inflammatory and antispasmodic, and consequently indicated in cases of asthma, flu and tropical diseases.

Eucalyptus globulus should essentially be applied through the skin by rubbing it over the ribcage, and not orally; if necessary, it may be equally advantageous to use the rectal route, suppositories being an easy way of assimilating a significant dose of essential oil, especially where children are concerned. Blended with other essential oils – *Rosmarinus officinalis b.s. 1.8 cineole, Myrtus communis, Ravensara aromatica, Laurus nobilis, Hyssopus officinalis, Lavandula vera*, etc. – it will be even more effective when massaged on the back at thorax level. We would also strongly recommended it be used by diffusing it in the air, blended, in that case, with *Citrus limonum*, which will attenuate its very pungent scent, and possibly with a little *Mentha piperita*.

The reputed hypoglycaemic properties of Eucalyptus essence do not seem proven to us; we think they may, on the other hand, relate to the Eucalyptus leaves, which contain other active principles of the essence. We will therefore basically reserve *Eucalyptus globulus* for broncho-pulmonary pathologies.

As a general rule, one should avoid massaging the chest with *Eucalyptus globulus* and apply it through the back in preference; in fact, a heavy dose of *1.8 cineole* – in addition to the very strong, characteristic odour of this essence – may give the impression that one is being stifled, which is obviously not the aim, particularly in cases of an asthma attack. We would also give a reminder that, as the essences are not water soluble in their natural state, it is strongly inadvisable to put essence of *Eucalyptus globulus* into one's bath, as is commonly recommended.

Eucalyptus globulus is a far more precious essence than it would appear and one need only use a little of it to appreciate its effectiveness.

Characterology

Whilst it is a misunderstood essence, *Eucalyptus globulus* indeed fulfils the paradox of simultaneously being one of the most profound essences as well as one of the most popularised from a commercial point of view; seldom pure and almost systematically rectified, it is most often a mixture of several Eucalyptus essences.

Pure essential oil of *Eucalyptus globulus*, however, possesses a flowery touch combined with a fragrance which is both dry and voluptuous, deep and tenacious, with an absolutely exceptional character.

In order to discover the characterology connected with the fresh, apparently straightforward, odour of this essence – one of extreme volatility – we must seek its archetype beyond the pretence of the outer world, and go past the ephemeral and the illusory in order to reflect, freely and without expectations, upon the eternal light shining in the deepest part of us.

"When I used to walk through the big Eucalyptus forests, I had trouble preventing myself from leaving my body", said Bashistya Shivananta, as if to set us on the way; the journey on which *Eucalyptus globulus* invites us is, in fact, a wholly inner one.

More an aspiration or a state of mind than a specific human being, *Eucalyptus globulus* appears as a meditating sage, whose aura one contemplates in order to assimilate its virtues. *Eucalyptus globulus* seems to breathe to the rhythm of life and, through his breath control, holds the secret of how to control the mind.

Eucalyptus globulus is a sage, a solitary, smiling yogi, secluded in asceticism at the top of the Himalayas, free from the grip of the senses and attachment. In tune with the rhythm of the cosmic breath, he hovers – like a royal eagle in majestic, inaccessible flight – above the temporal with which he was once familiar and is now transcending.

Gautama Siddhartha was a *Eucalyptus globulus* – a prince, married and the father of a family, having had his fill of earthly pleasures, but who one day wished to understand the mystery of human existence clouded by illness, old age and death; he became a hermit and, after a six-year quest, sitting under a sacred fig tree, liberated from passions and errors and then having gone beyond pain and death, he attained enlightenment, *Bodhi*. He became a Buddha.

Milarepa was also one – that great Tibetan yogi who, to purify himself, left to take up a hermit's life on Mount Kailasa, vowing not to come down until he had reached enlightenment. He lived on nettles, which he boiled in a clay pot, his only earthly possession. "Even this pot has been like a *guru* to me; it has revealed to me the law of the impermanence of all things and freed me from my last tie to the world", he said one day when the pot broke. "A solitary old man, walking naked, a song of praise springs from my lips – Nature is, for me, a book. With a steel-tipped stick in my hand, I cross the heaving ocean of life, master of Spirit and Light", he still sings throughout the world of glorified souls.

Like the tree which drains the marshes and purifies the air of the country where it grows, *Eucalyptus globulus* disperses the impure waters of a damaging and debasing affectivity to clean up the land and turn it into a garden full of flowers and fruits. His Buddhist perception of love can only be understood within the unity of spirit with a view to its ultimate merger with the Infinite. *Eucalyptus globulus* has made his own these words from the Bhagavad-Gita: "He who has found within himself inner joy, being blissful and lit from within, this yogi, on his way to becoming a Brahman, attains the supreme peace of a Brahman."

Although in spirit he remains above the world, *Eucalyptus globulus* does not cultivate contempt for attachment but, on the contrary, transcends it for he understands on what it is founded, like the very wise and enlightened Vasishtha, who taught Prince Rama, his disciple: "O Ramaji, if you must know attachment and if your soul aspires to it, then attach yourself to the holy image of an *Avatar*,[5] for one resembles that which one loves and serves with sincerity."[6]

Gladdened and elated by the transparent and invigorating freshness of its fragrance, he who inhales the scent of eternity in *Eucalyptus globulus* is invited on the most wonderful of journeys – one which leads him to himself. Detached from regret, not knowing fear, forgetting wars, grudges and existential divisions, he finds himself transported, light and free, on the wings of spirit to blend with the unutterable splendour of the Atman. "Liberated, the soul ascends to the supreme Light which is Brahman and identifies with him." *(Shankara)*

Within the human context, *Eucalyptus globulus* brings us a degree of expansion and considerable peace. He may only exceptionally appear in his archetypal form, which one must be able to encounter and recognise, but he inspires those who are guided by serenity – not through lax remoteness from material chance circumstances, but in stillness and "authentic breathing" which makes one think of that of the ocean in its

---

[5] *An Avatar is the visible embodiment of a deity.*
[6] *Yoga-Vasishtha.*

immensity, the mountains in their inaccessibility and Heaven and Earth in their unity.

Eucalyptus globulus brings us back to sound values – lively and original – and in that regard, its scent can disturb those who create of themselves a character full of barely justifiable social ploys – an approximate expression, and obviously restricting to their Ego. Very useful for recentring a scattered person who is the victim of respiratory spasms – symptoms of no longer being in balance with the world around – in low amounts, it acts gently and patiently, and is a remarkable supplement to other essential oils that help the Ego to incarnate and, as a result, assist in restoring the psychosomatic equilibrium, like *Cupressus sempervirens, Ravensara aromatica* and *Rosmarinus officinalis b.s. bornyl acetate, verbenone.*

It is quite obviously one of the best essential oils that one can discover, and one which helps us to reveal the best of ourselves.

"You are eternally present, my spirit, my God,
But your light undoubtedly dazzles and frightens me;
The fear of leaving, with regret, my past,
My tender memories, my physical attachments,
How much solitude before knowing you!
The path is long and my heart impatient, O Atman!
Thank you for understanding me, I know that you await me.
Tomorrow the sun will rise on the path,
In my turn, I will look at it,
In my turn, I will be a pilgrim."
Bashistya Shivânanta

Satureja Montana

And from the mountains and woods, flowers and high mosses,
In the warm and rarefied air, released in a gust,
Blows a wave of heavy, sweet scents,
Full of passion and sensual delights.
Leconte de Lisle

Origin and botanical portrait

A sun-loving plant, Winter Savory grows on the southern chalky hillsides at an altitude of between 300 and 1,000 m, but is also found beside the country roads of south-eastern France. It is a *Lamiaceae* which grows in clumps, like many other plants belonging to this family.

Satureja could come from the Latin *saturare*, meaning *to satiate* or from *satura*, which means "a dish garnished with all manner of vegetables" – an allusion to the use of the plant as a condiment. It is, however, more likely that this name derives from the Latin *satyrus*, coming from the Greek *saturos*, which gave the term *satyr* to the fourteenth century, due to the aphrodisiac qualities attributed to the plant.

There are two species of Savory in France from which essence is extracted:
- *Satureja hortensis L.*: annual or Garden Savory;
- *Satureja montana L.*: perennial or Winter Savory.

Satureja hortensis is a small species, 20 to 30 cm high in the wild, but over 1 m when cultivated. It grows spontaneously in dry, sandy and low altitude spots in the south of France. It is an annual herbaceous plant, and this clearly differentiates it from Winter Savory. *Satureja hortensis* is above all a cultivated plant which is cropped with a long scythe during the flowering period.

Satureja montana, which is more common in the wild, is a perennial sub-shrub growing in small (20 to 30 cm) close clumps. The plant has a compact appearance, and is stocky with spiky-looking stems which make one afraid of getting pricked if one touches them.

As far as the essential oil is concerned, *Satureja montana* is preferable to *Satureja hortensis*. It has a warm, strong, sharp smell and a bitter, burning taste. Nevertheless, this essential oil must be preferred to that of *Origanum compactum*, which contains between 60 and 75% of phenols (especially *carvacrol*), and is even more irritating and toxic to the liver than *Satureja montana*.

Properties and indications
HEBBD *Satureja montana*
p.o. flowering plant, *b.s. carvacrol, p-cymene*

Satureja montana, less concentrated in phenols and more balanced than *Origanum compactum*, is just as efficient an infection-fighting agent, but with a less immoderate effect on the body. It is an essential oil which is tricky to use and must, in general, be employed for short-term treatments in appreciable doses. Using it in minimal or – preferably – infinitesimal doses for a treatment related to the characterology is, of course, a different matter, since the toxicity of Savory is due to its high level of *carvacrol.* In substantial doses, it is recommended that it be blended with other essential oils that will refine its action without diminishing it (*Rosmarinus officinalis b.s. bornyl acetate, verbenone, Thymus vulgaris b.s. linalool* or *Salvia officinalis*, depending on the predisposing factors). As a general rule, it must always be blended with *Rosmarinus officinalis b.s. bornyl acetate, verbenone* which, on the one hand, is an excellent immune system stimulant and, on the other, due to its regulating properties on the hepatobiliary area, will enable the body to assimilate the phenols more easily. Nor must one overlook the fact that where there is an infectious pathology, the "terrain" is weakened and the eliminating functions, particularly the liver ones, affected; it is therefore not the time to force phenolic hepato-toxicity on them without counterbalancing such action. We know from experience that the theories advocating that the pure phenolic essences are more effective are inexact, since they do not take into account *in vivo* reactions, where phenolic assimilation combined with immunostimulation is of prime importance. Precisely this fact falls within the province of

Rosmarinus officinalis b.s. bornyl acetate, verbenone. Furthermore, a "terrain" treatment – even in cases of infection – is preferable to a mechanical action; thus, for uro-genital infections, blending it with *Salvia officinalis,* which does not itself have significant antimicrobic properties, proves beneficial because it regulates these functions and therefore prepares the way for the constructive action of *Satureja montana* whilst controlling its excesses, particularly the hyperthermal and caustic ones.

With these precautions in mind, *Satureja montana* is very helpful, especially when its immunostimulating properties are enhanced.

Its rather general infection-fighting properties act mainly and most efficiently at the level of the genito-urinary and gastro-intestinal areas, essentially for violent, acute infections. Recurrent infections, due notably to a "terrain" deficiency and to a psychological state which encourages such near chronicity, is more the province of *Thymus vulgaris b.s. thymol,* or even *Eugenia caryophyllata,* than *Satureja montana.*

Where children are concerned, phenolic essential oils should be avoided and alcoholic ones used (Thymus *vulgaris b.s. linalool,* for example). If serious or long-lasting pathologies are involved, an exception may be made with regard to *Thymus vulgaris b.s. thymol* administered in blended form by suppositories, but *Satureja* must in all cases be *excluded.*

Satureja montana regularises intestinal peristalsis and is indicated in cases of diarrhoea, flatulence and constipation, with *Cinnamomum zeylanicum* p.o. bark, *Eugenia caryophyllata* and, of course, *Rosmarinus officinalis b.s. bornyl acetate, verbenone.* It is advantageous as part of such a configuration as it gets rid of intestinal sepsis and destroys the pathogenic flora whilst preserving the saprophytic flora. For people who eat red meat and cooked pork meats, blending it with *Carum carvi, Rosmarinus b.s. bornyl acetate, verbenone* and *Laurus nobilis* can only be saving, although altering one's eating habits is, in any case, a priority.

Satureja is also hyperthermal and hypertensive. One must guard against high doses, for it becomes an excitant, toxic to the liver and harsh on the digestive mucous membranes. In the event of an imperative need for massive doses, it must be supplemented with another complex compound made up of *Anethum graveolens, Ocimum basilicum, Juniperus communis* p.o. berries and *Rosmarinus b.s. 1.8 cineole.*

In cases of fatigue and physical debility, *Satureja montana* is a good tonic, but must not be used excessively; treat it, in this case, as if it were a simple supplement. This direction is minor, and it should in general be preferred to the alcoholic essences, or else one should opt for *Eugenia* and *Cinnamomum zeylanicum* – always blended with *Citrus limonum* – which will give a lift to people who are physically depressed and subject to metabolic disturbances.

It has an analgesic action on infectious rheumatism, administered percutaneously and in a 3% dilution of vegetable oil of *Corylus avellana* or lipidic extract of *Hypericum perforatum*, blended with *Lavandula officinalis* and other gentle analgesic essential oils.

Let us nevertheless keep in mind that *Satureja montana* is counter-irritant and its cutaneous use sometimes causes erythema. Like all phenolic essential oils, it must never be used pure on the skin and must not be included in fumigations and inhalations, since it would, under such circumstances, cause violent irritation to the mucous membranes.

The fanciful and dangerous directions mentioned in some books concerning the use of phenolic essential oils are to be condemned absolutely. Only competent, experienced aromatherapists should use such oils, and we would again caution the reader against serious breaches by some authors who, by their remarks, turn aromatherapy into a dangerous, toxic practice.

In aromatherapy, a "terrain" medicine, we must avoid making symptomatology and especially combating an illness to the detriment of the body's metabolic and immune balance. *Satureja* is very effective, but must be used above all in cases of acute infectious pathologies. In such cases, substantial doses are vital, and the hepatobiliary area must be supported. When working with the characterology, minimal and infinitesimal doses allow prolonged use without problems.

In massive doses, we must not forget that it is hypertensive and toxic, and always dermocaustic if used in its pure state. Lipidic extract of *Hypericum perforatum* suits *Satureja montana* very well as a base oil.

Finally, do make sure that it bears the guarantee of purity (HEBBD certification) so as not to risk using *Origanum compactum* in place of *Satureja montana*.

Characterology

"And who are you to challenge and look me up and down with such arrogance? Know you not, rogue, who I am? The mighty bow down before my sword, and were it not that God is my protector, the Devil alone might dream one day to see me tremble." And the crafty fox replied with a smile: "Your words are true, my Lord, for I am he!"[7]

Exceptional beings do appear in our aromatic characterologies; have we not, in addition, met a few mythical spirits – the glorious Rosemary, the genial *Ravensara?* And a number of beautiful feminine figures, thrilling and inspiring, like *Chamaemelum nobile, Lavandula vera* and *Ocimum basilicum! Laurus,* too, has its archetype, whose spiritual credentials may seem beyond us, but it represents no less a man, one who is approachable and able to be shaken by the features of his personality; he, too, must move forward in order to evolve, and his essence must be completely transformed and become even more refined so that it may one day symbolise the nature of its original archetype. One day, no doubt, the world of smells will come to be in the image and likeness of its origins, when humanity is ready and brings in its wake the living forces of Nature... One day...

Satureja, an exceptional character, all things considered – in the spirit of the essence – is, himself also, only able to be comprehended from a human perspective, recognisable, moreover, not as a specific man but rather as a tendency which resides in each of us and is revealed to a greater or lesser extent, depending on our temperament. Due to the character, we do not see in it "the spirit of devilish temptation" or the "perverse tendency" that some religious-minded people would like to perceive in all men – striving, moreover, to maintain this view in order to preserve their prerogatives and justify their own excesses. We see in it, rather, an aspect of our personality, with its own reason for existing as well as its reason for evolving and transforming for the greater good of our deep nature, completely impregnated with the light our Ego which is still unable to manifest fully within the existential matter of our embodiment.

Satureja, then, is an exceptional being but one which it would be

---

[7] Sixteenth-century Provençal tale.

better to meet only on similarly exceptional occasions. Etymologically and perhaps actually, *Satureja* is a satyr – therein, in fact, lies his tragedy, his strength and his charm. A strange creature risen up from the depths of mythology, half-man, half-beast, one imagines him living in the woods, with horns and pointed ears, and the legs and hooves of a horse, but one would like to see and meet him, succumb to his charm and give way to his power: "O demon, why do you tempt me? I am a virgin and you know it, and my heart, I pray you, may not be sullied. My father has already promised me to the baron; my chaste breast, white as milk, is intended for him; ... O demon, go not; I will resist, but tempt me still!"[8]

Renowned for their debauched morals and lascivious appetites, the mythic satyrs personified the fertility of wild Nature; alongside the Bacchantes, they made up the bulk of Bacchus's procession, an earthy reflection of the celestial Dionysus, during the orgies intended to celebrate fertility:

"The earth rang out with the galloping of the centaurs;
They came from the echoing, far horizon,
And I saw, astride flying rumps,
Holding twisted thyrsi and bulging goatskins,
Limping satyrs stung by bees...
And the immense, frenetic dance,
Heavy hooves, light feet, fleeces, rumps, tunics,
Spun madly around me, whilst gravely I,
In passing, sculpted on the swollen sides of the vase
The whirling forces of life...
The dance, now dispersed and of which a gentle wind
Brought echoes of the faded din,
Turned with its goats, its gods, its naked women,
Its rearing centaurs and nimble fauns."[9]

With the permission of the gods, *Satureja montana*, the satyr of the mountains, pursues nymphs and vestals with vigour, makes nightly visits to respectable women, prompts gallant men to action and makes them impish, observes, noses about and in the shadows constructs the fateful

---

[8] Sixteenth-century Provençal tale.

[9] Henri de Régnier

design of tempting their ego, awakening their senses and testing their faith. He is the tempter, instrumental and dangerous, efficient and crafty as much as obedient, whom we see – not without a shiver – in the tales, legends and myths dedicated to the gods.

From an initiatory point of view, he has his reason for existing; he is the tempter in the desert who, three times, tests Jesus on the physical, emotional and mental planes. He asks him to change stones into bread, then to hurl himself from the temple and, finally, to reflect – from the mountain top – on all that might be his. The need to possess and stupid beliefs and pride are in this way respectively dominated by detachment, an act of will; by discernment, which confers wisdom; and by humility, inspired by divine love.

There resides in us all that which tests us, a part of our ego that forces us to choose between control of the senses and subjection to the desires. Omnipresent, it reveals to us what we are: "Look on the one who teaches you of your weaknesses as if he would show you the place wherein is found treasure", taught Buddha.

St Paul said to the Corinthians: "A thorn was given me in the flesh; three times I besought the Lord that it should leave me, three times He said to me: My grace is sufficient for you, my power is made perfect in weakness."

Like Job tested by Satan on the orders of the Lord: "Does Job fear God for naught?... put forth thy hand now, and touch all that he has, and he will curse thee to thy face." And the Lord said to Satan, "Behold, all that he has is in your power; only upon himself do not put forth your hand." *(Job 1:9-11)*

The tempter *par excellence* in Genesis, the serpent – "the most subtle of all the creatures of the field" – in enticing Eve to eat of the fruit of the tree of knowledge of good and evil: "You will not die. For God knows that when you eat of it, your eyes will be opened, and you will be like God, knowing good and evil", aroused the anger of the Lord, who said to it: "You will be cursed... upon your belly you shall go... I will put enmity between you and the woman; she shall bruise your head and you will shall bruise her heel" *(Genesis, 3)*. In this way was Eve, the human soul, enticed to give to the creative power she possesses (the sexual energy) – a horizontal direction, that of the creeping serpent – and to renounce thereby the vertical direction, that of the serpent upright and erect around the tree. Her heel was wounded before to Achilles, this weakness was already known.

In moving away from original unity – the Tree of Life – humanity experiences the duality of existence – the tree of knowledge of good and evil. This eternal dichotomy is also that of the sun and moon, day and night, Dionysus and Bacchus, symbolically expressed in myths and traditions.

In Egyptian mythology, *Satureja* is an aspect of Seth, the brother and murderer of Osiris, the solar god, whom he cut into fourteen pieces and shut up in a sarcophagus, a symbol of physical incarnation. Isis reunited thirteen pieces of Osiris, but the phallus remained in the Nile.

It is also Saturn, the god of the physical embodiment of divine energy, who castrates his father, Ouranos (Uranus), and swallows his own children – he is Saturn-Kronos, the god of time. *Satureja* is, equally, Mephistopheles – handsome with the beauty of the Devil, slender of body, with curly black hair, the magic of the seducer's look and impious words:

"I am the spirit who always denies

With good reason, for in the end, whatever is being created

Is certainly worth only being reduced to nothingness.

Would it be better to do nothing,

That there were no creation at all?

What you call sin, destruction,

In short, evil – all this is precisely my province."[10]

Nothing that is born will not, effectively, one day die, and the agent of this destruction – in the service of life and the cosmic plan – is also *Satureja*, the separator. Evil is only good misused, and what would day be without night to enhance it?

Hinduism, which personifies the two antagonistic forces operating in the world of existence through Vishnu, the Preserver, and Shiva, the Destroyer, symbolises *Satureja* through the *asura*, the "demons" in the service of the god Rudra, the terrible face of Shiva, whose son – in other words, manifestation – is Shani, the planet Saturn. A doctor and magician, Rudra is the lord of death and fertility.

---

[10] Goethe, *Faust.*

Satureja, in its earthly reality, defends biological life; "all this has been granted me...", says the tempter to Jesus, which corroborates its remarkable infection-fighting action, for his will is that physical life is perpetuated on earth. There is nothing surprising, then, in the fact that it was forbidden to grow Savory in convents, for it was supposed to attract the satyrs; with a strong, hot and sensual odour, *Satureja* is a powerful aphrodisiac, which awakens the instinctive forces in man and entices him towards voluptuous drunken revels. A volcanic fire, sleeping yet bubbling, *Satureja* is located in the *Muladhara*.[11]

"I adjure you, O daughters of Jerusalem,

by the gazelles or the hinds of the field,

that you stir not up nor awaken love

until it please!"[12]

Satureja is raw energy, instinctive and innate, which wisdom is able to channel and exploit – the dragon with the fiery throat also has wings. The fire which burns and destroys also warms the hearth and lights the lamp, if there is plenty of purified oil and it is not spilt.

May the five wise virgins and the five foolish virgins meet – the husband will be there and the oil shared out.

---

[11] First chakra, located at the sex organs.

[12] *The Song of Solomon, 2:7.*

Ravensara Aromatica

Fragrance is inherent in the flowers,
oil in the sesame seed, fire in the wood,
and in this way do the sages recognise the soul in the body.
The Avadanas

Origin and botanical portrait

Ravensara aromatica Sonn. (1782) is a tree 18 to 20 m high with reddish-grey bark; it is specific to the moist forests of Madagascar (there are six different species on that island, including a *Ravensara anisata*) and belongs to the *Lauraceae* family. It is also found on the island of Reunion in the cultivated state, and on the island of Mauritius. Also known as *Agathophyllum aromaticum Willd* (1799), *Laurus aromatica Baillon* (1870) and *Evodia ravensara Gaertn* (1791) – Havozo, Ravintsara, Voaravintsara and Hazomanitra in the Malagasy language (common names: Madagascar Spice, Clove Nut) – *Ravensara* is an abbreviation of the Malagasy words *ravina*, leaf, and *tsara*, good; it is "the tree with good leaves". The Malagasies use all parts of it (bark, leaves, fruit) as a panacea for the most diverse ailments, and even to take away the "evil eye"!

Greatly resembling the *Laurus nobilis* of our regions, *Ravensara aromatica* is a tall, leafy tree with dark, evergreen foliage. All parts of it are strongly aromatic; its reddish bark, used by the Malagasies for scenting rum, and its wood both contain an essence with an odour very reminiscent of Aniseed. The fruit has a smell comparable to that of Clove, Nutmeg and Aniseed. It is a much valued aromatic, hence its various names: Madagascar Nutmeg, Clove Nut and Madagascar Spice or Allspice, sold locally by pharmacies.

The essential oil is extracted from the young leafy twigs. There are probably several biochemical specificities, depending on where the tree grows in Madagascar. The composition of *Ravensara aromatica* is simple, without a specific compound, which makes such a smell, and above all, such remarkable properties even more astonishing.

Properties and indications
HEBBD *Ravensara aromatica*
p.o. twigs, *b.s. 1.8 cineole, eugenol*

A species reputed by ancient tribes to be a panacea against bodily and mental ills, *Ravensara aromatica* continues to be used as a valuable remedy, notably by the Malagasies, who administer it in conventional medicine – the leaves and bark of *Ravensara aromatica* are prescribed in the form of an infusion as stomachic and carminative, its crushed leaves as an ointment, and they also make a cough mixture from the macerated leaves.

The odour of *Ravensara aromatica* is very characteristic, and combines the freshness of the *1.8 cineole* with the gentle warmth of the alcohols and the dynamism of the *eugenol.*

Although relatively neglected in Western aromatherapy, essential oil of *Ravensara aromatica* is a basic essence with numerous properties and one which has the advantage of being devoid of toxicity. Like essences such as True Lavender and officinal Rosemary, *Ravensara* can be used – and even proves effective – for ailments which do not, on the face of it, fall within the province of its specific virtues. *Ravensara aromatica* is the essential oil we would recommend as the most indispensable – for it is without doubt the most versatile – if one were to have only one (even if we say the same about *Lavandula vera*).

Whether used internally or externally, for serious complaints or benign problems, it acts as rapidly as it does effectively. Our only reservation would perhaps be the risk of using it excessively – and therefore palliatively – though without iatrogenic effects in this instance, so revitalising and powerful is this essence. The characterology will, nevertheless, show us that this person is not inclined to keep people in a state of entropic dependency wherein they fail to take responsibility for themselves. Indispensable, therefore, wonderfully – the word is not too strong – efficient, its use is accessible to everyone, and whilst this must also be accompanied by discernment, one can be sure of getting the best out of it.

To begin with, *Ravensara aromatica* is an excellent antiviral agent, particularly for flu, used by way of a massage rub with *Eucalyptus radiata, Rosmarinus officinalis 1.8 cineole* and *Melaleuca quinquenervia*. For children, if necessary, dilute this lotion with vegetable oil of *Corylus avellana* (Hazelnut), since Melaleuca is slightly dermocaustic. Despite its all in all quite simple composition, as we have said, *Ravensara* has real infection-fighting and, in particular, immunostimulating properties. It is one of the essences to which one should turn as a preventative at the first signs of chills, shivers or tiredness. It can be used pure without any trouble and even children love it.

It is excellent for respiratory tract complaints, effective in cases of bronchitis, rhinitis and sinusitis, and also for more serious pathologies such as whooping-cough, with *Cupressus sempervirens*, or even against tuberculosis in company with the conventional remedies and accurate supervision; in this case, it needs to be blended with *Myrtus communis* and *Laurus nobilis*.

Ravensara aromatica is also astonishingly effective in cases of shingles and herpes, wherever the site of these ailments. For genital herpes, it must be used diluted with *Salvia officinalis, Helichrysum italicum* and *Melaleuca alternifolia* in a base of lipidic extract of *Hypericum perforatum*.

For shingles, add *Chamaemelum nobile, Mentha piperita, Lavandula vera* and *Eucalyptus radiata*. Given the significant psychological factor relating to shingles, other essences closely connected with the characterology may be included in the blend.

Ravensara aromatica is a nerve tonic and a mental and physical stimulant; it revitalises people suffering from physical and nervous fatigue, relieves the depressed and reassures the anxious. It acts on people who no longer enjoy life and doubt everything, especially themselves (add *Laurus nobilis* and *Mentha piperita*), those who no longer know where they are through lack of aims or ideals and who, their morale affected, suffer various pains as a result. These people may, in the long term, develop a chronic morbid state liable to foster serious pathologies, such as cancerous tumours. If necessary, blend *Ravensara aromatica* with *Cinnamomum zeylanicum* p.o. bark and *Eugenia caryophyllata* p.o. buds.

Ravensara aromatica, as an ointment blended with *Lavandula vera* and applied to the spinal column, soothes people who are stressed. In parallel with an in-depth treatment using this essence, it is good for stimulating the emunctories with *Rosmarinus officinalis b.s. bornyl acetate, verbenone,* for example.

It is also a muscular relaxant and pain-killer, able to be used in cases of joint pain – with *Thymus vulgaris b.s. linalool,* if there is acute rheumatoid arthritis; with *Lavandula spica,* if not. With *Eucalyptus citriodora* and *Lavandula vera,* it is applied by local massage in cases of cervico-dorsal arthritis.

Ravensara aromatica, particularly active even in low doses, acts to its full extent as a "terrain" treatment. An exceptional essential oil, it is non-toxic and is therefore, as it were, suitable for everyone. It is easy to use, although one should be aware that it has great potential for action at the psychological level. Ideal for those who want to "come out of themselves" in cases of depression or psychosomatic illnesses, it shakes up the lethargic and those who avoid their responsibilities. In this sense, it can be disturbing and not appreciated by some users or patients.

It is easy to blend, from wood to flowers and seeds to leaves; it is not too harsh on the fragile essences, nor inclined to fade with essential oils that are powerful and very strong from the olfactory point of view. It is, in any case, an essence worth discovering, with plenty of surprises in store, as the characterology suggests.

Characterology

Right from the start, to evoke *Ravensara aromatica* brings to mind the numerous trials that must be overcome by the conscious, determined man throughout his life, trials symbolically recounted through the various spiritual initiations – always kept secret – which contributed to maintaining virtue and spirituality on earth. Of all the ancient initiations, the Eygptian mysteries were, without doubt, the most intense and testing. Drawing its sources from the eternal mysteries relayed by divine inspiration through Hermes-Thoth – known as Hermes Trismegistus, the "thrice most great" – the Egyptian initiation spread its light throughout the world and illuminated the consciousness of prophets and philosophers, mystagogues and theurgists of all times and in all places.

After years of self-purification and endeavour, the would-be initiate – in imitation of the life and death of Osiris, the solar god killed and cut up into fourteen parts by Seth, the god of darkness, then reassembled and raised from the dead by his wife, Isis, the Mother Goddess – also went through tests and an initatory death. Shut up, like Osiris, in a sarcophagus by the hierophant, he descended into the underworld of his inner being where he died as himself, before being revived after three days – brought out of his lethargy by his Master – reborn as a "new Osiris", like Horus, the son of Isis, the Sun suddenly appearing from the shadows to light up the world.

Greece also had its mysteries, which were certainly influenced by those of Egypt since it is said that it was Orpheus – himself initiated at Heliopolis – who brought them to his homeland: "in truth, Orpheus brought back from the Egyptians most of the mystical initiations, the secret rites relating to his own travels and the invention of the myths concerning Hades. In fact, Osiris's rite of initiation is the same as that of Dionysus, and that of Isis appears almost identical to that of Demeter – only the names have been changed", points out Diodorus of Sicily. Thus Dionysus, the "twice-born" – son of Zeus who begat him in the form of a serpent and also called Zagreus, in other words "restored to life", or Iacchos when at Eleusis he was considered the son of Demeter (or sometimes of Kore) – scarcely had he come into the world than he was torn to pieces and devoured by the Titans, the dark and chaotic forces of the unconscious. Athena, the goddess of wisdom, just managed in time to rescue his heart, the abode of the divine spark, which she enclosed in a statue into which she breathed life, rendering Zagreus immortal. From the ashes of the Titans struck down by Zeus's lightning was born humanity; "we are therefore a part of Dionysus", comments Olympiodorus.[13] Such is the Orphic variant of numerous Dionysian myths, the most famous version of which makes the god the son of Semele, struck down after trying to gaze upon her lover, Zeus, in all his glory; Zeus tore the child from her womb and had him complete his gestation in his thigh. Only just born for the second time, with horns and a head crowned with serpents, Dionysus was dismembered by the Titans before being "reassembled" by Apollo (or by Rhea, the wife of Kronos). Consequently, Dionysus is, in reality, a thrice-born god – in body, soul and spirit – who died and was revived, androgynous in spirit, which pointed to his effeminate features: "a magician, an enchanter, from the land of Lydia, scented hair, fair curly and dishevelled, his eyes – the colour of wine – full of the dark charms of Aphrodite, he spends his days and nights in the company of virgins, laying before them the initiations of joy."[14]

Crowned with ivy and bearer of the thyrsus,[15] a multiform god: "Come, O Bacchus, show yourself in the form of a bull or a many-headed serpent or a lion, fiery of eye", Dionysus was a seer and healer, and his priest – when he was possessed in Bacchic trance – in turn read the oracles. The wine which Dionysus gave to humanity is a symbol of the spirit, the masculine principle, and the god's association with Demeter, who gave men the gift of wheat, a symbol of matter and the feminine principle, meant the Orphic mysteries were the celebration of the divine mystery of creation, relived in all initiations and celebrated in various forms in the various liturgies. One of the most telling was the initiation of Abraham, who received bread and wine from Melchizedek, after having vanquished the seven kings of Siddim – representing the stages of evolution – which gave him access to the great mystery of the two Masculine and Feminine Principles.

Orpheus, himself a priest of Dionysus, revived the passion of his Master in the mystagogues of Eleusis. He experienced these initiations in his soul and flesh for – in imitating Dionysus who descended into the underworld and brought his mother, Semele, back to Olympus, bestowing upon her the gift of immortality – Orpheus likewise journeyed there to seek Eurydice, symbol of the human soul reunited with the divine spirit; and he himself died, ripped to pieces by the Bacchantes, the orgiastic priestesses of the cult of Dionysus, who were jealous that they could not take part in the mysteries.

Yet death is but a stage, and he who seeks the truth must, like the initiate, pass through it with courage and determination.

"Entered into death, the soul experiences an emotion similar to that of the initiates to the great mysteries. That is why, as far as 'dying' and 'being initiated' are concerned, the two terms resemble one

---

[13] Commentary on *Phaeton* by Plato.

[14] Euripides, *The Bacchantes.*

[15] A staff around which were wound garlands of ivy and vines, a kind of caduceus.

another and the two things are alike. Firstly, the restless wanderings, the wearying detours and the endless, worrying advances into the midst of the shadows. Then, just before the end, all those dreadful things, the shudders and the tremblings, the torments and the terrors. But after that come the incredible light, the untouched places and the meadows, with the voices and dances and the solemn ceremony of the sacred sounds and holy apparitions."[16]

Thus, whosoever was seeking the light – a sage amongst men and a fool amongst sages – discovered how rough was the road traced before him by the hierophant, a living expression of the Dionysian spirit, the archetype of *Ravensara*. Before dying to the profane in order to be reborn to the sacred, he would drink from two cups held out to him: the first, initially sweet, then became appallingly bitter whilst the second, as burning hot as lava, gradually turned into a divine elixir. These two cups, explained the instructor of the initiation, are the cups of life: the first is that of the common, carefree man who enjoys the easily come-by sweetness of life but then knows only bitterness and pain; the second is the cup of initiation, difficult and gruelling, but the only one able to raise us to the light and unity of spirit.

But choosing is still not reaching the goal and if the seeker were, during the Egyptian initiations, to consider his quest long, and of scant compensation the promises to come, and if, weary of suffering and doubt, he were to ask: "When will I be allowed to lift the veil of Isis and breathe in the rose of Osiris?", he was told by his masters: "The truth is not given away; one finds it within or one does not. Pray and work."[17] This principle of *ora et labora*, later taken up by the alchemists, was and remains gospel to those for whom the human being – insofar as what there is of him capable of becoming perfect is concerned – must manage to join the spiritual to matter, in the example of that teaching in the *Upanishads*: "Those who are content to revere action founder in blinding shadows. As for those who revere meditation alone, they founder in a night even darker. For the light of the Truth is beyond simple action and meditation alone."

---

[16] Plutarch.

[17] According to the comments of Edouard Schuré

The archetype of *Ravensara aromatica*, whose universal basis permits us the eclecticism of our references, is the reflection of the higher consciousness of man, as immortalised by the driver of the chariot, Krishna, speaking to Arjuna, a symbol of human intelligence.[18] Revealing our Ego, he shows the ancient spiritual evolution – the painful, rigorous initiation, the eternal quest for fusion with the Divine – in the light of a new and ever-replenished day.

The spirit of *Ravensara* is found in many sages and masters, from Merlin the Enchanter, instructing King Arthur and his knights in the sense of duty and sacrifice; and from Socrates who, by his maieutics, delivered souls of their hidden treasures, to Paracelsus, an alchemist-doctor as brilliant as he was controversial, who treated the sellers of hope who were his contemporary counterparts as asses and madmen, but who fervently conceded to his Mother, Nature. *Ravensara* is also, in a certain sense, Gandhi, who treads the path of revolt and sacrifice with an aura of saintliness, referring his adversaries back to their contradictions in order to lead them to yield to his views, and serving as a mirror to reflect the ugliness and the grotesque in human nature imprisoned in the unconscious as much as the beauty of the soul sacrificed for a divine cause.

Like the Dionysian image, *Ravensara aromatica* is a complex character; retaining the spirit of initiation and the cult of mysteries of his archetype, he is humanly quite elusive and, surprising, often seeming to pass for someone other than what he needs to be or that one would like him to be. "There is every chance that those who instituted the mysteries for us were not ordinary men, but that they have spoken through enigmas..."[19]

Impelled by the sense of duty, tormented by the autocracy of his thoughts and the requirement of his credentials, matured by a profound, but often intransigent, sense of justice, he knows – like Lanza del Vasto – that "any wisdom that a sage tries to convey always has an air of madness about it".

Arousing many sentiments – from hate to devotion – acting straight to the point and without respite on behalf of an inaccessible design, he

---

[18] Krishna's Discourses with Arjuna in the *Bhagavad-Gita*.
[19] Plato, *Phaeton*.

remains alone in the middle of crowds, and his freedom of conscience and action in part explains the lack of orthodoxy of his behaviour; Dionysus, *Liber* for the Latin races, is a god who liberates. The urge to possess and the need to hold onto possessions, the temptations of wealth and knowledge are distilled in his inner alembic to extract the spiritual quintessence from all things. An apparent paradox, *Ravensara* has the patience granted through having perceived eternity and the impetuosity which demands immediate fulfilment.

"Thus the man who soundly uses similar means of remembrance, and who continues to initiate himself into the perfect mysteries, is alone in becoming truly perfect. And as he turns away from human preoccupations and seriousness and attaches himself with fervour to that which is divine, he incurs the reproaches of the crowd who consider him insane, but the crowd does not see that he is possessed by a god", commented Plato, justly, in *Phaeton*.

Loving people for what they are, with a genuine love that pardons but lets nothing pass, he tirelessly endeavours to lead them to the best of themselves, using irony, if necessary – considering, like Montesquieu, that "solemnity is the happiness of fools". He gives to each person not according to their expectation but according to their needs, and the awareness he represents guides determined souls towards their second birth, the rebirth of water and spirit, love and wisdom.

Ravensara aromatica is therefore a character of mythic proportions, more inspiring than actually present – a reflection of our own conscience, which displays its strength as well as its genius through the most diverse characteristics and appearances. An exceptional essence of unusurped reputation, it combines physical powers with metaphysical virtue, freeing our bodies of many ills and our souls from many torments – if, that is, personal effort and the will to improve are the price we are prepared to pay to benefit fully from its power.

Every therapist needing, in an ideal world, to consider his undertaking in the medical profession as a dedication, owes it to himself to meditate on the archetype of *Ravensara*, the spirit of Asclepius, in order to attract its abilities and be, in his turn – humanly speaking – a *Ravensara* seed for the greater good of the patients placing their trust in him.

Ravensara is, most certainly, the path of realised consciousness.

Rosa Damascena

In heaven reigns the sun,
amongst night lights, the Evening Star,
amongst precious stones, the diamond
and in the kingdom of perfumes,
the Rose queen reigns over the flowers
through the force of her beauty.
Calderon

Origin and botanical portrait

"A rose without scent is a flower which is missing a virtue for it to be perfect. When scent is added to the beauty of forms and colours, the result is a miracle", said J. Garnero, a perfumer from Grasse, a town in France near Nice and the hub of the perfume industry.

The Rose, which we like to believe is as eternal as love and as young as the new spring, is in fact a very ancient flower; it appears to have been on the earth since the Tertiary era to judge by various fossils dating back forty million years. Undoubtedly a native of central Asia, it has spread throughout the northern hemisphere, to the exclusion of the southern hemisphere where it is totally unknown in the wild. Depending on the species, it is able to tolerate polar cold and tropical heat, so much so that it is found as often in Siberia and Alaska as in North Africa and India. The word *Rosa* probably comes from the Celtic *rhood* or *rhund*, meaning red, and has given its name to its botanical family, the *Rosaceae*.

Cultivation of "wild" Roses in China goes back to five thousand years before our era. Under the Han dynasty (last two centuries BC), there was such a fashion for rose gardens that the emperors had to restrict the cultivation of Roses, which was encroaching on agricultural land and threatening food production.

The oldest European account on the Rose is a fresco in the palace of Knossos in Crete, dating back to about 2000 BC. Clay tablets also exist from Pylos, in the Peloponnese, which were used as receipts for the purchase of Rose oil (about 1500 BC).

The island of Rhodes, the name of which comes from *rhodon*, meaning Rose in Greek, testifies to the presence of wild Roses there, as on many other Mediterranean islands.

Shortly before our era, the Egyptians were sending cut Roses by boat to Rome (or more probably potted rose bushes about to flower), since Egyptian Roses flower two months before Italian ones; however, it was only with the Persian invasion (fourth century BC) that the Rose became established in Egypt.

The species *Rosa damascena*, with pink-red flowers, could correspond to the "Rose of Cyrene", some writers affirming that the *damascena* was long cultivated in North Africa, mainly in Tunisia, and the *damascena "semperflorens"*, a remontant species, to the "Rose of Paestum". Although some think that the *damascena* was introduced, or reintroduced, into Europe by the Crusaders, several sources seem to confirm this identity, notably Virgil who mentions the "rose gardens of Paestum which flower twice", as well as the description of this species as that of a "crowned rose" or "ready-made bouquet" to conjure up the buds of *Rosa damascena* which encircle the full-bloom flower in the centre. P.-J. Redouté, who painted the Roses of Marie Antoinette and Josephine, thus inscribed "Rosa damascena italica" at the bottom of his representation of the *semperflorens*.

The essence went unnoticed for a long time. The double distillation process is a much later discovery than that for Rose water; Saladin of Asculia, the doctor of the Prince of Taranto (end of the fifteenth century) describes in his *Compenditium aromatorium* the double distillation of Roses for producing Rose water and extracting the essential oil; Hieronimus Rubens and Porta, at the end of the sixteenth century, did similar experiments. In the East, the discovery of Rose essence, apparently unknown in ancient India – although certain lyrical and narrative texts such as the *Ramayana* lead one to suppose the contrary – probably go back to the seventeenth century, if we are to believe different historiographies of the Grand Moguls, and more precisely, the marriage of Princess Nour Djiban to the Grand Mogul Djihanghuyr celebrated in Kashmir in 1612. According to a narrative by the Venetian doctor,

Manucci, who was travelling in India: "The Princess took luxury to the extent of having a little canal filled with Rose water flow through the gardens. Whilst the Emperor was walking along this canal, they noticed a sort of scum that had formed on the water and which was floating on the surface. They waited until it got to the edge to remove it and then noticed that it was a Rose substance which the sun had heated up and, so to speak, gathered into a mass. The whole seraglio agreed in recognising this oily substance to be the most delicate perfume known in India. Art subsequently tried to imitate what had originally been the product of chance and Nature." The Princess called this substance *A'ther Djihanghuyr*, or perfume of Djihanghuyr; it was later called *Aether Gul* – essence of Roses, the Persian word *gul* meaning flower but also Rose, the supreme flower, and *a'ther* meaning perfume.

These days, one finds numerous varieties of Rose, but not all have a scent; hence our wild dog-rose, *Rosa canina L.*, common in the hedges along country roads, has a rather undeveloped, fleeting odour. By multiple crossbreeding between different species or hybrids, man has managed to create varieties of Rose with an extraordinary perfume.

Today, there are two main groups of species of Rose used in perfumery:
- the *centifolia*;
- the *damascena*.

The *centifolia* group is mainly grown in the Grasse region; these are the Roses called "Roses de Mai". *Rosa centifolia* (Pale or Hundred-leaved Rose) is a hybrid originally from the eastern Caucasus; already cultivated in antiquity, as Theophrastus seems to testify (see above), it had perhaps been reintroduced to Europe by the Crusaders and appeared in France at the end of the sixteenth century. "Rose de Mai" is probably a hybrid between Apothecary Rose (*Rosa gallica*) and Hundred-leaved Rose. Two types of Hundred-leaved Roses have been exploited in Grasse – one with very few thorns and the other with many; today, the variety introduced in 1895 by Nabonnand is cultivated.

There are also other varieties – the Lunier variety called "double" Rose de Mai, which is of no use to the perfumery industry and others whose cultivation has been abandoned, such as the so-called Auribeau variety.

The Hundred-leaved Rose is a shrub shaped like a bush, 0.5 to 1 m high, very readily throwing out suckers at the foot, but producing few flowers and requiring a lot of attention from horticulturists. It dislikes the late frosts and early heat, which destroy its flowers. In order to increase the number of blooms it produces, it has been grafted onto *Rosa indica major*.

The "Rosier de Mai" is traditionally grown in the Var department; it is also grown in Liguria, Calabria, Morocco, Lebanon and Syria.

The distilled Rose water found in France comes from the steam distillation of the "double" Rose de Mai.

The yields of essential oil from steam distillation of *Rosa centifolia* are too low (0.01%) for this species to be exploited like this on a large scale.

The *damascena* group is represented by *Rosa damascena*, which is mainly grown in Bulgaria and Turkey. Damask Rose is apparently native to the Middle East and its introduction (or reintroduction) to Bulgaria followed the invasion of the Balkan peninsula by the Turks in around 1500. Cultivation of it, not extensive in the Middle East, only began at the end of the seventeenth century in Bulgaria, where it has developed until today. It only began two centuries later in Turkey, where it was probably introduced as smuggled goods by an emigrant peasant from Bulgaria. Damask Rose, henceforth called Kazanlik Rose, is probably different from the original Damask Rose introduced into Bulgaria. From the end of the seventeeth to the end of the nineteenth centuries, this Rose developed numerous varieties of shape depending on geographical location and climatic conditions.

The influence of the outside environment and the action of man, who has perfected cultural techniques, have led to the selection of the thirty-petal shape, *Rosa damascena var. bulgarica trigintipetala roseus* – it is this Rose which is known as Kazanlik Rose.

Curiously, the Bulgarians do not have a proper word for the Rose – they use the Latin name *Rosa*, the Turish *güll* or the Greek *trindaphill*. And yet it is so deeply ingrained in their culture that one of their proverbs says: "If your heart is a rose, your mouth will speak sweet words."

It is from the floral buds of *Rosa damascena* that traditional and industrial distillers today extract its essential oil by steam distillation.

The best-quality essential oil comes from *Rosa damascena* bushes north of Plovdiv in Bulgaria, in the famous Valley of Roses, situated at an altitude of 300 to 500 m, between two mountain chains – the southern slopes of Stara-Planina and the northern slopes of Sredna Gora on the forty-second parallel. This valley is bounded by the towns of Klissoura and Kazanlik, and includes the valleys of Toundja and Strema (Kazanlik, Karlovo and Nova-Zagora districts).

Due to its very jagged relief resulting in micro-valleys irrigated by numerous streams and masses of moist air bringing large amounts of dew – vital to the Rose so that it can produce its essence – to the valley during the night, Damask Rose has, in this place, found the best conditions for it to flourish and create its inimitable perfume.

In Turkey, it is in the central-southern and south-western lake region of the Anatolian plateau that cultivation of *Rosa damascena* has developed. The distillation and extraction centres are located within a triangle demarcated by the valley of Keçi-Borlu, Lake Burdur and the valley of Isparta-Islamköi, situated at an altitude of between 900 and 1,100 m – ideal ecological conditions.

Moroccan Rose also seems to come from the *damascena* group; it is cultivated in the high valleys of southern Morocco, M'goun and Dades, between 1,200 and 1,500 m altitude. Damask Rose is also grown in Georgia (Tbilisi region), in the Crimea, Pakistan and India (in the Punjab and Uttar Pradesh).

There are other varieties of Rose cultivated for their essence: *Rosa rugosa Thumb.* in Japan, China and Korea; *Rosa gallica var. aegyptiaca* in Egypt; *Rosa bourbonica Desf. (Rosa gallica x Rosa chinensis)* in India; and *Rosa alba L. (Rosa gallica x Rosa dumetorum)*.

Rosa damascena Miller is a climbing shrub with a life-span of over fifty years and is a hardy plant able to reach a height of 3 m.

Four types of aromatic products are extracted from Turkish and Bulgarian *Rosa damascena*: the essential oil, the floral water, the concrete and the absolute, the latter two being reserved for the perfumery industry. The concrete is the result of maceration in a volatile solvent (benzene, hexane) of the floral buds; when this process has been completed, the macerate is distilled in order to separate the solvent from the aromatic extract – called a concrete – a thick mixture of wax, resin and fragrant constituents. The yield is between 0.2 and 0.25%.

The absolute is obtained by successive washes in pure alcohol, which makes it possible to purify the waxy molecules and other undesirable impurities, and cooling at a temperature of −20° to −25°C in order to precipitate the waxes. The removal of the latter enables a clear, liquid product, fairly concentrated in aromatic molecules, to be obtained – called an absolute – which is directly soluble in perfumes, unlike the concrete.

Of greater use is the essential oil obtained by steam distillation. It requires many precautions, given the fragility of the petals and the high volatility of the essence. As a result, the outlet temperature of the essential oil from the cooler is specific: between 25° and 30°C so that the stearoptens do not solidify in the condenser coils.

There is an essence in all parts of the flower, but the petals contain most. The essence content of the petals is highest from daybreak until about nine o'clock in the morning, when the temperature, humidity and light are favourably conjoined – temperature between 15° and 20°C, high humidity and light that is not too bright, since hot, dry and windy weather leads to a reduction in the essence level. Roses are picked at the end of May, the flowering season in Bulgaria and Turkey. Picking is done by hand and lasts four weeks; it begins at dawn (Paracelsus called the hour before sunrise *balsamiticum tempus*) and ends when the dew has disappeared from the petals. The blooms are placed in baskets which are emptied into sacks, then transported to the distillery before ten o'clock. After that time, the sacks are no longer accepted as the level of essence in the petals is too low (at seven o'clock the yield in essential oil is 0.033%, but at noon it is 0.025%).

The influx of sacks to the distilleries means it is not possible to distil them all quickly, but the flowers must not be left in the sacks because the temperature inside them can reach 45°C and lead to fermentation and enzymatic degradation processes; consequently, it is necessary to store the blooms in thin layers in air-conditioned storage warehouses to avoid spoiling. Although this procedure allows the integrity of the petal structure to be maintained, it does not prevent the most volatile aromatic molecules from evaporating, and in order to compensate for this, the flowers are sprayed with cold water. These precautions enable the petal essence to be preserved intact.

Harvesting begins as soon as the first buds have opened, that is to say, depending on how the season (from 15 to 25 May) progresses. Picking is done every morning from dawn by the women and young girls, who are generally paid 2 ct per kilo of picked petals.

A French traveller, M. Martinet, on arriving in the Valley of Roses on 7 June 1891, wrote: "The air we breathed was fragrant with the scent of the numerous fields of Rose bushes in the area, and especially of countless streams of Rose water which had been used for distillation and were running through the streets. The girls and boys from the village, their heads covered with Roses, had met in one of the public squares and were dancing the *horo*, the Bulgarian national dance. The whole country was jubilant, for the harvest was plentiful and, thanks to the good weather, the essence should be first class...

"M. Christoff admits that, on average, it takes a thousand Roses to produce 1 kg and, since a hectare yields 3,000 kg of Roses in normal years, about three million Roses consequently need to be picked during the season.

"The duration of the season varies – according to the temperature – between three and five weeks. Growers dread weather which is too hot and dry, for the Roses all bloom at almost the same time, which makes picking more difficult and less profitable; furthermore, the distillers are on edge and forced to work day and night.

"The sun also has the disadvantage of activating the essence loss that occurs to the detriment of distillation; it is in order to avoid such loss that the Roses are picked at first light and that picking is, for the most part, finished by six o'clock in the morning on normal days, and at eight or nine on days when there is an abundance of blooms.

"Mild, overcast conditions are best at picking-time. The pickers go along each row and remove all the open blooms and all the buds beginning to open, cutting or breaking the peduncle below the calyx with their nails... Each picker places her flowers in her apron or in a basket she carries on her left arm; all the Roses are then collected into sacks, which hold 20 to 30 kg of them, and taken to the factory. There, they are spread out in a cellar or other cool, tightly closed place, on an eight to ten cm layer where they are able to be kept, if absolutely necessary, for two days.

"The essence produced by white Roses being more abundant, but of lesser quality, than that of red Roses, a procedure for selecting the best of them is carried out when they are mixed in too great a number in the plantations."

Distillation is done in two stages as the essential oil is highly water-soluble. An initial steam distillation is carried out on the flowers; the yield, after separation of the essential oil from the floral water, is very low – this essence is called "direct essence". Since many aromatic molecules remain in the floral water, it is necessary to distil this as well; the essential oil thus recovered is called "indirect essential oil" and its composition is similar to that of the direct. The final essential oil is a mixture of direct and indirect essences. The ratio in quantity between direct essential oil and indirect essential oil is 1/3 to 1/5. The yields of essential oil by steam distillation of *Rosa damascena* are low, but are nevertheless double those of *Rosa centifolia*: 0.025-0.033%, that is, 2.5 to 3.3 tons of flowers for 1 kg of essential oil; in other words, three to four million flowers, including the calyces, are needed to obtain 1 kg of essence.

The composition of essential oil of *Rosa damascena* is extremely rich, but most of the constituents are in trace form. More than 275 constituents have been discovered in the essential oil of Bulgarian Rose, fifteen of which represent more than 90% of the composition; this has generated a large number of works starting from the end of the nineteenth century but, despite its inimitable perfume, the Rose remains a complete mystery.

The essential oil of Turkish *Rosa damascena* mainly differs from the Bulgarian variety by its scent, which is less ethereal and fragrant. Their biochemical compositions are very similar.

Properties and indications
HEBBD *Rosa damascena*
p.o. flowers, *b.s. citronellol, geraniol*

Since we are dealing with essence of *Rosa damascena*, we do not consider it reasonable to attribute "medical" properties to it and to use it as such. It can certainly palliate many ills, but is above all a balm to the soul, and in this sense, it affords each one of us what we hope to derive from it.

Nevertheless, in order to express its nature and fully reap its benefits, it must be used sparingly and gently. Handling essence of Rose without caution makes it transmute and renders its perfume bitter, whereas the care that we can – and must – bring to it enhances its delicacy even further, and personalises it according to whoever is using it. A sort of complicity must be formed between the person and Rose essence; rubbing a drop of it on the wrists or neck, or simply inhaling it, should symbolise a privileged touch, an almost ritual act – a mystical gesture. Harmony is established, and inner peace – by its presence – reveals how essential it is.

Essential oil of Rose is a miracle of Nature – certainly not the only one, but it is exceptional. Simply smelling it refines our sensitivity, takes us into an unknown world and seems to disperse the shadows of our worries, anxieties and sorrows. It shows us love, not only human love which is a gift as it is – possibly the finest – from existence, but spiritual love, and we would even say divine, were this term not over-used. Genuine perfume of Rose seems to come from another world; moreover, an initiatory tradition teaches that it was a gift from the planet Venus, which the Kabbalah associates with the sefir Netzach, love, found on the pillar of Clemency. Whatever credit one affords to legends and beliefs, the Rose seems to us to be a subject for meditation, an object of contemplation, a source of elevation.

Rare are those who dislike essence of Rose; to tell the truth, since we have been teaching aromatherapy, we have never met anyone who has an aversion to this scent. We like to see in this a sign of its universalism. Nevertheless, few – very few – people fully appreciate this quintessence; is it even possible to do so? Each day, it leads us to discover a new world; each time it is inhaled, it is an ever-new enchanting display and each of its fragrances reveals to us the existence of a world in which eternal rapture, and not habit, prevails. Did not Hafiz, inspired, say: "Here is spring returning with the charms of the Roses. See only their fresh cheeks and the bitter plant of sadness will be uprooted from your heart."

Rosa expands our awareness and, we think, leads to faith. And above all, it leads to respect: respect for the feminine principle and respect for Woman in all she symbolises by way of virtue, beauty, purity, tenderness and sacrifice, as well as fragility. She shows us that beauty – true beauty – can be contemplated, inhaled, but never profaned. True beauty, like love, is alive. Simply. Divinely.

Let us give thanks to it for being here.

Characterology

The Rose was born, says Anacreon, from the foam of the sea at the same time as Aphrodite. When the waves deposited the goddess of love on the shore, they also brought the seeds of the most beautiful of flowers: "Perfume for the Gods, fascination for mortal beings, a precious ornament for the Graces in the flowering season of love", the Rose was and remains the symbol of love and perfect beauty.

Sappho, in her time, sang in homage to the Rose: "If Zeus wanted to bestow upon the flowers a queen, it is the Rose to which this crown would fall."

In this way the flower of Aphrodite, whose beautiful brow it adorns, the Rose is connected with her and her story, sung about in countless legends and the subject of myths. Such was this allegory of the incarnation of the soul, recounting that originally, the Rose was white but became pink when Venus pricked her foot on one of its thorns and thus stained the petals with her blood. Another myth tells us that it was the blood of Adonis, the goddess's lover, who brought forth the Rose when he was killed by Mars, jealous of their love. We see here the expression of the androgynous soul of *Rosa*, and the symbol of love exalted as much as sacrificed.

In Thrace,[20] the homeland of Orpheus and the original site of the Dionysian cult, the Rose was one of the emblems of the son of Zeus; it is full of rich symbology, from the memory of the sacrifice of his mother, Semele – struck down by lightning after wanting to receive her divine husband in all his splendour – to the creation of the world by the Father of the gods, and to the purity and perfection of feelings towards which the Eleusinian mysteries led.

This attachment to the Master of the mysteries spread and Midas, King of Phrygia and Bromion in Macedonia, a great grower of Roses and

---

[20] Thrace covered Macedonia, present-day Bulgaria, European Turkey and part of Greece – in other words, the area in which Roses are traditionally cultivated. The Rhodope Mountains in the Balkan peninsula, from which "Rodon", the Greek word for Rose, derives, extend along this region.

pupil of Orpheus, set up the cult of Dionysus in his kingdom. Thus one sees Pindar, in one of his dithyrambs, invited to crown himself with Roses in honour of the "twice-born" God. The splendour of the spirit and the cult of Dionysian perfection are combined with feminine beauty, the mystique of Nature and a source of inspiration.

"Oh! How Beauty seems more beautiful when it is perfumed with Truth!", wrote Shakespeare, reflecting in these words one of the major principles of initiation, where the Rose is the emblem of the quest for God along the many roads of love.

Yet sometimes such love leads us – by many detours – to Eden, and the Rose then also becomes the symbol of human passions tainted with an eroticism that the myths knew how to exploit.

Perpetuating the Bacchic cult in their own way, the Romans offered vast quantities of Roses to the god Liber, whom they crowned with it, as well as his faithful, at the time of the *Vinalia priora*, festivals celebrating the new wine. The men would get drunk and the Roses, stripped of their petals, were tinged with purple like the celebrated passions.

Flower of Venus, and it was to her that the first buds of spring were dedicated. Whilst pure, young vestal virgins like Myrto – the future Queen of Persia beside Cyrus, healed by her virtue and unswerving faith – dedicated Rose petals to her in their unpretentious way, the goddess's feast day when the Venusian sign of Taurus, the Bull – the symbol of sexual activity and fertility – began was then a pretext for the most varied of libations. Roman courtesans crowned themselves with Roses and Myrtle, the two plants dedicated to this divinity, but the only significance of the Rose in this case was that of carnal love and sensual pleasures.

Passion, too, is part of the mysteries of the Rose, and the eroticism inspired by the double face of Venus – with her invitation to strip the petals from the sacred flower as one seeks to uncover feminine nakedness – is found in numerous cultures. In Hinduism, we see Kama, the god of love and Cupid's counterpart, throw five flowers, including a Rose, at those in whom he wishes to awaken desire.

But five is the number of renewal and of rebirth attained on leaving behind the four elements of matter. Thus the astral Rose of earthly love is a reflection of the cosmic Rose, Triparasundari, symbol of the Divine Mother, the universal Soul and image of her embodiment out of the primordial waters, rising up to bloom in all her splendour above them, like Lakshmi, the perfected beauty of creation, sitting upon a Lotus in the sea of milk.

The month of Roses, the month of May, used to celebrate Venus in Greek and Latin antiquity, and has always been dedicated to the Mother Goddesses.[21] With Christianity, it naturally became the month of Mary, and the white Rose became the symbol of the Virgin; the string of beads – formerly made out of rose-hips – consecrated to her is called the rosary.

Founded on ancient traditions, an old Provençal custom requires that on the first day of May, pretty little girls dressed in white, adorned with wreathes and garlands of Roses, take part in the May tree festival, the *mayo*. The festival of Pentecost, which generally falls in May, used to be called *Pascha rosata* (Pâques de Roses in French) – Rose Easter; this was the origin of the ancient pontifical custom of offering pious princes a golden Rose on that day.

The flower of Mary,[22] the Rose, in its mystical dimension, is a symbol of virginal purity. In *la Rappresentazione di San Tommaso* [The Representation of St Thomas], St Thomas blesses a woman and a fruit of the earth [apple] grows in her hand; she and her husband eat it and find it sweet, but the fruit makes them drowsy. Whilst sleeping, they both have the same dream in which they are offered a Rose whose beauty never fades. St Thomas appears, praises their chastity and then baptises them.

Sometimes a symbol of the wounds of Christ, the Rose is also that of the transmutation of his blood; it is said that the dog-rose spurted with

---

[21] May takes its name from the Sanskrit, Maya, which symbolises the power of creation, the shakti of Divinity, and is essentially personified in the Hindu religion by the wife of Shiva, Durga, or by that of Vishnu, Lakshmi. Maya Devi was the name of Siddhartha, the future Buddha; the Greek goddess, Maia, was the mother of the god Hermes.

[22] Miryam in Hebrew, Mariam or Maria in Greek; this name could, amongst other things, mean "Lady", the feminine of "Lord". A Christian tradition which plays on the Hieronymian translation of the Hebrew *mar yam* (drop of sea) – *stilla maris* in Latin – turns this expression into *Stella maris*, Star of the Sea, for the Virgin Mary, according to André-Marie Gérard.

the blood of Jesus when the crown of thorns was put round his head. The Rose also symbolises the Holy Grail which collects the blood, symbol of the moon, the receptive, loving soul receiving solar life, and which personifies the Virgin welcoming the Holy Spirit into her breast. Well before Teresa even, Christianity understood the depth of the Rose and associated it with her mystical quest, as testified by the Rosicrucians, whose fifth flower placed in the centre – on the heart of Christ – symbolises, amongst other things, the quintessence, divine life crucified in matter with the aim of transcending it.

Dante also, celebrating the flight of the angels between the Rose and God in the Divine Comedy, associated its mystique with the chivalrous spirit:

"Like a white Rose in bloom
the great chivalry appeared to me
of which Christ, by his blood, made his wife"[23]

Some people like to see in this a hymn to the Knights Templar, themselves persecuted during these dark years.

Beyond its spiritual purity, a source of inspiration and devotion, the Rose leads us towards the mysteries of creation and remains – like the Lotus in the East – a symbol of the cosmic wheel which turns the world in the spiral of time and space. Dante, again, dreams through the soul of Beatrice, his beloved, and having reached the last round of the heavens, sees a huge flower, both a Rose and rosette: "In the golden centre of the eternal Rose, which is expanding and moving by degrees, and which exudes an ever springlike perfume of praise to the Sun, Beatrice drew me."

Thus, in its cosmic dimension, it symbolises life, death and resurrection. Hecate, the goddess of the underworld, was sometimes shown with her head crowned with five-leaved Roses, and this is why it was the custom to decorate graves with Roses, a ritual intended to nourish the spirits of the dead. But Venus – fallen into human torment, the Evening Star, sorceress, erotic and funereal symbol – becomes again the Morning Star, "roseate-fingered Dawn", as Homer called her, the luminous, bountiful goddess.

---

[23] *Paradise, Song XXXI.*

The Rose, resuscitated, again lights up the world with its virginal brightness; for the death it symbolises is that which makes us live – an obligatory prelude to initiation – of the rebirth of water and spirit for which, offering their lives in sacrifice, heroes fall and spill their blood in the footsteps of Adonis or Christ.

"For them, the strength of the Sun shines brightly, whilst here below night is perpetuated; their abode is close to the city, in the meadow of Roses; some recreate themselves... by the sound of their lyre, and the flower of abundance blooms amongst them; a gentle fragrance spreads over the earth, and unceasingly they bring to the hearth... gifts of all kinds on the altar of the gods": thus Pindar described the abode of the blessed, worthy by their courage and self-sacrifice to cross the gate of mysteries in their soul.

But *Rosa*, surrounded with a halo of celestial light, could not be what it is unless it deigned to come down amongst men to assuage their ills, inspire their hearts and raise their souls.

Thus St Teresa, drifting between Heaven and Earth on her white cloud rent with suffering, sung during agony:

"Soon will I hear that sweet harmony

Soon in beauteous Heaven will I see you,

You, who came to smile at me in the morning of my life

Come smile at me again... Mother... now is the evening!...

I no longer fear the brightness of your supreme glory

With you have I suffered and now I want

To sing on your lap, Mary, about why I love you

And repeat eternally that I am your child!..."

Her true greatness lies in her simplicity, and her resurrection springs from sacrifice. So beautiful that she is impossible to describe, *Rosa* perfumes the air with her deep thoughts and brings to the aura of those who mix with her the iridescence of magical colours, diffuse lights and lustrous sparkle that, even so, never dazzle.

Little Sister of the poor, friend of the afflicted, you leave behind your princess's robe to dress in miller's clothing. The wheat you offer them grew in your heart, blessed by your light, watered by your tears, and into their outstretched hands, you divide the bread, baked in the fire of love that consumes your soul. Your suffering is theirs and their cries are a song that the child you bear raises up to the heavens.

For them, you are hope and yet you believe, in your simplicity, that you have nothing to offer but the fruit of your piety. Far, far from the sun which gave birth to you, you do not know who you are, and you are, little Sister, only closer to God because of it, for your gaze is taken from Him to lean, filled with your goodness and wet with your tears, over the starving child, over the dying old man, over the man reduced to the level of an animal, pulling in his state of emaciation the coach of rich men, and cursing his lot, lost, without dignity, awaiting death.

You burn in your faith and relive the Passion, but in the light of your love, like the Phoenix, you are reborn from the still glowing ashes of your consumed heart.

Little Sister, bountiful angel, the blood of sacrifice beads your brow and your hands hurt from holding your cross too tightly. Courage embraces you as much as does sorrow, and your prayer yields scent, like incense on the altar of the temple of your body, spreading its fragrance through the starry night through which you conduct the souls, serene and deified.

Bibliography

Abdeker ou *l'Art de conserver la beauté*, Paris 1792.

Ambelain Robert – *La Kabbale Pratique*, Niclaus, 1951.

André Fabienne – *Roses anciennes et contemporaines*, Roseraie André, St-André-de-Cruzières 1992.

Auclair Marcelle – *Vie de Sainte Thérèse d'Avila*, Seuil, 1967.

Bacri Etienne – *Le pouvoir invisible des odeurs*, Ça m'intéresse.

Bailey Alice – *La Guérison Esotérique*, Dervy, 1987.

Baumé A. – *Eléments de Pharmacie*, Paris 1762.

Behnam Martine – *Les Parfums à travers les littératures anciennes*, revue Parfums, Cosmétiques, Arômes, Paris 1979.

Bhagavad Gîtâ, La trad. Anna Kamensky, Courrier du Livre, 1988.

Bible, La trad. A. Chouraki, Desclée de Brouwer, 1989.

Bible, La Sainte trad. P. Segond, Sté Biblique de Genève, 1979.

Bott Victor – *Médecine Anthroposophique*, Triades, 1980.

Braun Lucien – *Paracelse*, Coeckelberghs, Lausanne 1988.

Brasillach Robert – *Anthologie de la Poésie Grecque*, Stock, 1991.

Capra Fritjof – *Le Tao de la physique*, Sand, 1985.

Carton Paul – *L'Art Médical, Le François*, Paris 1973.

Chevalier Jean et Gheerbrant Alain – *Dictionnaire des Symboles*, R. Laffont, 1982.

Coats Peter – *Les Fleurs dans l'Histoire*, Le Livre du Mois, Lausanne 1979.

Coggiatti Stelvio, Trechslin Anne Marie – *Roses anciennes – roses modernes*, Silva, Zurich 1985.

Colli Giorgio – *La Sagesse Grecque*, l'Eclat, Combas 1990.

Corbin Alain – *Le Miasme et la Jonquille, L'odorat et l'imaginaire social, 18e-19e siècles*, Aubier Montaigne, 1982.

Daudet Alphonse – *Lettres de mon Moulin*, Gallimard, 1979.

De Gubernatis Angelo – *Mythologie des Plantes*, Archè, Milan 1976.

Denton Michael – *Evolution, une théorie en crise*, Londreys 1988.

Desbois de Rochefort M. – *Cours Elémentaire de Matière Médicale*, Paris 1789.

Détienne Marcel – *Les Jardins d'Adonis, Mythologie des aromates en Grèce*, Gallimard, 1972.

Donato G., Minardi Branca E., Rallo A. – *Sostanze odorose del mondo classico*, Consiglio Nazionale delle Ricerche, Roma.

Ecole de Salerne, L' trad. de Ch. Meaux Saint-Marc, Paris 1861.

Fabre d'Olivet – *Les Vers dorés de Phythagore*, L'Age d'Homme, Lausanne.

Fliess W. – *Les relations entre le nez et les organes génitaux*, Berlin, 1896.

Fougère Paule – *Le Livre des Parfums*, R. Morel, 1972.

Fréderic Louis – *Dictionnaire de la Civilisation Indienne*, R. Laffont, 1987.

Gérard André-Marie – *Dictionnaire de la Bible*, R. Laffont, Paris 1989.

Gildemeister & Hoffman – *Les Huiles Essentielles*, tome 1, Tignol 1900.

Gildemeister & Hoffman – *Les Huiles Essentielles*, tome 2, Baillière 1914.

Gœthe J. W. – *La Métamorphose des Plantes*, Triades, 1975.

Grant Michael, Hazel John – *Dictionnaire de la Mythologie*, Marabout, 1990.

Graves Robert – *Les Mythes Grecs*, Fayard, 1979.

Guibourt N. – *Histoire Naturelle des Drogues Simples*, Paris 1876.

Halevi z'ev ben Shimon – *L'Arbre de Vie*, Albin Michel, 1985.

Hesse Hermann – *Siddharta*, Grasset, 1988.

Homère – *L'Odyssée*, trad. V. Bérard, Livre de Poche, 1988.

Ivanoff Mikhaël – *Amour, Sagesse, Vérité*, Izgrev 1946.

Ivanoff Mikhaël – *L'alchimie spirituelle*, Izgrev 1947.

Légende Arthurienne, La sous la dir. de D. Régnier-Bohler, R. Laffont, 1989.

Lao-Tseu – *Tao Tö King*, trad. C. con Lauer, Jean de Bonnot, Paris 1990.

Lapierre Dominique – *La Cité de la Joie*, R. Laffont, 1985.

Larchet Jean-Claude – *Thérapeutique des maladies spirituelles*, Ed. de l'Ancre, 1991

Lémery Nicolas – *Dictionnaire des Drogues*, Paris 1733.

Lémery Nicolas – *Pharmacopée Universelle*, Paris 1756.

Malnoy André – *Parfums liquides dans l'Antiquité*, Nancy 1929.

Mansfield Katherine – *Journal*, Stock, 1973.

Matthiole – *Commentaires sur Dioscoride*, Lyon 1680.

Mavéric Jean – *La Médecine Hermétique des Plantes*, Bélisane, Nice 1980.

Molière – *Oeuvres complètes*, Famot, Genève 1975.

Montain Bernard – *Tempéraments et groupes sanguins*, N.P.I., 1992.

Muchery Georges – *Magie Astrale des parfums,* Ed. du Chariot, 1952.

Ovide – *Métamorphoses,* trad. J. Chamonard, Flammarion, 1966.

Pagnol Marcel – *La Gloire de mon Père,* Didier 1964.

Pagnol Marcel – *Le Château de ma Mère,* Didier 1967.

Paracelse – *Oeuvres complètes,* Ed. Traditionnelles, 1984.

Paracelse – *Herbarius,* Dervy Livres, 1987.

Pelikan Wilhelm – *L'Homme et les Plantes médicinales,* Triades, 1962.

Penso G. – *Les Plantes Médicinales dans l'Art et l'Histoire,* Dacosta, Paris 1986.

Piesse S. – *Histoire des parfums,* Paris 1905.

Piesse S. – *Des Odeurs, des Parfums et des Cosmétiques,* Paris 1865.

Pline – *Histoire Naturelle,* Belles-Lettres, 1947-66

Requena Y. – *Acupuncture et Phytothérapie,* T.1, Maloine 1983.

Reutter L. Dr – *Les Parfums Egyptiens,* extrait du *Bulletin de la Société française d'histoire de la Médecine,* Paris 1913.

Rimmel Eugène – *Le Livre des Parfums,* Bruxelles 1870.

Ruasse Jean-Pierre – *L'indispensable en homéopathie : la matière médicale simple et le répertoire de base,* Techniced, 1992.

Rupescissa (Roquetaillade) Jean de – *De la Quinte Essence de toute chose,* Lyon, 1581.

Sansot E. – *Essai sur les Parfums.*

Shakespeare W. – *Les Comédies,* trad. P. Messiaen, La Guilde du Livre, Lausanne.

Shakespeare W. – *Les Tragédies,* (id.).

Shakespeare W. – *Sonnets,* trad. de F.V. Hugo, Paris 1857.

Sheldrake Rupert – *Une nouvelle science de la vie,* Ed. du Rocher, 1985.

Sheldrake Rupert – *L'âme de la nature,* Ed. du Rocher, 1992.

Schuré Edouard – *Les Grands Initiés,* Librairie Académique Perrin, 1983.

Skolimowski Henryk – *Eco-philosophie et Eco-théologie,* Jouvence, Genève 1992.

Steiner Rudolf – *Santé et Maladie,* Ed. Anthroposophiques Romandes, Genève 1983.

Süskind Patrick – *Le parfum,* Fayard, 1986.

Tagore Rabîndranâth – *Offrande Lyrique,* trad. A. Gide, Poésie Gallimard, 1971.

Theophrastus – *Enquiry into Plants, and Minors Works on Odours and Weather Signs,* London 1961.

Thérèse de l'Enfant-Jésus, Ste – *Poésies,* Cerf-Desclée de Brouwer, 1988.
Upanishads, Les trad. G. Garcet, ALTESS, 1991.
Valmiki – *Yoga Vasishtha,* trad. Hari Prasad Shastri, Archè, Milan 1977.
Winter Ruth – *Le Livre des Odeurs,* Seuil, 1978.

> *"It is Nature herself who instructs me;*
> *she is my mother and I obey her still.*
> *She knows me and I know her.*
> *The light which is within her, I have contemplated on it,*
> *I have proven it in the microcosm,*
> *and I have found it again in the Universe."*

Ph. Theophrastus Paracelsus

List of Oils by Property

abortifacient oils
    Mentha piperita
    Salvia officinalis
anaesthetic oils
    Mentha piperita
analgesic oils
    Eucalyptus citriodora
    Eugenia caryophyllata
    Juniperus communis
    Laurus nobilis
    Mentha piperita
    Sassafras albidum
    Satureja montana
anti-catarrhal oils
    Hyssopus officinalis
    Myrtus communis
anti-coagulant oils
    Helichrysum italicum var.
    serotinum
    Lavandula vera var. fragrans
anti-degenerative oils
    Laurus nobilis
    Melaleuca quinquenervia
anti-depressant oils
    Anethum graveolens
    Laurus nobilis
    Rosmarinus officinalis b.s. 1.8
    cineole
    Thymus vulgaris b.s. linalool
anti-emetic oils
    Mentha piperita
anti-fungal oils
    Cymbopogon martinii var. Motia
    Eugenia caryophyllata
    Lavandula spica
anti-infectant oils
    Cinnamomum zeylanicum
    Citrus ladaniferus
    Cymbopogon winterianus
    Laurus nobilis
    Lavandula officinalis
    Lavandula spica
    Melaleuca quinquenervia

Mentha piperita
Salvia officinalis
Satureja montana
Thymus vulgaris b.s. linalool
anti-inflammatory oils
    Citrus aurantium var. amara
    Commiphora myrrha
    Cupressus sempervirens
    Cymbopogon winterianus
    Daucas carota
    Eucalyptus citriodora
    Eucalyptus globulus
    Gaultheria fragrantissima
    Helichrysum italicum var.
    serotinum
    Hyssopus officinalis
    Juniperus communis
    Lavandula hybrida
    Lavandula spica
    Lavandula stoechas
    Lavandula vera var. fragrans
    Levisticum officinalis
    Mentha piperita
    Myrtus communis
    Ocimum basilicum
    Rosmarinus officinalis b.s. 1.8
    cineole
    Salvia officinalis
    Santalum album
anti-parasitic oils
    Eugenia caryophyllata
    Lavandula hybrida
    Pelargonium graveolens
    Rosmarinus officinalis b.s. 1.8
    cineole
    Thymus vulgaris b.s. linalool
anti-putrefactive oils
    Cinnamomum zeylanicum
    Eugenia caryophyllata
    Juniperus communis
anti-rheumatic oils
    Laurus nobilis
    Sassafras albidum

anti-sclerosant oils
  Laurus nobilis
antiseptic oils
  Cinnamomum zeylanicum
  Eucalyptus globulus
  Eugenia caryophyllata
  Laurus nobilis
  Melaleuca alternifolia
anti-spasmodic oils
  Ammi visnaga
  Anethum graveolens
  Cupressus sempervirens
  Eucalyptus globulus
  Gaultheria fragrantissima
  Helichrysum italicum var.
  serotinum
  Laurus nobilis
  Lavandula spica
  Lavandula vera var. fragrans
  Ocimum basilicum
  Rosmarinus officinalis b.s. bornyl
  acetate, verbenone
  Salvia sclarea
antiviral oils
  Cupressus sempervirens
  Cymbopogon martinii var. Motia
  Eucalyptus citriodora
  Helichrysum italicum var.
  serotinum
  Ocimum basilicum
  Ravensara aromatica
aphrodisiac oils
  Mentha piperita
  Ocimum basilicum
  Satureja montana

bactericide oils
  Eugenia caryophyllata
  Laurus nobilis
balancing oils
  Ravensara aromatica

calming oils
  Lavandula vera var. fragrans
  Ocimum basilicum
cardiovascular oils
  Laurus nobilis
cholagogue oils
  Mentha piperita
  Ocimum basilicum

Rosmarinus officinalis b.s. bornyl
  acetate, verbenone
choleretic oils
  Mentha piperita
  Rosmarinus officinalis b.s. bornyl
  acetate, verbenone
cicatrisant oils
  Cistus ladaniferus
  Helichrysum italicum var.
  serotinum
  Lavandula hybrida
  Lavandula officinalis
  Lavandula vera var. fragrans
  Melaleuca quinquenervia
  Salvia officinalis
circulatory oils
  Rosmarinus officinalis b.s. 1.8
  cineole
cleansing oils
  Cinnamomum zeylanicum
  Eugenia caryophyllata
  Juniperus communis
  Mentha piperita
  Rosmarinus officinalis b.s. bornyl
  acetate, verbenone

decongestant oils
  Anethum graveolens
  Cupressus sempervirens
  Mentha piperita
  Ocimum basilicum
  Pistacia lentiscus
  Rosmarinus officinalis b.s. 1.8
  cineole
  Rosmarinus officinalis b.s. bornyl
  acetate, verbenone
decontractant oils
  Lavandula vera var. fragrans
depurative oils
  Daucus carota
  Thymus vulgaris b.s. thymol
disinfectant oils
  Cinnamomum zeylanicum
  Eugenia caryophyllata
  Lavandula vera var. fragrans
diuretic oils
  Anethum graveolens
  Daucus carota
  Levisticum officinalis
  Rosmarinus officinalis b.s. bornyl

acetate, verbenone

eliminating oils
Rosmarinus officinalis b.s. bornyl
acetate, verbenone
emmenagogue oils
Cupressus sempervirens
Lavandula spica
Salvia officinalis
expectorant oils
Eucalyptus globulus
Laurus nobilis
Lavandula spica
Mentha piperita
Ravensara aromatica
Rosmarinus officinalis b.s. 1.8
cineole
Salvia officinalis

fungicide oils
Laurus nobilis

haemorrhagic oils
Artemisia herba
Salvia officinalis
Thuya occidentalis
harmonising oils
Lavandula vera var. fragrans
heart regulators
Lavandula vera. var. fragrans
heart tonic oils
Lavandula spica
Rosmarinus officinalis b.s.
camphor
hypertensive oils
Mentha piperita
Rosmarinus officinalis b.s.
camphor
Salvia officinalis
Satureja montana
hyperthermal oils
Cinnamomum zeylanicum
Satureja montana
hypnotic oils
Ocimum basilicum
hypotensive oils
Rosmarinus officinalis b.s.
camphor
Salvia officinalis

immunostimulant oils
Cupressus sempervirens
Eugenia caryophyllata
Laurus nobilis
Mentha piperita
Ravensara aromatica
Rosmarinus officinalis b.s. bornyl
acetate, verbenone
Satureja montana
Thymus vulgaris b.s. linalool
Thymus vulgaris b.s. thymol

infection fighting oils
Cinnamomum zeylanicum
Cymbopogan winterianus
Satureja montana

lipolytic oils
Rosmarinus officinalis b.s. bornyl
acetate, verbenone
Salvia officinalis
liver tonic oils
Rosmarinus officinalis b.s. 1.8
cineole

mucolytic oils
Anethum graveolens
Cupressus sempervirens
Eucalyptus globulus
Helichrysum italicum var.
serotinum
Laurus nobilis
Lavandula spica
Mentha piperita
Rosmarinus officinalis b.s. 1.8
cineole
Rosmarinus officinalis b.s. bornyl
acetate, verbenone
Salvia officinalis
muscle tonic oils
Cinnamomum zeylanicum
Rosmarinus officinalis b.s. 1.8
cineole

nerve regulating oils
Citrus aurantium var. amara
nerve tonic oils
Daucus carota
Laurus nobilis
Mentha piperita

Origanum majorana
Ravensara aromatica
Thymus vulgaris b.s. linalool

pain killing oils
Anethum graveolens
Helichrysum italicum var.
serotinum
Lavandula spica
Mentha piperita
Ravensara aromatica
Rosmarinus officinalis b.s. 1.8
cineole
Rosmarinus officinalis b.s.
camphor
Thymus officinalis b.s. linalool
pancreatic regulators
Daucus carota
purifying oils
Mentha piperita
Rosmarinus officinalis b.s. bornyl
acetate, verbenone

rebalancing oils
Citrus aurantium var. amara
Cupressus sempervirens
Origanum majorana
Rosmarinus officinalis b.s. bornyl
acetate, verbenone
Salvia sclarea

regenerative oils
Citrus aurantium var. amara
Daucus carota
Laurus nobilis
rejuvenating oils
Citrus aurantium var. amara
Laurus nobilis
Melaleuca quinquenervia
relaxing oils
Ocimum basilicum
Ravensara aromatica
revitalising oils
Eugenia caryophyllata

sedative oils
Chamaemelum nobile
Citrus aurantium var. amara

Ocimum basilicum
Salvia sclarea
soothing oils
Ocimum basilicum
spasmolytic oils
Citrus aurantium var, amara
stabilising oils
Thymus vulgaris b.s. thymol
stimulating oils
Anethum graveolens
Cinnamomum zeylanicum
Cupressus sempervirens
Mentha piperita
Origanum majorana
Ravensara aromatica
Rosmarinus officinalis b.s. bornyl
acetate, verbenone
Thymus vulgaris b.s linalool
Thymus vulgaris b.s. thymol

tonic oils (general)
Thymus vulgaris b.s. linalool
toning oils
Cymbopogon martinii var. Motia
Lavandula vera var. fragrans
Mentha piperita
toxic oils
Cinnamomum zeylanicum
Satureja montana

uterine tonics
Eugenia caryophyllata
Mentha piperita

vasocoronarodilatory oils
Helichrysum italicum var.
serotinum
Laurus nobilis
vermifuge oils
Cinnamomum zeylanicum
viricide oils
Eugenia caryophyllata
Laurus nobilis
Lavandula spica
Mentha piperita
Ravensara aromatica

Index

In the interests of space the full categorization of oils has not been quoted (see Section 1): where there is more than one sub-type of an essential oil the minimum terms necessary for differentiation have been used (e.g. Lavandula, Salvia).